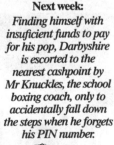

The going is soft

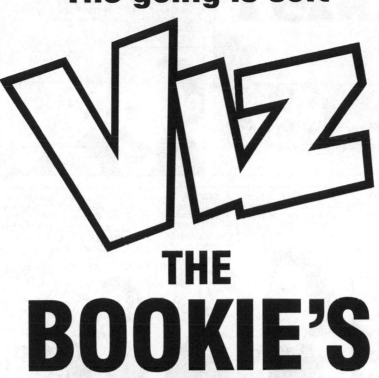

VIZ
THE BOOKIE'S PENCIL

A Blanket Yankee of Odds-on Favourites from issues 232~241

Hot tips

Honest Graham Dury and Honest Simon Thorp

Each-way bets

Mark Bates, Peter Brooker, Alex Collier, Terry Corrigan, Jeff Dugdale, Simon Ecob, Tom Ellen, Chad Elliott, Barney Farmer, David Glasper, Lee Healey, Andy Hepworth, Carl Hollingsworth, Davey Jones, Marc Jones, Martin Meeks, Richard Milne, Paul Palmer, Tom Paterson, Cat Sullivan and Kent Tayler.

Stewards' enquiries

Ian Westwood and Stephen Catherall

Published by Dennis Publishing Ltd
30 Cleveland Street, London W1T 4JD

ISBN 9 781781 065433
First Printing Autumn 2016

Subscribe online at www.viz.co.uk
Find us at facebook.com/vizcomic and twitter.com/vizcomic

HERE YOU GO, DOLLY...TURKEY WITH ALL THE TRIMMINGS.

OOH, SMASHING!

I'VE BEEN LOOKING FORWARD TO THIS CHRISTMAS DINNER.

LEG OR BREAST, LOVE.? OR A BIT OF BOTH..?

OOH, NO TURKEY FOR ME, ADA, THANKS.

DO YOU NOT WANT JUST A LITTLE BIT ON THE SIDE OF YOUR PLATE?

OOH NO. I DON'T LIKE IT. IT'S TOO DRY IS TURKEY. I CAN'T SWALLOW IT DOWN.

SHALL I PUT YOU SOME GRAVY ON IT, THEN DOLLY?

NOT FOR ME, ADA. NO GRAVY ON MINE, TA. GIVES ME LOOSE MOTIONS, DOES GRAVY.

WHAT ABOUT SOME YORKSHIRES.? YOU'LL HAVE SOME YORKSHIRES?

CAN'T EAT 'EM, ADA, ON ACCOUNT OF ME COELIAC'S DISEASE. THEY INFLAME THE BOWEL LINING AND IT SLOUGHS OFF.

SAUSAGES, THEN DOLLY..?

BEST NOT, LOVE. THEY REMIND ME TOO MUCH OF DOG DIRTS. I DON'T WANT TO BE SAT HERE HEAVING ON ME DINNER.

VEGETABLES, THEN. SURELY YOU CAN MANAGE A FEW ROASTIES AND CARROTS, DOLLY. SPROUTS..?

NOT ON THEIR OWN. I COULDN'T JUST EAT 'EM ON THEIR OWN. OOH, NO. THAT WOULDN'T BE RIGHT AT ALL. ANYWAY, I'VE GOT TO LEAVE ROOM FOR ME PUDDING.

SHORTLY...

OOH, NOT FOR ME, ADA. I COULDN'T EAT ANOTHER THING.

RIGHT! IF YOU'RE NOT TOO BUSY FARTING ON WITH OTHER PEOPLE'S IRONING, WOMAN, PERHAPS YOU COULD SPARE ME FIVE MINUTES TO DISCUSS MY CHRISTMAS LIST

OH, YES, MY POPPET

HERE'S THIS YEAR'S TOYS 'R' US CATALOGUE, AND I'VE CIRCLED THE TWENTY ITEMS WHICH...

TWENTY?

YES...TWENTY...

PROBLEM?

OH...

NO..ER...NO.

GOOD... ANYWAY, AS I WAS SAYING, I'VE CIRCLED THE TWENTY ITEMS WHICH I DON'T WANT, SO YOU CAN JUST GET ME THE REST.. I'VE SET MY HEART ON THEM.

IMAGINE MY LITTLE FACE ON CHRISTMAS MORNING...

CHRISTMAS MORNING...

AREN'T YOU GOING TO OPEN THE REST OF YOUR PRESSIES, MY LITTLE CHRISTMAS ANGEL

WHAT!? NO! THROW THEM OUT... THEY'LL BE RUBBISH COMPARED TO THIS BOOM-CO RAPID MADNESS BLASTER ...IT'S FANTASTIC!

IT FIRES SINGLE MISSILES, OR YOU CAN PUT IT ON RAPID FIRE TO PUMP OUT 20 SHOTS PER SECOND.

OH, I'M SO GLAD YOU LIKE IT

IT'S ALL I REALLY WANTED

OH, I ALMOST FORGOT... I'VE GOT YOU A PRESENT

YOU DESERVE IT, MUMMY...

DON'T SAY ANYTHING... JUST OPEN IT

M..ME? ...BUT...

OH..TIMMY. OH, MY LOVE. I...I DON'T KNOW WHAT TO SAY.

OH, TIMMY... THIS IS THE BEST CHRISTMAS EVER...SOB! THANK YOU. SNIFF!. MY ANGEL.

TREMBLE! RIP!

RIP!

RIP!

WELL...PUT IT ON!

BRAP-AP-AP-AP-AP-AP-AP-AP-AP-AP-AP-AP-AP!

COME ON... MOVE ABOUT A BIT, YOU LAZY OLD TOILET! MAKE A RUDDY SPORT OF IT FOR ME

LETTERBOCKS

STAR LETTER

WHY didn't Joseph Merrick, the Elephant Man just grow a really long fringe? I have to admit, I think there was a bit of "Look at me! Look at me!" about him.

Toby Carvery, Galashiels

IN these uncertain times, where on earth is the Queen Mother when she's needed to rally the British public like she did so well in World War II? Come on, Ma'am. Your subjects need you.

Timmy Tibbs, e-mail

APPARENTLY if there is no pavement and you have to walk on the road, you should always face the traffic so as you can see any vehicles coming. Well, if a car was going to hit me, I think I would rather not know.

Ross Kennet, e-mail

**Viz Comic
P.O. Box 841
Whitley Bay
NE26 9EQ**
letters@viz.co.uk

THEY say a woman's work is never done, but my missus is sitting in front of the telly with her feet up. What's going on there?

Alan Heath, e-mail

WHY do people always say "As the crow flies"? I was watching a couple out my window the other day and the little fuckers were flying in all directions.

Bartram Oddie, Tooting

WHEN you really think about it, Custer might have been okay at the Little Big Horn if he'd just kept the noise down a bit. He was only supposed to be attacking a few Indians, but I reckon the noise woke up all the neighbouring tribes who came over to see what all the kerfuffle was about.

Steve Plantagenet, Cromer

IT makes you think when you consider that JFK, the most powerful man in the world was killed by a lowly library worker. As a result, I personally never drive past my own local library with the top down on my car. I always thought that the only people who worked in libraries were nerds and timid, plain-looking nymphomaniacs, but why take the chance?

William Andben, Cornwall

DID you know, if you combined all the Premier League football teams' stadiums, then the total area would be the equivalent of around 20 football pitches.

Derek, e-mail

IT seems like every other church is raising money to repair their roof. What the fuck are they making church roofs out of these days? Sugar paper?

AB of C, e-mail

SEEING as the *Jeremy Kyle Show* utilises the CIA-developed Lie Detector system, I think the next step for getting his guests to spill the beans should be waterboarding. They wouldn't necessarily tell the truth, but they'd certainly tell Kyle and the audience what they wanted to hear, which would be great television.

Pogle Wood, Hampshire

IF God really did appear to Moses on mount Sinai, how come he made him write all the commandments on tablets of stone? It must have been murder on his fingers. Surely conjuring up a nice A4 feint-lined jotter pad wouldn't have been too much of a stretch for an omnipotent deity?

Andrew Pandy, Carlisle

IN all those cowboy films, they always had to build a new scaffold every time there was a hanging in town. They must have taken the last one down because they reckoned it would never be needed again. Clearly Americans have always believed the death penalty is a deterrent.

Tarquin Rumble, Tring

WHEN will people realise that "do you want anything from the shop?" is a rhetorical question?

Alex Zeal, e-mail

WHY do porn actresses insist on keeping their stilettos on even though they've removed everything else? Anyone who's taken off a pair of tracksuit bottoms with their football boots still on knows it's no timesaver. Besides, worrying about them putting a hole in the sheets really throws me off my stroke.

Dave Anderson, e-mail

THEY say that geese are social creatures, but I'm not so sure. A flock of them flew over our house the other day, doubtless off to warmer climes as usual, but they seemed to be arguing like fuck, even more than my own family argue when we go off on our yearly holiday. And that's saying something.

Crystal Tipsworth, Leicester

I BET after being savagely attacked by one a few years ago, Roy Horn out of Siegfried & Roy will give tigers a bit of a wide berth for a while and perhaps spend more time at home enjoying his hard-earned wealth.

Hector House, Birmingham

LYING LITTLE SHIT

HAVE YOU JUST TRACKED POOP THROUGH THE LIVING ROOM AGAIN?!?

ERRR...

NO?

TOP TIPS

CIGARETTE ends placed in a thermos flask filled with boiling water make for a cheap alternative to expensive electronic cigarettes.
Derek, e-mail

AVOID accidents when shaving your bollocks by first practising on kiwi fruits.
Roders, e-mail

DISABLED bays make ideal short stay parking spaces for people "just nipping to the ATM" at Asda and Tesco.
T O'Neill, e-mail

GENTS. Liven up the dull chore of washing your penis by pretending that you are sprucing up a mouse for a country show.
Paul Doolan, e-mail

MEN. Did you know if you begin sex by singing, "Bow! Chicka Wow Wow!" and winking while shooting her with finger guns, you get to masturbate instead?
Greg Payne, e-mail

FOOL your neighbours into thinking you have had a car accident by smashing in the front of your car with a hammer.
Chris Sheenan, e-mail

WHEN you catch a mouse in a humane trap, violently shake the trap for 30 seconds to teach the little fucker a lesson. That way it will be less likely to come back when you release it.
Gerry Paton, e-mail

MOBILE phone users. If you are having connection problems, simply lift your phone up higher by several inches. It should then instantly connect to the satellite which is currently orbiting at approx 35,800 km above the earth.
John Mason, e-mail

HAVE an extra twenty minute lie-in in the morning by getting up halfway through the night to crimp one off and brush your teeth.
Tam Crawley, e-mail

DEPARTMENT of Transport. Change the "keep two chevrons apart" signs on motorways to "keep one chevron apart," then save a fortune on paint by simply missing out alternate chevrons.
Nick Stansbury, e-mail

toptips@viz.co.uk

I NOTICED recently that if you say the name of ageing British pornographer Ben Dover quickly, it sounds a bit like 'bend over.' No wonder he makes mucky films.
Mr R Torque-Wrench, Truro

WITH reference to Mr Torque-Wench's letter *(above)*, it always tickles me when I see someone whose name reflects their profession. I recently read about a farmer called Geoff Farmer, and I once saw a cook on *Saturday Kitchen* called Paul Cook. However, the most amazing was a dominatrix whom I visited last night called Madam Whiplash. I couldn't believe my eyes when I first saw her card in the telephone box.
Clive Shipton, London

WHAT'S to stop a footballer flicking the ball up and balancing it on his head like a seal, and then his team mates forming a protective circle around him and the whole lot just walking across the opponents' goal line? As long as he didn't pass the ball to any team mate, nobody would be in an offside position. No opponent could break the protective cordon as that would be a challenge off the ball, nor could they try to kick the ball off his head as that would be a high foot and deemed dangerous play. It seems absolutely foolproof to me. I understand it wouldn't lead to an exciting game of football, but we're going to have to do something to get past the group stage at the 2018 World Cup.
Gritley Mews, Nottingham

WOULDN'T it have been terrible if Her Majesty the Queen had cocked her leg and farted at the Cenotaph during the two minutes silence?
Hapag Lloyd, Runcorn

THEY say that "You don't know what you have until it's gone." Bollocks. I had a Vauxhall Astra 1.6i hatchback last night. I'm 100% sure because I remember parking it up. And now some bastard has nicked it.
Frank Butter, Leeds

I'M amazed at how many people say they don't understand the rules of cricket. It's perfectly simple; the team with the most 'runs' win. Then there's something to do with 'innings,' 'overs' and 'wickets.'
Ben Vowles, e-mail

I RECENTLY overheard a gravel-throated OAP boast: "I'm really good at scratchcards." I wonder if anyone has heard a less cogent claim to a skill than this?
B. L. ZeBubbe, e-mail

EVERY time people talk about something being "the size of Wales" I am left confused as I have no realistic grasp of how big an area that might be. Do any of your readers know how many football pitches Wales is equivalent to?
Miko Stromstedt, e-mail

I WAS saddened to hear that porn actor Ben Dover and his wife Linzi Honey have divorced. I wonder if he'd been telling her that he was working late, whilst he was actually having sex with other women.
TFI Friday, Galshiels

DID you know, if you combine the total areas of England, N. Ireland and Scotland, then the remaining area of the UK would be roughly the size of Wales.
Derek, e-mail

I HAVE turned my shower curtain round the other way so that I get the nice picture while in the shower and not the plain side where it's been sewn up. Do I win £5 for being clever rather than funny?
Ross Kennet, e-mail

WHENEVER someone is described as having a 'girl next door' look, I always feel a bit confused. The girl living next door to me is an unemployed, glue-sniffing nutcase with no front teeth.
Aindsley, e-mail

I MISS the good old days when the likes of Screaming Lord Sutch were larger-than-life characters on the political stage. Those salad days when a ridiculous ex-public schoolboy twit would make broad, wide, sweeping promises that we all knew that he couldn't and wouldn't keep, have long since passed. I'm sorry but they just don't make 'em like that any more.
Hector Twos, Hull

I ONCE met the actor Sean Bean and he had extremely large thumbs. 'Murderer's thumbs' my granny would have called them. I'm not sure why she thought murderers would have large thumbs, unless they were a strangler in which case they would perhaps be an advantage. Not that I'm accusing Sean Bean of being a murderer, you understand. As far as I know he has never killed anyone, I'm just saying that if he did, he would probably do best to strangle them.
Ada Coleslaw, Putney

ROGER MELLIE

FTV

The Man on the Telly

MORNING, TOM... HEY, I'VE HAD A **GREAT** IDEA FOR A SHOW

...WHAT'S MY RUMOUR?

A CELEB COMES ON AND THE PANEL HAVE GOT 20 QUESTIONS TO GUESS WHAT THE RUMOUR ABOUT THEM ON THE INTERNET IS... HIM OFF BLUE PETER WHO GOT THE MILK BOTTLE STUCK UP HIS ARSE...

MARC ALMOND WITH HIS 2 PINTS OF SPUNK IN HIS STOMACH... HE'S UP FOR IT, TOM... I'VE SPOKEN TO HIS AGENT...

...HIM OFF RADIO 4...EDDIE MAIR... APPARENTLY, HE GOT HIS...

...YOU ALRIGHT, TOM?

RUB! RUB!

ROGER... YOU'VE TWEETED A PHOTO OF YOUR GENITALS TO YOUR 1.2 MILLION FOLLOWERS

NO I **HAVEN'T**... HAVE I?

I SENT ONE TO SUSANNA REID, BUT I THOUGHT IT WAS A DIRECT MESSAGE. I MUST'VE PRESSED THE WRONG BUTTON... WHAT AM I LIKE, EH?

JESUS!...THAT LOOKS TERRIBLE, DOESN'T IT, TOM?

YOU'RE TELLING ME, ROGER!

TO: @susannareid
@rogermellie_.to: @susannareid
hey sweet tits. hows this for an early riser? ;-) lol

I SHOULD NEVER HAVE TAKEN IT FROM ABOVE. THE PERSPECTIVE GOES ALL TO FUCK

MAKES IT LOOK LIKE I'VE ONLY GOT AN INCH AND HALF SWINGING ABOUT

I HAD HALF A TEACAKE ON AT THE TIME AND ALL, TOM... NOT THAT YOU'D TELL FROM THAT ANGLE...

I LOOK LIKE BOBBY FUCKIN' **DAVRO**!

LET'S DO THIS THING PROPER

FLASH!

THERE WE GO... LET'S GET IT SENT TO HER...

PING!

OH, YES, THAT'S BETTER... IT LOOKS PROPER **BEEFY** FROM UNDERNEATH... HAS SUSANNA REPLIED TO ME YET, TOM?... DIRTY BITCH

NOT YET, ROGER...

...BUT YOU'VE PRESSED THE WRONG BUTTON AGAIN... AND 4,000 PEOPLE HAVE RETWEETED IT...

...4,500...

...5,000...

HA! HEY, I'M FUCKING **USELESS** WITH TECHNOLOGY I AM, TOM.

ROGER!...HOW CAN YOU BE SO **FLIPPANT**?

...THIS IS A DISASTER... AN ABSOLUTE **DISASTER**!

NO, IT'S A BIT OF PUBLICITY, TOM. I MIGHT EVEN GET MY BLUE TICK ON TWITTER

NO... YOU DON'T SEEM TO UNDER-STAND, ROGER... THIS IS A CAREER ENDER...

...THERE'S NO COMING BACK FROM THIS... YOU'RE FINISHED, ROGER

BREEP! BREEP!

...FINISHED!

BREEP! BREEP!..

BREEP! BREEP!..

HELLO!?. YES...YES... YES...ERM... OKAY...

...I'LL JUST ASK HIM...

ROGER...ERM... IT'S THE PRODUCER OF *MOCK THE WEEK*...HE'S SEEN YOU'RE THE TALK OF THE NET... HE WANTS TO KNOW IF YOU CAN GO ON THIS WEEK'S SHOW

OOH... I THINK I CAN MANAGE THAT, TOM

YES, HE CAN...YES...OKAY... GREAT... SORRY, GOT TO GO. MY MOBILE IS RINGING...

DIDDLE! DIDDLE! DEE!

HELLO!?..YES...YES... YES... OKAY... SURE...

...I'LL ASK HIM

ROGER...DO YOU WANT TO BE THIS WEEK'S GUEST PRESENTER ON *HAVE I GOT NEWS FOR YOU*?

FUCK IT!.. WHY NOT?

BREEP! BREEP!

TEN MINS LATER...

...8 OUT OF 10 CATS, NEXT THURSDAY?... YES, THAT'S FINE... OKAY

CELEBRITY POINTLESS? SORRY, HE'S DOING *THE ONE SHOW* ON MONDAY, *BBC BREAKFAST* AND *LOOSE WOMEN* ON TUESDAY...

I'M AFRAID NOT... HE'S DOING *KEITH LEMON*, *GRAHAM NORTON* AND *CHATTY MAN*... HE COULD SQUEEZE YOU IN ON SUNDAY...

GREAT BRITISH BAKE OFF AND *QUESTION TIME* ON THURSDAY?... SURE...

OH, SORRY, NO... HE'S DOING *ANDREW MARR*...

FUCK ME, TOM... SUSANNA REID'S JUST PM'D ME A PHOTO

A *SHOCKING* undercover *SHOCK* report that will *SHOCK* all readers!...

THE UK is being swamped by a tidal wave of overseas layabouts. The proud land that once ruled the waves is now a haven for foreign benefits scroungers from Poland, Croatia, Lithuania and other so-called European countries. And it's easy to see what's bringing them here - *the most generous welfare system in the western world*. Welcome to...

A special undercover report by Viz columnist and prospective UKIP Parliamentary Candidate **Charlie Pontoon**

SOFT TOUCH BRITAIN

"ROMANIAN single mothers with thirty kids raking in *a million pounds a week*... Disabled Serbs being given *twenty-bedroom mansions with ramps*... Free Harley Street medical treatment for *AIDS-riddled Bulgarian sex offenders*...

It reads like a work of fiction but it's *TRUE*. And it's *YOU* - the hard-working British taxpayer - who's picking up the bill for these horror stories.

The welfare state was set up as a safety net to protect the most vulnerable members of society - our old folk, our war veterans, kiddies in leg-braces who were born here and whose parents were born here too.

But its original purpose has been forgotten. And now any British granny who needs a hip replacement has to get behind the queue of Italian porn stars getting their tits blown up on *OUR* NHS. It's making us the laughing stock of the world.

I recently spent *ONE WEEK* undercover, finding out just how easy it is for a foreigner to milk the system. And what I discovered *rocked me to my very foundations!* In my worst nightmares I couldn't have dreamed what a simple task it was for a foreigner to climb on board Britain's benefits merry-go-round.**"**

Da Da Da Da Da Da Day 1

The Citizens Advice Centre...

I DRESS myself up as a Polish immigrant straight off the ferry - with a black donkey jacket, heavy boots and false Lech Walenska moustache - and go to the Citizens Advice Bureau. Shown into the waiting room, along with dozens of other scroungers, I am given a cup of tea. *Ring-Ching!* £1.50 off the poor taxpayer before I've even sat down.

When my turn comes I am called to a desk by a volunteer called Sue, who asks me a series of questions. I give false information, claiming I haven't eaten for three days and have nowhere to stay. However, instead of politely suggesting I hop on the next banana boat back to the Balkans, Sue gives me directions to a nearby Salvation Army hostel.

When I arrive, there's yet another cup of tea and a hot meal waiting for me, and I'm told by the old lady on duty that "there's plenty more where that came from." Of course there is... *it's all-you can eat at the Soft Touch Britain buffet.*

Da Da Da Da Da Day 2 y 1

The Food Bank

EVERY hardworking Briton knows that the cost of food has gone through the roof in recent years. Putting three square meals on the table every day is getting harder all the time. Unless, of course, you're a Serbian asylum seeker.

I arrive at my local food bank disguised as a busker from Belgrade, complete with corduroy cap, red spotted neckerchief and accordion. I tell the vicar in charge that I haven't made any money for a month due to a slow puncture in my accordion bellows. I tell him my wife's dead and I've got five hungry children to feed.

My accent isn't very good and he looks a bit suspicious. A quick call to the Serbian Embassy would show my story of woe up for the tall tale it is, but Holy Joe can't even be bothered to pick up the phone. After all, he's not picking up the bill either ... YOU are.

Without further ado, he hands over a luxury cardboard hamper including a loaf of bread, a tin of Heinz Bangers'n'Beanz and a small carton of Utterly Butterly. The grub for me and my fictitious family of five looks delicious, but as a taxpayer it leaves a sour taste in my mouth. *Because Serbs tuck in for free in Soft Touch Britain, leaving US to pick up the bill.*

The NHS

WE ALL felt pride when the Health Service was celebrated during the opening ceremony of the 2012 Olympic Games. But the country should be ashamed of the way this already overstretched institution is squandering billions of pounds providing free treatment for people who have never paid a penny in National Insurance.

Wearing leather shorts and covered with blood I lie down in the fast lane of the M6, claiming to be a German tourist who has been knocked over. The paramedics arrive within minutes and quickly see that I am uninjured and the "blood" is in fact tomato ketchup. But instead of getting a well-earned jackboot up the strumpfs, I am gently helped into the ambulance and taken to a nearby psychiatric hospital. Here I am seen by a consultant - £250 an hour to Tommy Taxpayer but not a pfennig to Freeloading Fritz. I pretend not to speak English and an interpreter is provided - a snip to taxpayers at £100 an hour. I can't speak German so I pretend to be deaf.

The consultant goes out and returns with another, equally expensive colleague. They both look concerned and arrange for me to stay in overnight for observation. Next morning, after a hearty free breakfast I am handed a bottle of powerful anti-psychotics and sent on my way with an open invitation to come back and stay if I feel unwell again.

The total cost of this crazy escapade must run into many hundreds of pounds, but at no point am I asked to put my hand into my lederhosen and cough up. And they thought I was mental - *it's complete madness like this that is bleeding Soft Touch Britain dry.*

Emergency Services

I RECENTLY met a man in the pub who knew someone - *British born and bred* - who called out the fire brigade when their cat got stuck up a tree. They came out and rescued it alright... and then sent them a bill for £2500! I decide to find out how much a Frenchman would pay for the privilege of dialling neuf neuf neuf in the UK.

Disguised as a typical Gallic immigrant - in a stripy Breton shirt, beret and winkle-pickers, I empty a few cans of petrol around the ground floor of my house before setting it alight and hightailing it upstairs to escape the conflagration. After about five minutes of screaming out of my bedroom window, two fire engines pull up outside, each one worth the thick end of two hundred thousand quid. Within seconds, a brand new turntable ladder is making its way up towards me.

Although I am already dizzy from inhaling the thick black smoke billowing up from downstairs, I ask the yellow-helmeted fireman who throws me over his shoulder how much this rescue is going to cost me. "Don't you worry about that, sir," he tells me. "Let's just get you to safety." Once on the ground I am given oxygen - once again free - and another overnight stay courtesy of the Burns Unit of my local hospital.

About the only bit of schoolboy French I remember is "Garcon, le bill s'l vous plait." *But it seems that's a phrase no snail-chomper will ever find himself using in Soft Touch Angleterre.*

Housing

WITH MY house burned to the ground, it's time to find somewhere to live. A British person doesn't stand a chance of getting on the council house list, but disguised as a pregnant foreign migrant - in a niqab with a cushion pushed up the front - I know I'll be holding the keys to a luxury 10-bedroom house by the end of the day, with a big fat housing benefits cheque tucked down the back of my burka.

Once again, I pretend not to speak English and when a translator is provided I pretend to go into labour, screaming that my waters have broken. In a state-of-the-art £100,000 ambulance I am rushed to the local maternity unit, where my ruse in uncovered as I am wheeled into the operating theatre for an emergency Caesarian section. As soon as it becomes evident that I am not a Muslim asylum seeker and am, in fact, a white Englishman, a quick phone call is made to the council housing office. Surprise surprise! Moments later, the offer of a million pound mansion for me and my immigrant brood is summarily withdrawn.

What clearer example could there be of the double standards operating in Soft Touch Britain?

Legal Aid

WITH lawyers commanding fees of up to £500 an hour for their services, anyone in Briton will tell you that the price of justice can be very steep. Fortunately for me, as I stand in the dock of my local magistrates' court dressed a Spanish matador, I know that unlimited legal aid will be coming my way. My brief - *provided for free courtesy of the hard-working British taxpayer* - informs me that I am being charged with a series of offences, including defrauding a food bank, endangering life on the motorway, arson and attempted benefits fraud.

On advice, I plead guilty and the hearing is over within the hour. But as I look around at all the lawyers, judges, stenographers and policemen crammed into the room, I reflect there can't have been much change out of £10,000 to provide the trial I am enjoying. But am I asked to chip in a few pesetas to help cover the costs? No senor!

Is that justice? Judge for yourself... in Soft Touch Britain.

Prison

SLOPPING out begins spot on 7.30. Disguised as a Greek trawlerman, I leave my cell carrying a bucket of my own faeces and make my way to the communal sluice on the landing. With good behaviour I could be out in three months, but why bother? It's like a holiday camp in here, and of course, my six month jaunt in jail will be fully funded... *by Joe and Jill Muggins.*

And don't let them tell you that prison is hard. It's like a five star luxury hotel in here. Breakfast is two sausages, scrambled egg and a fried tomato with as much toast and tea as you like. On the outside, an Englishman would have to shell out the thick end of a tenner to enjoy such a sumptuous spread. But for me, Spiros the Greek, it costs nothing. They say there's no such thing as a free lunch? Well you try telling that to the millions of foreign criminals who are living high on the hog in Soft Touch Britain's prisons. *In here, there's free breakfast, lunch and evening meal every day of the week.*

Next Week: Charlie Pontoon and a friend go undercover in a pantomime cow costume to expose the Halal meat industry that is flooding Britain's chip shops and pizzerias.

Hen Cabin

Look at the size of *that* bastard.

Christ! I ain't never seen one that big before...

Wh-what are you going to do with it?

Call it a Turkey King Wing and knock 'em out a quid a pop.

Where's the rest of the bird?

Out back with the other fifty.

Fifty?

How much did that lot cost?

Fuck all.

Sounds a bit iffy...

Let's just call the cunts nature's fuckin' bounty.

Everything else we turn into this.

What is it?

Pulled turkey.

Ain't that a pork thing?

Not anymore. Is everywhere. Pulled this, pulled that –

The fuckin' pricks can't get enough.

Other bits are too big to fry so I boiled one whole then smashed it with a hammer.

Mix in salt and batter dust and there you go. *Pulled*.

Bleccch!

Splutter!

Tastes just like our chicken!

I'll put the new posters up.

You get back there and start fuckin' pluckin' and pullin'.

Here, you said they was turkey!

I said we was going to *call* it turkey...

Where the fuck is it from?

Free range.

Yeah, but free where?

You'll see pal, you'll see, but take my word for it –

– if this shit sells we'll be there every day from now 'til cunting Christmas!

And so

Later

How'd we do?

Sold out, cleaned up. We'll nip over to restock first thing.

Next day

Always wait for 'em to settle.

I spunked about ten quid of ammo up the wall other day trying to bring 'em down.

What if they *don't* settle?

They will.

BLAM

Cunts here for fuckin' food.

Just like us...

We Wish You a Mer-Ray Chris-Mears!

A survivalist's guide to finding this year's Christmas Gifts in Mother Nature's very own shopping mall

WE all love going out to do our Christmas shopping at 4 o'clock on 24th December when the stores are at their most festive, bustling with busy customers enjoying the final few merry moments of the present-buying season. *But what if the worst should happen and we take a wrong turning on our way to the shopping mall?* Hopelessly lost in a dense forest with no shops in sight, could we still manage to get hold of all the presents our loved ones are expecting to find wrapped up under the tree on Christmas morning?

Believe it or not, prezzies for every member of the family can easily be made from stuff found lying around in the woods; bark, leaves, moss and fungus can all be fashioned into traditional gifts of every description. And now we've teamed up with salad-shy survivalist *RAY MEARS* to bring you this handy guide to using nature's bounty to give your loved ones just what they've always wanted this Christmas...

To Dad
Mer~Ray Chris~Mears

FOR DAD, You can't go wrong with hankies, golf tees or a book. And Mother Nature's miraculous woodland harvest provides everything you need to delight any Dad on Christmas morning.

A *dock leaf* is nature's handkerchief. Once torn into a square, it can monogrammed with your dad's initials in his favourite colour (for black ink use crushed blackcurrants; for blue ink use crushed blueberries, and for red ink use crushed mice).

The forest floor provides everything you require to fashion an excellent tee for any golf-loving father. Simply stick an empty *acorn cup* onto the end of a short twig using a blob of amber resin, which can be obtained from a pine tree by boring a hole into it.

Finally, if you're dad's a bit of a petrolhead, follow animal tracks through the undergrowth until you find where a fox has thoughtlessly deposited a big pile of *steaming shit*. Voila! Nature's very own Jeremy Clarkson book.

To Mum
Mer~Ray Chris~Mears

WHAT MUM wouldn't love to find a bottle of perfume, a hairbrush or a pair of gloves waiting for her under the tree on Christmas morning? If you can't find the mall, you can do all your Christmas shopping in the woods.

Britain's forests are awash with a myriad of enticing natural scents. *Flower petals* boiled in half a coconut over a moss fire produce an intoxicating perfume to rival Chanel No.5, Le Jardin de Max Factor or Shine by Heidi Klum. If your mum prefers a more exotic, musky aroma, search for a tree trunk where a *deer* has squeezed its anal glands and soak strips of its bark in a puddle.

A nice hairbrush is always a welcome gift, and you can make one by glueing *conker cases* onto the shoulder blade of a dead sheep using blobs of mud.

Alternatively, make a stylish pair of green gloves by using *nettle* "cotton" to stitch two *horse chestnut* leaves together. Or, if she wants a stylish black velvet pair for a fancy "do", cut the ends off a couple of *moles* and pull their innards out through the hole at the bottom.

To Grandad
Mer~Ray Chris~Mears

WHAT GRANDAD wouldn't love a nice new wallet, a pair of slippers or a soap on a rope in his Christmas box? Once again, everything on your shopping list is free from nature's very own department store.

Luckily, the mouth of a fully grown common British *frog (Rana temporaria)* is exactly the same width as a credit card. Simply empty out a a frogskin by carefully stamping on it and you with be left with a smart, green, waterproof leather-look wallet that any grandad would be thrilled to receive as a gift.

You might imagine that a pair of slippers would be hard to fashion in the middle of a wood, but you would be wrong. Simply hollow out foot-shaped holes into two disused *wasps' nests* to make Gramps a comfy air of puffed-up carpet slippers. They're made of paper, so it's easy to apply a traditional tartan pattern using any ink you have left over from monogramming your dad's handkerchief.

Soap, or sodium stearate, is a natural substance found in many animals and plants. Simply boil some of these down until you

ANY GRANDMA would be over the Moon to receive some pot-pourri, a box of jellied fruits or a china teapot for Christmas. And all these things can be simply obtained after just a few minutes of foraging in the woodland shopping mall.

Pot-pourri is one of the most abundant stocking fillers to be found in the biosphere. Simply pick up a handful of *twigs*, *leaf litter* and *pine cones* from the forest floor and pop them into a plastic bag or crisp packet which you can find in any tree, bush or hedge. Tie it up with a nice pink ribbon made by peeling the stem of a *rhubarb*.

Fruits, such as *crab apples*, *rosehips*, *blackcurrants* and many others grow abundantly in woodland glades and forest copses. Make sure you pick non-poisonous ones for Granny, before jellying them and covering them in sand. Then arrange them sixteen to a box in two layers of eight. Don't forget to include a *birch-bark* card explaining which flavours are which

so Granny can take her pick of her favourites.

Old ladies love tea, and a gift of a handmade teapot will remind them of Christmas every time they use it. Dig down into the riverbed until you hit *clay*, then mould it into a teapot shape, including spout, handle and lid, before firing it in a *beechnut* kiln until it turns into bone china. Don't forget to add a little sticky-out lip into the back of the lid so it doesn't fall out when Granny's pouring out her afternoon cuppa.

FRUIT JELLIES taverners

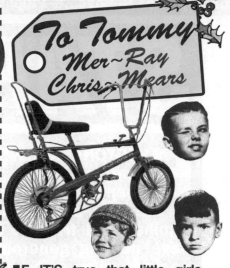

To Tommy
Mer~Ray
Chris~Mears

IF IT'S true that little girls like ponies, then little boys like bikes, board games, and Stretch Armstrongs. Happily, for any parent who gets lost on the way to the shops, the natural ecosystem of the woods is a ready source for all these things and more.

You might suppose that a serviceable BMX could be made by bending *springy branches* into the wheels, forks and frame, with a soft *bracket fungus* making a comfortable Brookes-style saddle. But anyone who tried to build such a machine would simply be wasting their time, as there is a copious supply of abandoned bikes lying at the bottom of every woodland pond and stream in Britain. Simply take your pick of the various styles, sizes and colours available, give it a quick polish with a squirrel and Bob's your uncle.

If your lad already has a bike, then a boardgame always makes a great present. Peel a large piece of *bark* off a tree to make a Monopoly board, and use *acorns*, *berries* and *droppings* as counters. Instead of London Streets like Piccadilly, Marylebone and Community Chest, use things you would find in a forest like Beech Tree, Oak and Doggers; be as inventive as you like. Or why not make a Mousetrap set using twigs - nature's plastic - and a real life mouse?

Stretch Armstrong was one of the most popular boy's toys ever, and my woodland version, made from a *deer's entrails* filled with mud, is even better than the real thing.

To Grandma
Mer~Ray
Chris~Mears

To Sally
Mer~Ray
Chris~Mears

toy can be made from any woodland creature, such as hares, foxes, rabbits, otters and owls.

CHRISTMAS is really a time for our children, of whom a half are usually girls. And which little girl could resist a soft toy, a jigsaw puzzle or a real-life pony of her very own on Christmas morning?

It's every little lady's dream to wake up on December 25th to discover that Santa Claus has brought her a pony of her very own. Well, if you get lost in the New Forest on the way to Toys'R'Us this year, that dream could come true for your daughter, because the woods are crawling with the things, and they don't officially belong to anyone. Simply lassoe the nearest one using a rope woven from *ivy stems*, which can later be converted into a bridle for riding it round.

Following DEFRA's hugely successful culling programme earlier this year, Britain's forests are full of *gassed badgers*. To turn one of these into a cuddly, soft toy, simply skin it and sew the hide back together, stuffing it with *leaves* and *feathers*. In fact, a cute soft

With their trademark interlocking lobes, *oak leaves* are Mother Nature's jigsaw pieces. To make a challenging puzzle that will delight any teenage girl, simply fit 1000 of them together into a big flat rectangle and paint a picture of One Direction on them, before breaking them apart and putting them in a box with the same picture painted on the lid.

are left with a ball of soap, which can be stuck on the end of a loop made from a rope-like plant, such as *bindweed*, *goose grass* or *dodder*.

MONOPOLY

STAR HUMBUG!

EVERYONE KNOWS that Christmas is a time for giving. It's a special season when the generous spirit in us all comes to the fore as we exchange gifts with our families and friends. Even those of us who have nothing generously dig deep into our pockets, even going into debt to ensure that our loved ones have a smile on their faces come Christmas morning. So how much more generous are the ones who DO have money to spend - the wealthy stars who we invite into our homes each evening?

We put the celebs to the test to see how deep they dig into their Christmas pockets

To find out, we teamed up with ex-burglar now gone straight **Nosher 'Straightman' Bent,** who used his knowledge of 40 years in the housebreaking business to jemmy his way into celebrity homes to see just what presents they had splashed out on for those they love...

Xmas Casefile 1

Name: Bruce Forsyth
Gaff: Surrey
Net worth: £25m

TWINKLE-TOED gameshow host Brucie regularly handed over conveyor-belts full of expensive gifts to winning contestants on the *Generation Game*. According to BBC insiders, licence-payers actually picked up the tab for all those swish fondue sets, teasmades and cuddly toys, so will Brucie's largesse be as impressive when he's stumping up the cash from his own pocket?

OUR MAN waited for the *Strictly* star to leave his Surrey mansion for his weekly round of celebrity golf before making his move. Once over the wall it took just a couple of forceful pushes with a yard-long jemmy to force open the doors of Brucie's conservatory. Inside the house everything was spick and span, with framed photographs of Forsyth and showbiz pals, such as Cilla Black, Sammy Davis Junior and Bob Carolgees, all set out on the top of a white grand piano.

After a thirty year career as a housebreaker, our man had a hunch that the Christmas presents would be hidden in the back of the wardrobe, so he made his way up the wide, white-carpeted staircase, lined with photographs of Brucie at the Royal Variety Performance or on the stage of the London Palladium, to the master suite. In the wardrobe, behind a rack containing several pairs of patent leather tap shoes, was the entertainer's Christmas shopping.

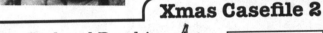

Our man ransacked his way through it, and made a few shocking discoveries. Forsyth had splashed out on a £10,000 diamond necklace and matching earrings for his Miss World wife Wilnelia. Nice to see it, to see it nice. But, whilst the price was right for his current missus, it was all wrong his former spouses Anthea Redfern and Penny Calvert, for whom he appeared not to have bought gifts. Despite a personal fortune estimated at £25million, he hadn't spent a single bean on his exes. There was nothing for that pair, not in this game.

Didn't he do not well!

Before he left the house, our man took the necklaces, several watches and Brucie's CBE medal in order to make it look like a genuine burglary had taken place.

Xmas Casefile 2

Name: Richard Dawkins
Gaff: Oxford
Net worth: £15m

EVANGELICAL atheist Dawkins is well known for his blasphemous ongoing campaign against religion, so our man wasn't expecting to find any evidence of the Christian celebration of the nativity in his plush Oxford townhouse.

EX-BURGLAR Bent first rang him up to tell him that his mum had been run over by a bus in Cheltenham and had been taken to hospital. Two minutes later the shaken professor was out of the house on a mercy dash and it was a simple job for our man to shin up a drainpipe onto the garage roof and make his way in through the first floor bathroom window, which had been left open.

Once inside he was amazed to discover that Dawkins had decorated his house for Christmas, with paper chains hanging from the ceiling, cards on every surface - many of which depicted scenes of the birth of our Lord which the *God Delusion* author finds so laughable - and with a big tree set up in the corner of the living room. The presents were already arranged under the tree, and our man lost no time in opening them to see what they were. And what a shock he got. The best-selling author may have made millions from his God-bashing books, but he appeared to have done all his Christmas shopping on a shoestring at his local Poundland. For his wife, *Dr Who* assistant Lalla Ward he had bought a non-branded bubble bath gift set. His daughter Juliet had fared little better, and on Christmas morning was set to unwrap a shower mat and a pack of 24 felt pens. Meanwhile, the woman who brought him into the world, his mother Dolly Dawkins had just a box of After Eight-style mints with the ingredients written in Arabic to look forward to. Total spend on Christmas gifts: £4.

Talk about the selfish gene? This millionaire Oxford don is at the top of the evolutionary tree when it comes to penny-pinching.

Before he left the house, our man took an expensive Bose stereo and pulled pictures off the wall, as though he had been looking for a safe in order to make Dawkins think he had been the victim of a real robbery.

Xmas Casefile 3

Name: Carol Kirkwood
Gaff: London
Net worth: £8m

AS FIVE times winner of the coveted Weather Presenter of the Year Award, you might expect *BBC Breakfast*'s Carol Kirkwood to present a warm front at this time of year. But as it turned out, nothing could have been further from the truth.

OUR MAN rose early to take the opportunity of breaking into her South London flat at 6.30am, safe in the knowledge that he would be undisturbed whilst she was appearing live on the television. Calling on decades of experience when he was a real burglar, he made short work of the elaborate security system and gained access by forcing a casement window with a long-handled screwdriver.

On the dining room table, waiting to be wrapped, were several gifts for her fellow broadcasters. Shockingly, Louise Minchin was clearly set to receive a jar of honey that had been given to Kirkwood as a birthday gift by keen beekeeper Bill Turnbull, whilst Turnbull himself was set to get a scented candle that Kirkwood had received the year before in a BBC Christmas party bran tub. Meanwhile, popular business editor Steph McGovern had fared little better, and was

set to open nothing more exciting than a copy of Joe Swash's autobiography *King of the Jungle* on Christmas morning.

Never mind the winter temperatures, Kirkwood's gifts were decidedly below average for the time of year.

Before he left the house, our man performed a sex act into Kirkwood's underwear drawer and stole several bras in order to make it look like she had been targeted by an obsessed pervert fan.

Xmas Casefile 4

Name: Bernie Ecclestone
Gaff: Brazil
Net worth: £75bn

WHAT BERNIE lacks in stature he makes up for in the size of his wallet and his wife's tits. But does he also compensate for his lack of inches by displaying huge generosity in the festive season?

OUR MAN broke into the F1 supremo's luxury motorhome just as the lights went out at the start of the Brazillian Grand Prix, cutting a hole in the floor to gain access. It may only have been the second week in November, but the racing magnate's Christmas shopping had already been done and all his presents were laid out on his leather-topped desk.

However, the gifts - one each for all the Formula 1 drivers - were not the Rolex watches, diamond encrusted cufflinks and giant bottles of Champagne you might expect the pint-sized billionaire to hand out. They were Christmas tree angels that he had glued together himself from toilet roll tubes, ping pong balls and cotton wool, each with wings made from half a doily sprayed gold.

The total outlay on Pritt, glitter and pipecleaners must have been less than a fiver, a drop in the ocean for a man of Ecclestone's unimaginable wealth. Perhaps he had spent so much on his glamorous 35-year-old wife's Christmas gift that it had left him a little short? Not a bit of it.

For our man unwrapped Fabiana's parcel to reveal that penny-pinching Ecclestone had handmade her present too - a picture of a racing car made out of dry pasta shapes glued to the back of a Cornflakes box.

He may take poll position when it comes to wealth, but Bernie's starting at the back of the grid when it comes to generosity.

Before he left the Winnebago, our man took £40 in cash and did a shit on the carpet to make it appear that the robbery was the work of an opportunist thief.

RUSSELL BANNED!

INARTICULATE polemicist *Russell Brand* has called on Britain's young people to BOYCOTT Christmas this year. The pipecleaner-legged ersatz polymath, 41, condemned the festive season as "a tradition that has been cynically hijacked by the capitalist forces of multi-conglomerisational tyrannywyranny."

Speaking at a press conference to publicise his new CGI animated feature *Rabbit Santa*, where he voices the part of the Easter Bunny who is forced to take over when Santa Claus comes down with the flu on Christmas Eve, Brand implored the nation's youth to rise up and take control.

ivory

"It is time to seize the reins of the festive season from the grasping hands of our plutocratic overlords," he announced. "For too long, this special holiday that should be the preservation of all the peoples of the world irregardless of race, creed, colour or beliefs, has been subsumed by the private hegemony of the political elite in their ivory towers."

And the Artful Dodger-voiced political philosopher urged Britons to create a new, revolutionary type of Christmas for themselves. "I have a dream where everyone in the world has their own celebration based on love, equality, freedom, meritocracy, and nuts and berries," he proffered. "In the world I dream of nobody has a house that's any bigger than anybody else's house and nobody has any money or any possessions, and there's no hatred or crime. There's just infinitessimal love and peace and beautiful flowers in this garden of Edam that is perfidious Albany," he struggled.

banker

Warming to his theme, the Manuel's granddaughter-fucking dialectical epistemologist issued a rousing call to action. "The proletariat must rise up as one and decimalise big business," he said. "And they must not rest until every last conglomerate, oligarch, magnet

EXCLUSIVE!

Man of the people Brand campaigns for end to capitalist Christmas

and corporation has been smashed to smivvereens."

navy

"All except Bertelsmann SE & Co. KGaA, the vast multinational that publishes my books," he continued. "And Warner Brothers, who my agenty-wagenty is talking to about doing Rabbit Santa II: Merry Eggsmas for next Chrimbly-wimbly."

Revolting: Russell Brand, who launched into a loggorrhoeic broadside against the festive season yesterday.

DR VAN HELSING, VAMPIRE HUNTER

Transylvania, 1883. The full moon casts its icy light across the deserted streets of Knöchelbruch. Deserted save for one solitary creature - a denizen of the night - which flits towards an open window at the Ürlaub Inn...

Next morning...

Scream!!!

What the devil...?!

I heard your cry. What is it?

It's the young lady, sir. She's been visited in the night.

Visited? What on earth do you mean?

Visited, sir. Ravaged in her sleep by Nosferatu... the Lord of Darkness!

My God!...

There is only one man in Transylvania can prevent my fiancée from becoming one of the Children of the Night!

There isn't a moment to lose!

Jonathan Harker knew that time was of the essence. For Count Dracula had already laid claim to the soul of his beloved, and would certainly return that night to take possession of her earthly body. Only Dr Van Helsing the famed Vampire Slayer could now save her from the torment of eternity as one of the undead...

Knöchelbruch Surgery Dr Van Helsing

SURGERY 1 2 3

Help me! In God's name! I must see Van Helsing now!

HAVE YOU HAD YOUR GARLIC JABS?

Family member a vampire and need to talk to someone?

By all that is holy, woman, open the glass!

Please ring bell for attention

My fiancée lies in bed, the victim of a vampire! I must see Van Helsing this moment! Please, I beg of you.

DING! DING! DING!

I'm on my lunch till one-thirty.

1 2 3

THWUMP!

ring bell for attention

HAVE YOU HAD YOUR GARLIC JABS?

45 minutes later...

1 2 3

Thank God! At last!

Please ring bell for attention

Where is Van Helsing! I must speak with Van Helsing!

Have you made an appointment?

No! No, it's my fiancée...!She's been bitten on the neck by a malevolent denizen of the netherworld!

Hmmm...

I can fit you in with Dr Grüber... 4:30 next Wednesday.

No! I must see Van Helsing! Only he can stop Dracula's infernal contagion from spreading! In God's name, woman, even as we speak that monster's diabolic poison will be coursing through her veins!

If it's a genuine emergency you could try the Satanic Succubus Walk-in Centre in Schulter Aus Gerenkt.

TING-A-LING-A-LING!

Schulter Aus Gerenkt?! But that's over the mountains! The pass will be blocked with snow at this time of year!

Well that's not Dr Van Helsing's fault. You should have made an appointment in plenty of time.

HAVE YOU HAD YOUR GARLIC JABS?

Fraülein Müllerlicht? Dr Van Helsing, surgery one.

A NOTE ABOUT WOODEN STAKE PRESCRIPTION CHARGES

As you can see, doctor's very busy. Lots of people come in with vampire bites.

I implore you! The good doctor must see her today!

Please...

...Once the sun sets, her transformation into a demonic revenant will be complete.

In the name of humanity, woman! *Call him! Call Van Helsing!*

Sigh!

I'm so sorry to bother you, Dr Van Helsing, only there's a gentleman here says his fiancée has been bitten by a Dracula...

No... no, he hasn't.

Yes, doctor. I told him that, but he says the pass will be blocked...

Yes, I told him that.

No, he doesn't want Dr Grüber. He's insisting on seeing you.

Yes, doctor. It is, isn't it.

Thank-you. I'll tell him.

Dr Van Helsing has very kindly agreed to see you at the end of surgery. If you would like to come back at four-thirty.

Thank-you from the bottom of my heart...

...you and the good doctor both.

I shall return at the appointed hour, of that you can be sure.

You may have to wait if doctor is running late.

At four-thirty...

Sorry. Surgery is closed.

But I am here to speak with Dr Van Helsing as arranged!

Ah, I'm afraid he has been called out on a very urgent appointment.

I say, good shot, Van Helsing.

Thank-you, Kronos.

Right, this one for three over.

The End

LETTERBOCKS

**Viz Comic P.O. Box 841
Whitley Bay NE26 9EQ
letters@viz.co.uk**

STAR LETTER

I READ somewhere that the old Roman gladiators used to practise with wooden swords and only used the steel versions for actual tournaments. Wouldn't it be nice if the North Koreans could take a leaf out of their book and fire off wooden nuclear missiles when testing their ballistic weapons? A few South Koreans might get splinters, but when you consider the alternative it's a no-brainer really.

Pip Pirrip, London

I WAS checking over my son's history homework and realised that he had mistakenly written that Napoleon was exiled to St. Helens, (rather than St. Helena) in 1815. I had to laugh as I explained to him that although the Republic hated Bonaparte for many things, not least for the loss of some 380,000 troops during his disastrous Russian campaign of 1812, they obviously didn't hate him enough to exile him to St.Helens.

Perkin Warbeck Liverpool

IT'S all very well Spanish hotel staff kicking people out of the pool for urinating in the water, but I notice that the Spanish word for swimming pool is "piscina". I'm not making excuses for bad behaviour, but they were sort of asking for trouble when they came up with that name in the first place, if you ask me.

Humphrey Cushions, Tring

THEY call horse racing "The Sport of Kings", but I've never clocked any members of the Royal Family coming out of my local bookies. Plenty of the local arseholes and blokes in shell-suits, but no kings.

Dirk Steele, Luton

WATCHING *The Snowman* this Christmas, I couldn't help wondering how long it will be before the boy in the pyjamas contacts the Yewtree squad to accuse the snowman of shoving his icy cock up his arse. How sad to think that another much-loved TV icon will shortly find himself banged up on a nonce wing.

Stuie, e-mail

I AGREE with the writer of the above letter. Sadly, I reckon if *A Christmas Carol* happened today, Ebenezer Scrooge's sudden interest in his employee's young son would probably be misconstrued as grooming.

Derek, e-mail

THEY say "Gentlemen prefer blondes". Well I've just watched a bongo flick and the bloke doing the two blondes in that was no gent in my book. Apart from the "Cut Here" neck tattoo and his Brummie accent, he actually called one of them a "dirty bitch" whilst she was performing anilingus on him. Charming. A true gentleman would have pretended not to notice and let it go without passing comment.

Maxwell Axolotl, Leeds

I'M currently doing a poo in Asda. Can any readers beat that?

Mike Brunt, e-mail

PS. I'm in the toilets, not in the vegetable aisle or anything.

POSTMAN Pat has been on telly for twenty-seven years and his black and white cat Jess is still going strong. Can any other readers think of a cat that has outlived Jess? I would Google it myself but I can't be bothered.

Ross Kennett, e-mail

A LOT of people have no time for East European immigrants these days, but I reckon they get a bad press and it was that Dracula bloke who fucked it all up for them. As the most infamous Romanian to illegally enter the UK (in a container via Whitby), he never looked for a job, spent all day in bed and then went out at night causing all kinds of bother. People have long memories, you know.

Bert Flavoursome, Hull

I RECKON that if the major Christian religions changed the Sabbath to, say, a Tuesday or Thursday night when there's fuck all on telly, they'd double their church attendances in one fell swoop. Throw in some nice cheese with the altar wine and bingo!

Brian Nettlesting, Cromer

THE C4 TV show *What Happens In Kavos* took an unexpected turn this week when some teenage drunks made arses of themselves on holiday. I'll certainly be tuning in again next week to see if the writers manage to pull off any plot twists to rival this.

Ian Graham, e-mail

IT'S no wonder that rich Russians flock to our casinos. When you consider their version of roulette, I know which one I'd prefer.

Bartram Owlpellet, Hull

WHILST I was sat eating my lunch the other day, a few women on the table next to me were talking about the tragic circumstances in which their various family members had died. I was suddenly concerned that if some unrelated incident happened to make me laugh, then it might appear that I was incredibly insensitive and amused by their trauma. Luckily I was reading *Viz* at the time, so there was really no need to worry.

Shenkin Arsecandle, e-mail

I DON'T know why people think so highly of owls. They're cowards in my book. Notice how they will only ever come out at night when all the other birds have gone to bed and then act like they own the place. They won't face up to magpies or crows though. I saw one the other night as I was cutting through the park on my way home from the pub. He tried to stare me out but as usual, he didn't do fuck all else.

Arthur Pewty, Denton

100% GENUINE BORED HOUSEWIFE

HAVING watched the extensive coverage of the Nelson Mandela memorial service, I can't help wondering why no similar fuss was made following PW Botha's death in 2006. He was South African President for a credible 8 years, beating Mandela's 5 years in the job. What's more, Botha was not to my knowledge an ex-jailbird. It's political correctness gone mad.

Lemmy Lurch, e-mail

THEY say that cockroaches would survive a nuclear war, but I can tell you for a fact that is simply not true. Not that I have any evidence, I just find it incredibly fucking difficult to believe.

Ben Nicol, e-mail

HOW did Jesus not have a crib? His dad was a carpenter.

Ross Kennett, e-mail

WHY are tea towels called tea towels? They are used to wipe wet plates, cutlery and work surfaces. I have never once used one to dry a tea bag or inserted one into an overfilled cuppa to partially soak up its contents and thus avoid it spilling when lifted. They must think we were born yesterday.

H. McCheesoid, e-mail

I RECEIVED a parcel today and I drew a dick for the electronic signature.

Alakh Saini, e-mail

ACCORDING to the *X-Factor*, One Direction have "taken over the world". If this is indeed the case, I sincerely hope their views on nuclear disarmament are the same as mine.

Ryan, e-mail

THAT Google Images is rubbish. I just typed in 'Peter Busby' and none of them was me.

Peter Busby, e-mail

THIS morning I sat up in bed waiting patiently for Alfred, my butler, to bring me a big plate of eggs Benedict and a copy of the Gotham Gazette. But then I remembered. I'm not Batman.

Kirk Jones, e-mail

IF Hitler was so popular with his so-called "diehards" during his final days in the bunker, how come they didn't have a leaving do for him once his intention to commit suicide was made known? One way to gauge your popularity, I've always found, is to see how many people turn up for the leaving do piss-up. But there was not even a card passed round for the Führer, as far as I'm aware.

Herbert Trumpwell, Goole

GARAGE BANNED!

Some things *THEY* don't want *YOU* to know about garages

with bonkers looney former Hereford Utd goalkeeping nutjob David Icke

● **YEARS** ago, someone invented a garage door that never wore out and never needed replacing. To protect their interests, the illuminati who run the up-and-over garage door industry bought up the rights to the design and had the man who invented it killed in a staged road accident.

● **THERE'S** a garage in the grounds of Buckingham Palace with a shapeshifting alien car in it that belongs to the Queen. But don't look for it on Google Earth, because you'll just see a fountain, because the image has been doctored by the lizards who run the internet.

● **THERE'S** an equation that explains everything in the universe. The mathematicians who worked it out were killed in a staged hot air balloon accident by the US military who keep the equation behind some tins of paint in a garage at Area 51 in Roswell.

More unbelievable truths next time, garage conspiracy fans! Dave

SCARLETT Johansson is to be commended for her recent candid assertion that both men and women should be able to enjoy pornography. Any time she wants to pop round and watch my well-worn copy of *Ben Dover's Anal Amateurs Volume 3*, she will be more than welcome.

N Urquhart, e-mail

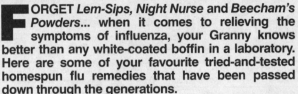

Granny Knows Best!

Your Home Flu Remedies with Grandma *Hilda Knows*

FORGET *Lem-Sips, Night Nurse* and *Beecham's Powders*... when it comes to relieving the symptoms of influenza, your Granny knows better than any white-coated boffin in a laboratory. Here are some of your favourite tried-and-tested homespun flu remedies that have been passed down through the generations.

● **MY OLD** nan used to swear by what she called her "Instant Flu Salve" - a mixture of lemon juice, hot water and sugar with a ground-up Paracetemol tablet dissolved in it. When we were ill, she would serve them up for us once every four hours, no more than four times in any 24 hour period. She wouldn't give them to children under twelve years of age, pregnant or breastfeeding women, or people who were presently on other medications. And if symptoms persisted, she consulted a doctor.

Hilda Feltchbreath, Leeds

● **MY GRANNY** used to gut a cat and strap its innards to my chest as soon as the first symptoms appeared. And what she called her "moggy poultices" worked a treat. After a week of coughing, sneezing and aching, I would be well on the road to recovery.

Keith Curtains, Hull

● **WHEN WE** had the flu, our nana used to make us put our heads under a towel and inhale the fumes off a burning ping-pong ball. "It'll either kill you or cure you," she used to say. And she wasn't wrong. Six of my brothers and sisters died after this treatment at a young age and two of us got over our bouts. However, we were both left with lifelong lung problems.

Yootha Clubfoot, Tring

TOP TIPS

SIT on the floor and thread a scaffold pole down each leg of your shorts, then get two friends to pick you up and carry you around by those poles. Hey presto, your own sedan chair.

Harry Scammell, e-mail

PORN actresses. Ensure you have the correct amount of money before ordering a pizza for delivery.

George Spiggot, e-mail

SIMULATE coming home after a night out by getting up at 3am, smoking 3 fags and drinking half a bottle of whisky. Then smother your face in chilli sauce, get back into bed and pester your wife for sex.

Captain Pistachio, e-mail

THEATRE companies. Save money this season by hiring an extremely tall Snow White alongside seven "dwarves" of average height.

Ros Smith, e-mail

IN these days of austerity, you can make cheese last longer by grating it instead of slicing it. If you then win the lottery, a car-jack and an empty paint tin can be used to make a handy press to reconstitute the grated cheese.

Nick Lyon, Cornwall

DUTCH burglars. Make less noise while breaking into houses by wearing soft-soled shoes as apposed to traditional wooden clogs.

Steve Ramsey, e-mail

CONVINCE friends and neighbours that you're about to host an Ambassador's Reception by buying bulk supplies of Ferrero Rocher from your local Cash & Carry.

Arnold Bumfluff, Cornwall

CHEDDAR, Red Leicester and Danish Blue cheese cut into small disks make ideal savoury Smarties. Draw an "S" on the front to make them into savoury Skittles.

George C Hill, e-mail

BIRDWATCHERS. Avoid all those cold mornings standing in the woods with heavy binoculars around your neck by simply hiring a private detective to watch the bird for you. That way you will get regular reports about the bird in the comfort of your own sitting room.

JD Pocket, e-mail

toptips@viz.co.uk

TINRIBS

YOUNG TOMMY TAYLOR'S BEST PAL WAS A FANTASTIC ROBOT CALLED TINRIBS

D.J. '14

I FOUND THIS OLD PRINTING PRESS IN THE SCHOOL BASEMENT...

SO I THOUGHT WE'D USE IT TO PRODUCE A SCHOOL MAGAZINE!

OH DEAR! THE LETTER "O" IS MISSING FROM THE TYPE BLOCKS!

IT'S GOING TO BE TRICKY WRITING A WHOLE MAGAZINE WITHOUT USING THE LETTER "O".

NOT TO WORRY, HEADMASTER!

I'LL JUST PEEL THE LABEL OFF ONE OF TINRIBS'S SOUP TINS...

SNIT SNIT

...AND USE IT TO MAKE A SERIES OF PAPER-CUTS ON MR SNODWORTHY'S LIPS!

GNNN

THERE - HIS LIPS ARE ALL WET WITH BLOOD, NOW...

NEXT WE JAM TINRIBS'S FINGER UP MR SNODWORTHY'S BOTTOM, TO GIVE HIS MOUTH THAT "OOH" SHAPE

OIT!

SLAM! SLAM!

AND HEY PRESTO...

...NOW YOU CAN PRINT AS MANY BLOOD-RED LETTER "O"S AS YOU WANT!

GOOD WORK, TAYLOR! NOW LET'S GET THIS MAGAZINE WRITTEN!

FIRST, WE'D BETTER DO AN ARTICLE ABOUT THE DINNER LADY HAVING A CALAMITOUS BREAST IMPLANT.

EVERY SUCCESSFUL MAGAZINE REQUIRES A "MY CALAMITOUS BREAST IMPLANT NIGHTMARE" ARTICLE.

CLANG

I HAVEN'T HAD ANY KIND OF IMPLANT, YOU IMPUDENT PUP!

OUCH! OH DEAR - THEN OUR MAGAZINE IS DOOMED TO FAILURE!

MY ROBOT CHUM TO THE RESCUE AGAIN!

AK!

I'LL JUST FORCE TINRIBS'S ARMPIECE DOWN MR SNODWORTHY'S THROAT, TO MAKE HIM THROW UP.

THAT'S THE WAY, MR S!

BLURRGH!

FILL MY ELECTRONIC AMIGO'S RUBBER GLOVE HANDS WITH YOUR VOMIT!

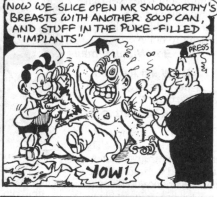

NOW WE SLICE OPEN MR SNODWORTHY'S BREASTS WITH ANOTHER SOUP CAN, AND STUFF IN THE PUKE-FILLED "IMPLANTS"

YOW!

WHAT A TERRIFIC STORY FOR OUR MAGAZINE...

"SAUCY TEACHER'S CALAMITOUS FIVE-NIPPLED SPEWY BOOB-JOB NIGHTMARE"!

SO, SHORTLY

I'LL GIVE THEM A STORY FOR THEIR POXY MAGAZINE...

"FUMING TEACHER'S RELIEF AT FLATTENING STUPID ROBOT WITH SLEDGE-HAMMER"!

SPROING

WOW!

THE HAMMER'S BOUNCED OFF THAT TIN TWIT'S RUBBER BALL HEAD!

HI! I'M BARBIE!

MEANWHILE

HELP! THOSE TEENAGE HOODLUMS HAVE STOLEN THE SCHOOL SILVER CUTLERY!

SCHOOL KITCHENS

SILVER

BOYS

WE'LL ESCAPE OVER THE ROOF OF THOSE TOILETS, DUDE!

FO' REAL!

CLONK!

CLUNK!

SILVER

OOF!

OOYAH!

YOU SHOULD FEATURE MR SNODWORTHY IN YOUR MAGAZINE, HEADMASTER — HE'S A HERO!

PRIDE

HE STOPPED THOSE TWO YOUNG CUTLERY THIEVES, OUTSIDE THE SCHOOL TOILETS!

HMM! YOUNGSTERS, YOU SAY? TOILETS?

I THINK I HAVE JUST THE ANGLE THAT THIS STORY NEEDS...

AND

CONGRATULATIONS SNODWORTHY! YOU MADE THE FRONT COVER OF OUR MAGAZINE!

SCHOOL MAG

FAT PAEDO TEACHER BUMMED YOUNGSTERS IN TOILET NIGHTMARE

AND OUR FIRST EDITION IS SELLING LIKE HOT CAKES!

SCHOOL MAG PERV!

EACH DAY, millions of us turn to a tabloid to keep abreast of what's happening in the world. Whatever news is breaking in politics, showbiz and sport, at home or abroad, we'll read about it first in our favourite red-top. But, as we leaf through our daily paper, how many of us ever stop to think about the huge team of dedicated professionals that work round the clock to produce it? Let's take a peek behind the scenes to find out...

1 The Editor
The buck stops at the editor's desk; every single word in the paper is his or her ultimate responsibility. Unless something results in criminal charges, in which case they knew nothing about it and were on holiday every time they didn't know it was happening.

2 The Proprietor
The press magnate owns hundreds of newspapers around the world, not to mention countless television companies, radio stations and social media platforms. His international business empire - coupled with the fact that his finances are so labyrinthine that he pays no tax - have brought him unimaginable riches. But it is not the lure of wealth that drives him to voraciously gobble up media outlets like a tramp eating chips. For he is at heart a humble man, who is fuelled by a passion for the truth as he sees it, and he will go to any length to make sure that the whole world is kept appraised of his opinions, twenty-four hours a day.

3 The Prime Minister
You wouldn't expect to see the country's premier secretly visiting a newspaper office, apparently sucking up to the editor and proprietor. As holder of the country's highest office, his dealings with the press are required to be completely above board. But don't worry - he's here in a personal capacity, not on official business. As inhabitants of the same Cotswolds village, he is a close friend and neighbour of the paper's editor, and has just popped round to return some personal items which she left at his house when she was round for a country supper. Some cynical people might think that such a close relationship with the editor of the country's most influential paper might compromise the premier's position, but it doesn't.

4 Downing Street Press Officer
So, if the PM is here on personal business, why is his Press Officer with him? Well, by a huge coincidence, he too is a friend of the editor and has also dropped by to return some personal items which she has left in the back seat of his car. And in another bizarre twist, the aide to Britain's top politician is himself also a former editor of this very newspaper who was forced to resign over a misunderstanding that was nothing to do with him and anyway he was on holiday when it happened. The fact that he has been given a job in the very heart of Downing Street has led certain people to speculate that there is some sort of clandestine conspiracy operating to allow the paper's proprietor to influence government policy in return for favourable media coverage in the run-up to the next election. In fact, nothing could be further from the truth and those people should hang their heads in shame.

5 The Chief Constable
This senior officer has a weekly column in the Sunday edition of the paper which keeps readers up-to-date with all that is going on in the world of law and order. Because, like all policemen, he is semi-literate at best, the chief constable's byline and photograph appear at the top of a column that is ghost-written by a veteran reporter in the tertiary stages of acute liver failure. In return for this, and for various other services that are too complicated to go into here, the Chief Constable is paid a quarter of a million pounds a year.

6 Fashion Correspondent
Young and enthusiastic, the paper's fashion correspondent has a wide-ranging brief covering everything from the latest clothing trends to youth culture. By an amazing coincidence, she also happens to be the teenage daughter of the Chief Constable. But it's not a case of nepotism, whatever the cynics might think. With 2 GCSEs in textiles and English language under her belt, she managed to beat off stiff competition for the job from legions of fully-qualified journalists and the Deputy Chief Constable's daughter. By another amazing coincidence, once she's filed her copy it is binned and completely re-written by the same veteran reporter in the tertiary stages of acute liver failure who writes her father's column.

7 The Private Investigator
Most people are happy to speak to newspapers, knowing that they only report the truth in a fair, balanced and non-judgemental way. However other people, who have clearly got something to hide, are less keen on allowing the press to pry into their dirty secrets. That's why the paper is forced to keep a private investigator on its books. Whatever he does, whether he's hacking into a murder victim's phone, going through a celebrity's bins to look for AIDS medicine packaging or blagging the confidential medical records of a politician's sick child, his expertise ensures that the truth will out, however uncomfortable it is for those trying to conceal it. In order to protect his anonymity and enable him to bring crooked, untrustworthy people to justice, he must work undercover, and so he is paid in cash under a variety of assumed names.

8 IT Man
The production of a daily newspaper generates a vast quantity of electronic correspondence. E-mails and internal messages between journalists, editors and management all take up huge amounts of memory on the newspaper's computer network. As a result, this IT man has been called

The Topical Commentator 10

in to free up space on the system. He has strict instructions to search for any emails to, from or mentioning the editor, and delete them from the cache without reading them. As well as that he is regularly required to remove the hard drive from the editor's lap-top, cut it in half with an angle grinder and smash the pieces with a lump hammer before throwing the shattered fragments into the Thames under cover of darkness, also due to pressure on memory space.

The Star Columnist 9

Controversial and refreshingly politically incorrect, this opinionated writer courts controversy. In his weekly broadside, filed from his villa in a gated community in Florida, he fearlessly holds forth on a wide variety of hot-button issues about the state of Britain. From race relations to immigration and from asylum seekers to foreigners taking all the jobs, no topic is too emotive or controversial for him to tackle in his own inimitable way. And don't get him started about the gays!

The Topical Commentator 10

This writer's task is to crank out a platitudinous, wikipedia-fuelled eulogy about a celebrity who's just died, explaining how they had meant an awful lot to him when he was growing up. And if no-one of note happens to have passed on in a particular week, he must be ready, without thinking, to quickly produce 500 words on any topical subject the editor throws at him. The picture of him at the top of his column was taken when he was twenty-three.

The Agony Aunt 11

Years ago, the agony aunt would offer sound advice to readers who wrote in with their problems. Whether they were lovelorn, in emotional turmoil or worried about their health, she'd offer words of wisdom and comfort to help them through their troubled times. However, circulation pressures mean that these days she spends her time making up soft porn stories and ordering junior reporters to strip off and re-enact them in their underwear.

The Story Source 12

The reporters at our tabloid know that an important scoop can come from literally any source. Something as apparently insignificant as a hacked voicemail message on a TOWIE star's phone, a false Sheikh who's entrapped a minor soap actor into buying him drugs or builders who have been working in a famous celebrity's house and have stolen some scandalous Polaroids of his wife being orally pleasured by the family dog could all lead to the next big headline story which leaves a public figure's reputation in tatters. Here, a prostitute is being paid to provide candid pictures of a famous person who has been paying her for kinky sex. But the celebrity need not worry - the secret of his sordid sex romps is safe with the paper. As long as he agrees to front a series of TV ads and appear as Santa Claus at their Christmas party, the photos will remain in the office safe, only being taken out occasionally to show to people in nearby pubs.

HOWARD GREEN WAS MY VALET

JEEVES, HUDSON, CARSON... the list of famous butlers is literally endless; faithful, unflappable retainers who serve their masters with calm, measured composure. From early in the morning to late at night they're always on call, organising every aspect of their employers' lives down to the minutest detail. They are discreet to a fault, and never reveal what goes on above or below stairs, no matter how salacious, saucy or scandalous.

UNTIL NOW! Because former butler *HOWARD GREEN* is set to sensationally break the professional valet's code of silence and exclusively tell *Viz* readers about his experiences butling for some of the most well-known faces in showbiz.

He told us: "Pop stars, Hollywood heart-throbs, soap stars, sporting icons and politicians ... I've butled for them all and now it's time to reveal some of the shocking, hilarious and downright outrageous things I've seen behind some of the most exclusive front doors in the world."

Celebrity butler lifts the lid and spills the beans

His master's vice: Green butled for porn star Dover.

> *A good butler is always the soul of discretion. If, when he enters his master's bedroom first thing in the morning to open the curtains and hand him a freshly-ironed copy of the Times and a china cup of Earl Grey tea, he sees that he has had female company overnight, he must not miss a beat. The butler's code of conduct states that he must not make eye contact with the lady in question, but merely politely enquire of his employer whether he wishes another place set for breakfast.*

naked

This rule was stretched to its very limits during the two years when I butled for pornographic actor and film director *BEN DOVER*. I remember on one occasion entering the master's boudoir to find him apparently *in fragrante delicto* with no fewer than twenty-five naked young ladies at once. As it happened, Mr Dover hadn't noticed me come in, as he was engaged in a sexual act that rendered his ears and indeed eyes temporarily obscured, so I coughed politely to attract his attention.

'Would sir like me to set another twenty-five places for breakfast?' I asked. 'Yes, thank-you Green,' came the muffled reply. 'That would be splendid.'

little creatures

Twenty minutes later, Mr Dover and his guests were sat in the breakfasting room, tucking into kedgeree, devilled kidneys and soft-boiled plovers' eggs, and chatting about how the morning's "shoot" had gone. It was then that I realised that my master had been making one of his pornographic films in the bedroom and I had inadvertently blundered onto the set. My understandable embarrassment was only compounded by the fact that my appearance made it into the final edit, and viewers of *Ben Dover's Gaping Cunts 26* can still enjoy my cameo role if they fast forward through the first 49 minutes of relentless hardcore jizzing.

Mr Dover was a splendid employer, but so much of my day was spent bending over to pick up discarded lingerie and wipe up bodily fluids that it began to have an adverse effect on my back. After two years I was forced to hand in my notice and relinquish my position in his household."

Doherty household was Shambles

"Another position that provided me with a great deal of satisfaction was the eighteen months that I spent in the employ of the drug-addicted singer and musician Mr *PETER DOHERTY*. It was an unconventional household, if I may say so, and provided quite a challenge for a manservant such as myself who had cut his domestic service teeth butling for some of the most refined and people in the land.

My daily duties were, nevertheless, quite routine. My employer quite often entertained guests until the early hours, and each morning I rose at six to clear up the apartment, which I would invariably find bestrewn with used crack-pipes, blood-stained syringes and dead bodies. After tidying up, it was my responsibility to press my master's suit for his morning's court appearance on drug possession charges, also readying a second and third shirt for any subsequent hearings or appeals regarding previous offences that may be coming up later in the day.

In a traditional household, it is the butler's duty to keep the master's cellar is kept well-stocked with fine wines and vintage port. However, whilst in the employ of the erstwhile BabyShambles frontman, it was incumbent upon me to ensure that my employer had a plentiful supply of crack cocaine and heroin. Such was his voracious appetite

> *...After tidying up, it was my responsibility to press my master's suit for his morning's court appearance on drug possession charges...*

for illicit narcotics that I found myself often required to venture out several times a day to meet with his dealer.

true stories

Usually this wasn't a problem. I built up quite a rapport with the gentleman in question, and the cash transactions typically went off without a hitch. However, on a couple of occasions, minor misunderstandings arose which led to me being shot - once in the abdomen and once in the lower back. I must say that Mr Doherty was a marvellous employer at such times, and whenever I was shot, stabbed or beaten up by his "man", he always relieved me of my duties to allow me time to recuperate from my injuries.

Eventually I was forced to reconsider my position after a Mexican drugs cartel bound me with insulating tape and drove me around in the boot of their car for three days. I suffered a deep-vein thrombosis, heatstroke and dehydration, and after I came out of hospital I explained to Mr Doherty that, with much reluctance, I had decided to leave his employ. Needless to say that, ever the gentleman, he was marvellous about it and gave me a wonderful reference."

Leftie Bragg got Red Mist

"One of the most unexpected celebrities who employed me as a butler was left-wing singer **BILLY BRAGG**. Although he made his living singing protest songs at picket lines and CND marches, he was completely different once he got behind the front door of his Devon mansion, Bragg Towers. Inside, his "man of the people" mask came off and the true Billy was revealed as the hoity-toity snob that he really was.

He insisted on being addressed as "Sir William" or "your Lordship" at all times, and I always had to be immaculately dressed in starched collar, tailcoat and white gloves. Everything had to be presented to him on a sterling silver platter - even his daily ironed copies of The *Morning Star* and *Socialist Worker*. However despite the rigorously-enforced indoor dress code, I was instructed to never leave the house in my butler's uniform in case I was spotted by one of the papparazzi who hid in the bushes in the grounds. When

Nothing to Bragg about: Working class hero Billy liked to keep truth about his massive stately home from public.

> **❝ Mr Bragg was furious and took a riding crop to me, whipping me across my legs, back and buttocks... ❞**

I went out to fetch coal for the fire or to feed Bragg's pack of foxhounds, I had to don a checky lumberback shirt, a denim jacket, tatty jeans and Dr Marten boots. As soon as I was back inside I had to change back into my frock coat and bow tie.

I remember on one occasion, the groom was off sick and I had to pop over to the stables to polish Mr Bragg's polo boots. I hadn't had time to change out of my formal attire, and a few days later a picture of me crossing the lawns appeared in the *Daily Mail* with the sarcastic headline: '*Billy Liar! Hypocrite Bragg Employs Butler*'. Mr Bragg was furious and took a riding crop to me, whipping me across my legs, back and buttocks. '*You blithering oik! You've ruined everything!*' he screamed.

Eton

Fortunately for Mr Bragg, he knew the newspaper's proprietor as they both had children at Eton, and he managed to convince them that the photograph showed a striking miner who was on his way to a fancy dress party as a butler to raise funds for the Militant Tendency.

officers

I've been a butler for nearly thirty years, and over that time I've seen many changes in the world of domestic service. Whilst it may have been acceptable years ago for an employer to beat his below-the-stairs staff, that is not the case today.

I accept that I had done wrong, but by thrashing me in front of the other servants, Mr Bragg overstepped the mark and I felt that I could no longer remain in his employ. I gave his lordship three months notice and left Bragg Towers forever."

Meringue, y' Lud!

"It is part of the butler's mantra that when his master calls, literally nothing is too much trouble. A good gentleman's gentleman will go to the ends of the earth to keep his boss happy. But some employers stretch this principle to the limit... and beyond. And one such was millionaire businessman and *Apprentice* star **SIR LORD ALAN SUGAR**, for whom I found myself butling a couple

> **❝ ...he wanted me to come up with a completely new cereal that was to appeal primarily to short, wealthy men in their 60s... ❞**

of years ago. I had seen Sir Sugar on the television and so I was aware of his pugnacious, perfectionist personality; it was clear that he demanded nothing less than excellence from everyone around him,

which is surprising when you consider the quality of Amstrad products. But nothing I had seen of him on the television could have prepared me for the rude awakening I had in my first day on the job.

The telephone by my bed rang at four in the morning and his Lordship brusquely announced that he wanted breakfast served at six on the dot. Nothing unusual about that; many successful people like to get the day off to an early start. But he then added that he wanted me to come up with a completely new and original cereal that was to appeal primarily to short, wealthy men in their 60s. He said that the British breakfast market was worth over £4billion a year, and I was to invent a new one, including packaging, a TV ad and full promotional strategy, and pitch it to buyers from the country's four leading supermarkets and on-line food retailers.

dog

I was a little sleepy, but I managed to come up with a sort of healthy toasted granola with meringue pieces. I couldn't decide whether to call it Tycoon Flakes, Golden Sir Alans or Rich Krispies, but I eventually plumped for Lord Sugarpuffs. My advertisement was to feature a man dressed as a meringue bouncing off a trampoline into a giant bowl of granola and milk. It was an ambitious idea, and by the time actor playing the meringue arrived for filming it was 5.45; I was pushed for time and I

have to admit that I rushed the editing. But it was ready for showing when Sir Alan came through the frosted glass door and sat down at his enormous breakfast table.

I pitched Lord Sugarpuffs to him, and he just sneered. He said that I had completely misjudged the market, as meringues were for children, not 60-year-old millionaires. What's more, he said the packaging was wrong, telling me: "It looks more like a box of bloody washing powder." And he was even more critical of my commercial. "It's a bloody joke," he said. "Unfortunately, nobody's laughing."

power clown

I was mortified. I have spent my career bending over backwards to provide good service to my employers. Before this, I had never fallen short. I explained that I was passionate about giving good domestic service and promised that, if he gave me another chance, I would give 10,000% and not let him down. But his Lordship accused me of being "a liar, a bullshitter and a schmoozer." Then he delivered his hammer blow.

"I like you, Green. You're a nice bloke," he said. "But there's no prizes for being nice in this game, and this whole breakfast has been a dog's dinner." He pointed his finger at me, and I knew what was coming next. **❞**

"You're fired."

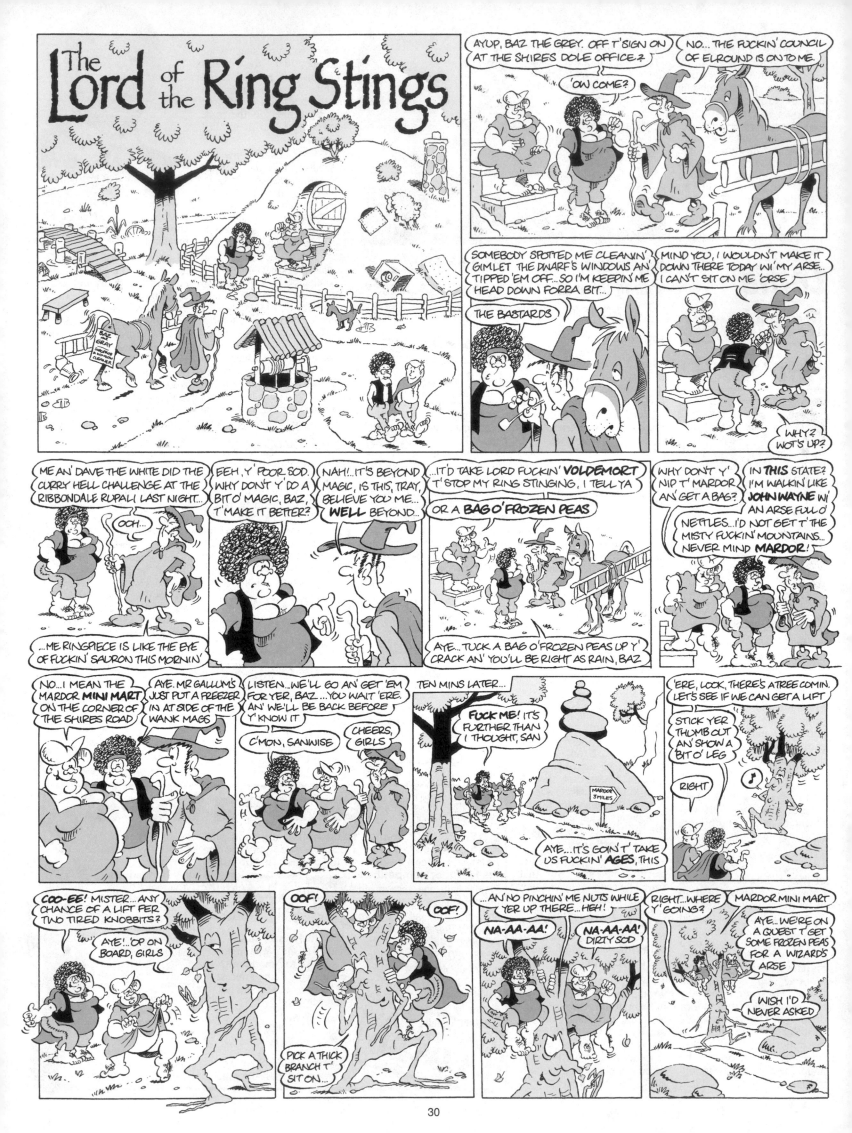

Continued over...

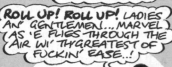

35

LETTERBOCKS

Viz Comic P.O. Box 841 Whitley Bay NE26 9EQ : letters@viz.co.uk

STAR LETTER

ACCORDING to an Oxfam report, half of the world's wealth is owned by 85 people, enough to fit on one London bus. They illustrate their report with a photo of the 159 London bus which runs from Paddington Basin to Streatham. Why anyone so wealthy would want to go to Streatham is beyond me. And why go by bus? Surely they'd have Rolls-Royces.

Alan Heath, e-mail

I ALWAYS enjoy watching *Lawrence of Arabia* when it comes on the telly. But even though it won lots of awards, I can't help thinking that perhaps it missed a trick. During one of the many scenes where they are camping in the desert, perhaps a busty young woman doing morning exercises could have had her bra suddenly fly off. I know the film is based on a true story but for all we know, this may well have happened.

Talbot Rothwell, Firkham-on-Sea

WHY is it that the people who are signed off with broken backs on the personal injury adverts are always well enough to appear in their own reconstructions? I'm no benefit-fiddling expert, but surely appearing on national TV falling off a ladder or slipping on a banana skin is a schoolboy error?

Matt Neave, e-mail

WELL done to the Newcastle jury who acquitted the two Glaswegians who bit actor Clive Mantle's ear off in self defence. I've long suspected Mantle of being the sort of monster who wakes at four in the morning and attacks drunken Scotsmen with his ear. Now it's been proved beyond reasonable doubt that that's the kind of man he is. Shame on him.

Geordie Bob, Newcastle

DURING the recent bad weather I have noticed that it's only the rivers that have flooded, whilst none of the canals in Britain burst their banks. So it seems to me that the answer is to simply replace all the rivers with canals and the job's a good one. All these big wigs down at the Environmental Agency should start earning their salaries with some lateral thinking instead of just blaming God.

Otis B Driftwood, e-mail

I SPOTTED this pair of tits on the surface of Mars. Do I win Star Letter?

Jake Cuthbertson, Middlesbrough

IT'S a shame they shot that poor giraffe at Copengagen Zoo. I would have happily had it. I'm out at work most of the day, but the lady from next door could have let it out at lunchtimes for a shit.

Ian Ping, Hull

HAVING just watched Tottenham Hotspurs v Manchester United, the commentator informed me that Man Utd were "away." Well assuming United are the ones who play in red, they were definitely there. In fact they won 2 - 0.

Miss F Boildegg, e-mail

I WISH ITV and Channel 4 would stop 'recapping' after every commercial break in their documentaries. Anyone who has been watching from the start knows what's going on. And anyone who comes in halfway through, well fuck them.

Crompton Wells, Tooting

DOES anybody wonder whether porn actor Ben Dover ever gets a furball?

Rev J Foucault, Truro

WITH reference to Rev. Foucault's letter *(above)*. What with the insistence nowadays on pornographic actresses shaving their pudendae all the time, I doubt very much whether Mr Dover ever brings up a furball. Whereas I'd imagine his predecessors in the 70s and 80s were bringing them up on set right, left and centre.

Fr Trevelyn Humbleman, Bodmin

I'VE just discovered that 'bonk' spelled backwards is 'knob'. Do any of your other readers know any words that are slightly saucy and make another slightly saucy word when spelled backwards? And 'tit' doesn't count because that's the same word both ways.

Jarvis Winkle, e-mail

THE Weather Girls sang with great confidence in 1982: "For the first time in history it's gonna start raining men." But if I'm not mistaken, that milestone was passed in 1941 when the paratroopers of the German Luftwaffe mounted Operation Mercury on Crete. Those Yanks take the credit for everything.

L Mills, e-mail

DO you think the Queen removes her white gloves when she wipes her arse, and if so does she bother to wash her hands before putting them back on? If there is anyone working in the royal laundry who has seen skidmarks on the inside of the her majesty's gloves, could they let me know?

David Mitson, e-mail

WHY don't people forearm smash each other any more?

Willy Mack, e-mail

BE KIND, RETWEET

Ha ha ha ha!

Gotta tweet this...

Gnn!

Mwuh!

Meanwhile in Wigan

Ha ha!

And Plymouth

Ha ha.

Anything?

Two retweets and a favourite.

Bit shit...

Hold still mate!

One quick pull we're laughing.

We should give him the cider.

Then he'll need to piss.

THEY say that certain types of music can take you to another place. This is very true; I was in the pub the other night and a James Arthur song was playing on the jukebox, so I went to another pub.

Peter Crompton, e-mail

WHY do folk think crotchless knickers are so sexy? Me and my girlfriend tried them and she couldn't stop laughing at my bollocks swinging out the gap.

Skipper McKipper, e-mail

WHAT'S all this women's cricket nonsense? Whatever next, men's dish-washing and nappy-changing competitions?

Peter Busby, e-mail

IMAGINE my surprise when I put a nob of butter in my frying pan and it turned into a "knob of butter." Can any of your readers beat that? Naturally, I put my foot through the oven and sent Lurpak the bill.

Gozo Gary, e-mail

✵ *Hmmm! Your picture aroused suspicion in the Viz office, Gary. Whilst the butter has clearly melted into a knob shape, complete with balls, shaft and glans, we suspect that a finger has been drawn down the top of the butter to produce the hog's eye. Of course, we can prove nothing and are giving you the benefit of the doubt, safe in the knowledge that if you have lied you will one day have to answer to a higher authority than us.*

PEOPLE say a bird in the hand is worth two in a bush. If you were holding something like a peacock or maybe a big owl or something, and in a nearby bush there was just a couple of seagulls or crows, then maybe it would be true. But what if you were holding a small pigeon or a budgie and there were two ostriches or golden eagles in the bush? And why would anyone be in that situation in the first place? People are strange.

George C Hill, e-mail

I'M really glad they made *Horny Shaved Housewives 13*, because I found that *Horny Shaved Housewives 12* left me with so many unanswered questions.

Ben Nicol, e-mail

HOW come cowboys always eat bacon and beans at the chuck wagon, yet you never see a pig in a western? Also, saloon doors seem to serve no purpose beyond making everyone look round when someone comes in. You can't lock them and if you did any thief would just walk under them and rob the till.

Edith Clunge, e-mail

WE'RE all familiar with the lifestyles of the people featured on *Benefits Street*, but in the interest of fairness, how about a reality series about fatcat corporate leeches called *Gated Community Tax Dodgers?* Come on Channel 4.

Sarah E Hall, e-mail

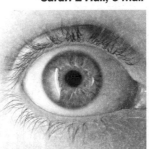

DAVID Attenborough claims that eyes came about as a result of Darwinian evolution. But in the Bible, Proverbs Ch.21 v.12 clearly states that God invented eyes. They can't both be right.

Tim Rusling, e-mail

TOP

LIFEGUARDS. Take your big chair home and use it at the family dinner table. Up there you'll have a good view of the area and can rush down to help anyone you see struggling with their dinner.

Spock, e-mail

ADVERTISERS. Stuck for a jingle for your latest project? How about some fucking whistling over a cunting ukulele?

Lowell Mills, e-mail

I DETEST visits from my Scotch brother-in-law as he always insists on bringing whisky with him. I wouldn't mind, but his stuff is always 15 years out of date.

Ian Docherty, e-mail

YOU never hear anything from The Horse Whisperer nowadays, do you?. I hope he isn't signing on because those bastards behind the glass always pretend they can't hear you and make you talk loud just to show you up.

C Dullworthy, Buxton

WHILST reminiscing on happier, more innocent times, I thought it might be nice if you could print some pictures to bring back memories of yesteryear. Perhaps a dog running out of a butcher's shop with a string of sausages hanging out of its mouth. Or maybe a schoolboy in a doctor's waiting room with a saucepan stuck on his

head. Failing that, how about a picture of a bloke kissing a bird's arse?

Uncle John, e-mail

MINI designers. Save time designing the next model by simply putting the plans of the last model on a photocopier and blowing it up slightly larger.

Philip Morley, e-mail

PROVE to your girlfriend that men can multi-task by thinking about her sister when having a wank.

D Slade, Oxfordshire

PRETEND you are a Premier League footballer by drawing all over one of your arms in Biro.

D Slade, Oxfordshire

ESTATE agents. 'Consists of', 'comprises' or 'is comprised of' but NOT 'comprises of'. Get it fucking right for once.

Dr Eric Queef, e-mail

SCIENTISTS in Australia. Find out the weight of the Earth by simply turning your kitchen scales upside down.

Mr Bobs, e-mail

THE ink tubes from Bic pens make ideal vaulting poles for spiders interested in athletics.

B Terrier, Surrey

UNSURE whether you're going to fart or follow through? Simply tuck the legs of your trousers into your socks and release a 'test dose'. Then examine your socks for signs of contamination. If all is clear, proceed. If not, visit the lavatory.

Dolly Giblets, Truro

AFFIX chicken wire over the top of a shopping trolley to make an ideal 'mobile home' for a parrot.

D Slade, Oxfordshire

ASPIRING actors. Avoid spending money on acting classes by just pretending to be a good actor. That's what acting is.

Ed O'Meara, e-mail

PRETEND you're a barmaid by standing outside a pub dressed in black with a fag dangling out your mouth.

Colonel Toothpaste, Tring

TIPS

toptips@viz.co.uk

IN the interests of recycling and saving the planet, wouldn't it be a good idea to use the little plastic discs left over from the centres of CDs and DVDs to make shirt buttons for the homeless?

Claudette Bonnaire, e-mail

Comedy Legend Returns to Stage

By our Comedy Correspondent Mr B. Gumby

IN A MOVE guaranteed to delight comedy fans the world over, the legendary *Monty Python Dead Parrot Sketch* yesterday announced that it is to reform. And such was the interest in the news that tickets for the shows sold out in *five minutes*.

The constituent words of the classic sketch have not been heard together in public since the early eighties, and in recent years fans of the 517 letter groups had given up hope of ever hearing them in public again.

But at a packed press conference in London's West End, the sketch's various words, a little greyer but still unbowed, announced that they would be performing a live reunion.

The locutions, some repeated as many as seven times, will perform a number of dates at the O2 Arena with a world tour possible in the future.

negotiations

Speaking for the aggregation of phonemes, the word 'plumage' told reporters: 'The time seemed right to give it one last go around the block before we're all too old."

According to insiders, negotiations were tricky, with the word

Registering a complaint: Some actors saying the words yesterday

'boutique' holding out for a film rather than live show. And the word 'fjords' was initially totally opposed to the whole idea.

"The sketch would not have been the same without the word fjords. It would probably have been replaced by 'mountains' or 'lakes' which would not have had the same comic effect," they said.

"But in the end it agreed as it had a potentially expensive divorce settlement on the horizon," the source added.

EXCLUSIVE!

Dough-No!

BRITAIN'S BAKERS were last night in a state of panic as the nation's doughnuts were struck by a mystery virus. The infection, known as 1DV16, causes the popular sticky treats to become shrunken and flaccid, and if left untreated can lead to the jam leaking out the side.

The contagion was first identified in a small batch of French doughnuts imported from the continent back in January, but has spread rapidly throughout the country and has been identified in doughnuts from places as far apart as Lands End, John O'Groats and Leeds. It is now believed that up to 90% of UK doughnuts could be affected.

"This is a disaster for the industry," said Richard Hearne, spokesmen of the British Guild of Master doughnuteers. "It is no exaggeration to say that if this virus isn't eradicated, we could be looking at the end of doughnuts in Britain."

"Bakers are standing on a precipice, staring into the abyss," he added.

Bakers in Jam over Doughnuts

Meanwhile, food industry chiefs are understood to be urgently looking at a series of drastic measures to halt the spread of the virus. These include:

● *A BAN* on the import of doughnuts from overseas, especially France

● *RESTRICTIONS* on the movement and sale of doughnuts

● *TOUGH PENALTIES* for shops selling doughnuts in multi-packs where conditions are ideal for IDV16 toxins to flourish

eclair

The new infection comes hot on the heels of other patisserie-borne epidemics, including Mad Eclair Disease, Meringue Flu and Bovine Spongecake Encephalopathy, which have decimated the UK baking industry.

agutter

"We've been making doughnuts in this shop for four generations," said Dover baker Frubert Bollywood. "There's never been anything wrong with them before, but now every batch I take out of the fryer is limp and has all jam leaking out."

"I have to take them out the back and burn them on a pyre. It's heartbreaking," he added.

adrainpipe

Prime Minister David Cameron said that Downing Street was setting up a specialised emergency committee to deal with the crisis. "We're going to call it MAMBA, because like COBRA it's the name of a snake and it sounds really cool and rock," he told reporters.

"The first M and A will probably stand for Major Action and the B more than likely will be for Bakery or Bakers."

"If anyone's got any ideas what the middle M and the last A could stand for, we'd love to hear them. Send me a DM on Facebook or a tweet," Mr Cameron added.

Doughnut touch: Closely-packed bakery shelves are ideal breeding ground for virus.

DOUGHNUTS

DOUGHNUTS are the tasty treat we all love to eat, but have you ever stopped to wonder: *What are they? Where did they come from? Who owned the smallest one ever made and exactly how small was it?* Here are...

1 UNLIKE peanuts, Brazil nuts and cashew nuts, doughnuts don't actually contain nuts, so they're perfectly safe for allergy sufferers to eat. But wait - they may have been produced in a factory where nut-based products are handled, and so could well contain minute traces of nuts, certainly enough to cause a violent allergic reaction that could prove fatal.

2 THE founder of the Krispy Kreme doughnuts empire was notoriously bad at spelling, and genuinely believed that the words "Crispy" and "Creme" were spelled with a K. By the time his error was pointed out to him, it was too late as he had already had all the boxes printed. Luckily he was better at doughnut making than he was at spelling, and his business went on to be hugely successful.

3 THERE are two different types of doughnuts, known as "ring" and "jam" doughnuts.

Both of them have a hole in the middle, in the former case one which penetrates the doughnut along its radial axis and in the latter case, one encased concentrically within the doughnut itself.

4 MATHEMATICIANS are able to describe the two different types of doughnut in terms of their topological structure. Consisting of one unbroken plane enveloping an intrinsic hole, the jam doughnut is a *sphere*, whilst the ring donut is known as a *torus*.

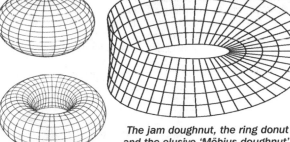

The jam doughnut, the ring donut and the elusive 'Möbius doughnut'.

Geometric topologists at the Krispy Kreme Institute in Massachusetts are thought to be working on a third type of doughnut, with three planes and two holes.

5 REGULAR readers might expect the smallest ever doughnut to have belonged to the world's smallest man Calvin Phillips. They might furthermore suppose that the said doughnut was about the size of a Polo mint or Cheerio. However, they would be wrong, because Phillips suffered from a severe peanut allergy, and studiously avoided doughnuts in case they had been produced in a factory where nut-based products were handled. Even a minute trace of minute traces of nuts found in a doughnut the size of a Polo mint or Cheerio would have been enough to cause a fatal allergic reaction. In fact, so serious was Phillips's allergy that he never went anywhere without an Epipen the size of a gramophone needle.

6 THE smallest ever doughnut ironically belonged to Robert Pershing Wadlow, the world's tallest man. The doughnut, which was three-quarters the size of a normal doughnut, was presented to the nine-foot tall Illinois giant by Chang and Eng Bunker, China's fattest Siamese twins.

7 ASK a motorcyclist if he'd like a doughnut and he'll probably rev his bike up so fast that the back wheel loses traction and the bike pivots around the braked front end, leaving a circular black trail of burnt rubber - or "doughnut" - on the tarmac.

8 ACTUALLY, come to think of it, you'd probably have to ask him to "do a doughnut", rather than whether he'd "like" one, for him to do that.

9 LOTS of tv characters have been named after doughnuts, such as Doughnut out of *The Double Deckers* and many, many more.

10 BRINSLEY Ford, who played Doughnut's fellow gang member Spring in the series, later went on to find fame as the drummer out of reggae band Aswad. However the group never managed to top the charts with a song about doughnuts. Or anything else for that matter.

A Hole Lot of Memories

☆ *Stars of stage, screen and train robbery reminisce about doughnuts* ☆

Buzz Aldrin, *Astronaut*
"I'll never forget my first doughnut, because I was stood on the Moon when I was eating it. My mom had packed my snap-tin before we blasted off from Cape Canarvinal, and popped a doughnut in as a special treat for when I got on the lunar surface. It tasted delicious, but the problem was I got all sugar and jam round my mouth and I couldn't wipe it off because of my space helmet. It took a whole week before I got the chance to take my hat off and wipe all that sticky gubbins off my face."

Ronnie Biggs, *Late Train Robber*
"As a simple East End lad growing up on the bombsites after the war, doughnuts were an unimaginable luxury to the likes of me. So I had wait until I'd done the Great Train Robbery before I had enough folding stuff in me old back sky rocket to afford one. The day after the blag, I went to the nearest bakery to our hideout and bought myself a bag of four with a fifty knicker note. I think this must've raised suspicions a bit and we were caught by the filth a week later."

Shirley Bassey, *Flingtitted Diva*
"I always request half a dozen strawberry jam doughnuts as part of my backstage rider when I'm doing a concert. But I can't eat them, because I insist that they are covered in diamonds and they would break my teeth if I took a bite. If the diamonds aren't big enough, or there's too few of them stuck to the doughnuts, I have a tantrum and scream until I'm sick."

Ben Dover, *Auteur*
"Doughnuts are packed with carbohydrates, protein and calories, so I always eat a dozen big ones to give myself an energy boost just before I go on set to perform. When you see me licking my lips in one of my films, it's not in anticipation of all the ladies' fannies and tits I'm about to get, I'm just licking the sugar and jam off."

Simon Cowell, *Talent Magnate*
"Whenever I fancy a doughnut, I get a runner to go out and buy thousands of them for me. Then I have them paraded in front of me while I look bored. Then, over an arse-numbing twelve-week selection process, I whittle down the doughnuts until I'm left with just a single winner, which I then eat."

Kim Jong-Un, *Despotic North Korean Nutjob*
"You don't get cheeks this chubby from avoiding doughnuts, I can tell you! I love 'em, and though it pains me to say it, I have to admit the most delicious ones are Krispy Kreme ones made by evil, decadent, capitalist pigs in America. I have a selection box of a dozen assorted flown over from a Krispy Kreme store in Pittsburgh PA every day. After they are delivered to the People's Palace, everyone involved in their import - from the pilot of my presidential jet to the servant who brings them to me - is thrown to a pack of hungry dogs. Each box of doughnuts costs about 250 lives and my favourite flavour is Chocolate Dreamcake. Yum yum!"

Fay Ripley's Believe it or Not about PIANOS

IN THE olden days, no home was complete without a piano, and every evening was spent singing round it. But nowadays, with the advent of video games, 3D television and 24-hour on-demand internet pornography, the old-fashioned "Joanna" has sadly fallen out of favour. In fact by 2007, sales of upright pianos were so poor that Prime Minister Tony Blair appointed petrolmouth motorhead Jeremy Clarkson as the country's new "Piano Czar", charged with the task of making pianos cool again. However, in his usual outspoken style, the *Top Gear* host made a number of controversial and offensive comments about pianos, and was quickly removed from his post.

THE 20TH century's most famous concert pianist was Bobby Crush (real name Robert Crushworth), who was best known for his friendly stage persona, flamboyant costumes and cheeky winks to the audience whilst playing. Like his musical hero Liberace, Crush's hands were bedecked with priceless rings containing diamonds, rubies, emeralds and Swarovski crystals. Indeed, so valuable was his stage jewellery that Crush routinely kept a gun in his piano stool to fend off theft attempts whilst tinkling the ivories at northern working men's clubs and Butlinses. Several times during his career, he was forced to keep would-be robbers at bay during a performance.

WHEN Uri Gagarin's Vostok rocket blasted off on April 12th 1961, the first man in space wasn't alone. For Soviet scientists had also jammed an upright piano into his capsule, with the intention that Gagarin should become the first human to play the Russian national anthem whilst in orbit. However, the cockpit was so cramped and Gagarin's spacesuit gloves were so bulky that the hapless cosmonaut found it hard to hit the correct keys or operate the sustain pedal successfully, and his performance was littered with bum notes and false starts.

ON D-DAY in August 1944, one of the first British soldiers to land on Omaha Beach was honky-tonk pianist Russ Conway, seconded from ENSA by special request of US Army General George Paton in a bid to boost Allied morale. Seated at a specially-constructed upright amphibious landing piano, Conway was pushed up the Normandy beach-head whilst performing a medley of his popular hits, including *China Tea, Side Saddle* and *Toy Balloons*.

IN THE prudish Victorian era, piano legs were kept covered up in case their erotic curves inflamed the passions of the gentleman of the house. We can look back on such times and laugh about it now, as modern pianos have unsexy square legs that can be safely left on show. Instead of resorting to fantasising about piano legs, twentieth century men instead are able to slake their desires with a bewildering selection of internet pornographies, including gilf gonzo, German self-scat and Asian babes POV double facial.

Next week: Fay Ripley's BELIEVE IT OR NOT about **Harpsichords**

41

Real life Time Lord breaks silence after 51 years

"I AM WHO, I AM!"

EVERY SATURDAY teatime since 1963, millions of viewers have tuned in to watch the latest exciting episode of *Dr Who*. Whether battling the Daleks, fighting the Cybermen or being chased by giant spiders from Metabilis 3, for more than half a century the Doctor's time-travelling adventures have kept us thrilled as we peek at the screen from behind the settee. But even as we watch his latest narrow escape from the evil clutches of yet another alien foe, we know it's all just pretend. Or at least, we think it is…

The Doctor will see you now: Reg with a cardboard cut-out of his real-life Tardis, which was at the garage having a new fan belt put on when our photographer called round.

For a South Wales man has now come forward who claims *he* was the original inspiration for the character of Dr Who. Unemployed supermarket trolley collector Hilton Dullard says that he is a real Time Lord from the planet Gallifrey, and that a BBC employee got the idea for the long-running sci-fi serial after meeting him at a party.

He told us: "I met a bloke who worked in television at a house-warming in Caldicot back in 1962. We got chatting and I told him all about my adventures fighting monsters through space and time in my Tardis."

EXCLUSIVE!

"On reflection, I probably should have kept my trap shut. But it was just a bit of small talk. It never occurred to me that I was handing them the idea for a long-running smash hit TV series on a plate," he continued.

"A couple of weeks later I put the telly on just as the first episode of *Dr Who* was starting. I couldn't believe what I was seeing. The character on screen was me in everything but name," he added.

Dullard listed a catalogue of similarities between his own life and that of the TV Doctor:

- *Both travel through time and space in a blue police box which is bigger on the inside than it is on the outside.*

- *Both use a sonic screwdriver to fix things.*

- *Both wear floppy hats, bow ties and colourful knitted scarves.*

- *Both have waged a series of battles against extra-terrestrial foes on alien planets that look like disused gravel pits.*

Dullard told us: "I really don't mind the beeb taking my life and turning it into a popular and long-running television show. It's actually quite flattering. But they've had to leave the most interesting parts of my adventures out of their scripts. Because, whilst *Dr Who* is a show aimed at children, most of what I get up to on my intergalactic time travels is certainly not suitable for pre-watershed viewing, I can tell you."

Now, in an X-rated tell-all memoir, Dullard, 38, is set to lift the lid on his galaxy-wide bed-hopping life.

telly

"Just like the real Doctor off the telly, I'm 900 years old and I've regenerated twelve times. It just so happens that my latest incarnation began in 1976 in the Maternity Unit at Monmouth General Hospital. And after being around for so long, you can bet I've had my share of amorous adventures across the Universe and through time," he added.

"I'll never forget this one time. The Tardis was playing up, pulling to the left, so I landed on the nearest planet to do a few running repairs. I went for a look round and as luck would have it I got captured by some alien wasp creatures. They were about the same height as a man, and walked on two legs. Their top pair of legs was used like our arms, and their middle pair of legs just stuck out at right angles and bounced up and down when they walked. They took me back to their hive, which had doors, rocky, uneven walls and a completely flat floor.

george

They took me to their leader. I couldn't believe it when I saw him; he was just a big brain in a large perspex jar. He had no mouth, but I was able to hear his thoughts and he sounded a bit like Bungle from Rainbow speaking through a Stylophone. Every time he spoke, the brain sort of lit up as if there was a light bulb inside it. He said I was an invader on his planet and ordered his wasp-like minions to sting me to death.

florence & fred

When you've been a Time Lord as long as I have, you learn a few things about how to deal with hostile life forms. I quickly used my sonic screwdriver to blow the fuse on the giant brain's life support apparatus. There was a big flash - a bit like a theatrical squib going off - and the light in the brain started to flash.

fred & ginger

All the time while this was happening, its voice was getting higher and higher, saying the same thing over and over again. Then the floor started shaking and lumps of very lightweight rock began to fall from the cave roof and bounce off the floor. All the wasps were crushed to death

Continued over…

Wasp a rip-off: Dr Who insect monsters were copied from Hilton's story.

as the whole hive collapsed. Luckily I managed to get out just in time.

There, waiting for me outside in the gravel pit was a beautiful woman wearing a dress made from a material I'd never seen before. It looked a bit like those sheets of silvery plastic that are left over after sequins have been punched out of them. She was also wearing a lot of silver eye make-up, a pair silver motorcycle boots and her hair was like tinsel. She explained that she was the Queen of the planet and her people - the Moebians - had been enslaved by the wasp men but now they were free - all thanks to yours truly.

planet

That's where the television episode would have ended, but in real life things went a bit further, I can tell you. As a thank-you for rescuing her planet from the evil aliens, she said I could do anything I wanted with her, sex-wise. And let me tell you, I did, to her tits and everything! And remember that silvery tinsel hair I was telling you about? Well, the collar matched the cuffs, if you know what I mean. And once I'd gone off I jumped in my Tardis, nipped back 20 minutes and did it all again!"

The TV doctor is a loner, whose relationship with his companion is never anything but professional. However, says Hilton, in real life nothing could be further from the truth.

"On telly, the Doctor always has

an attractive young female such as Lala Ward, Jo Grant or Billie Piper as his assistant, although he always keeps his relationship with them on a professional basis. The most he ever gets off one of his companions is a peck on the cheek after he's saved them from the Daleks. But in real life nothing could be further from the truth, and I've had it off with every single one of my assistants.

express

One of my assistants was a Stone Age warrior woman who I picked up during a trip to fight some Sontarans on another planet in the third sector of the Andromeda Nebula. When I got there, they were about to sacrifice her to some maggot monsters when I rescued her in my Tardis.

She was very attractive, with surprisingly clean hair and good teeth and a sort of bikini made from chamois leathers. She spoke a primitive form of English - a bit like a Red Indian from an old cowboy film - so she was able to make it clear to me that she was happy to express her gratitude to me in a physical way. Well I'm 900 years old and I've been round the block a few times, so I didn't need telling twice.

thompson

I decided to do her over the control panel and moments later we were at it like knives, lost in throes of her animalistic cavewoman passion. During one particularly forceful thrust up her I accidentally knocked a lever that sent the Tardis into warp drive, making the perspex cylinder in the middle of the controls go up and down in time with my pushes. Before I knew it we were travelling through space and time at a hundred times the speed of light. It was an intoxicating feeling and I knew I couldn't hold on much longer.

hingsen

In the end I shot my bolt just as we went over the event horizon. Anyone who's ever had an orgasm whilst travelling at a hundred times the speed of light through the central vortex of a black hole will know how shattering that is. At such a point of singularity, the concept of time has no meaning and an instant can last for eternity. Despite this, thirty seconds later my Charlie was back on the slack so I gave it a couple of wipes on my scarf and set the Tardis coordinates for my home in South Wales again.

mathius

I recounted this adventure to the man at the party and thought no more about it. But imagine my surprise when I turned on the telly the next Saturday to see *Dr Who*'s new companion Leela - a sexy Stone Age warrior woman in a chamois leather bikini. I sent the BBC a bill for £25 for the copyright on my story and characters.

Have they paid it yet? *Have they Daleks."*

Another time Hilton was forced to send the BBC a bill for £25 was when they took yet another idea from his real life time-travelling adventures and turned it into a Dr Who series - the Sea Devils.

"The Sea Devils were clearly based on a race of creatures I encountered on the planet Siluria that I also told the man at the party about. But of course, the soft, sanitised children's version of the tale that they showed at teatime on a Saturday night was nothing like the real life adult adventure that I was involved in on the other side of the Milky Way.

I was forced to land on the planet's surface after getting caught in a tractor beam when I went out in the Tardis to get some milk and a paper. It was an alien world unlike any I'd ever been on anywhere in the universe, but it looked a bit like Brighton beach. Suddenly, as I wandered about on the pebbles, these strange creatures began emerging from sea.

whole lotta

They were about the same height as a man, but they had reptilian heads and green scaly skin, with the scales particularly big where the head, arms and legs joined the body They wore strange clothes that looked like a string vest that had been ripped a bit, and they moved slowly and deliberately as they surfaced, almost as if they were just standing up after kneeling in the shallow water.

They captured me and took me back to their undersea lair,

which had more netting and shells hanging from the roof, and once again a very smooth floor, where they tied me to a chair. Then the Queen of the Sea Devils came in and I couldn't believe my eyes. She was as beautiful as her subjects were ugly. She was the same colour as them, but on her it looked more like make-up than scaly amphibian skin. She wore a long spangly dress with a big collar sticking up, a slash up the side with one of her legs sticking out, and a big hole down one side in the middle so you could see her stomach. She looked as bit like a green Rula Lenska.

she'd always wanted to have sex with a Time Lord, but if I disappointed her I would be put to death

Diabolical: Idea for undersea monsters the Sea Devils was stolen by BBC man at party, says Dullard.

She explained that she'd always wanted to have sex with a Time Lord. She said she'd set me free if I satisfied her, but if I disappointed her I would be put to death by her Sea Devil minnions. With that she undid a clasp at her neck and her clothes fell to the floor. Despite being green and having lobster-like antennae sticking out of her head, her tits and fanny were just like you'd get on a normal woman, and I got to work.

Having to perform under that sort of pressure would leave most men desperately trying to thumb in a slacky. But life and death situations are meat and drink to me, and I rose to the occasion magnificently, taking the Queen to heights of ecstasy she had only ever dreamt about, over and over again till we both collapsed exhausted on the floor.

As we lay in the undersea afterglow of our passion, she

...she said I could do anything I wanted with her, sex-wise. And let me tell you, I did... to her tits and everything!

Companion piece: Time Lord's cave-woman assistant was a sight for dinosaur eyes.

My friend Billie: A photo of Daisy taken outside his tardis. Dullard believes the similarity to Piper is more than coincidence.

told me I had given her one so well that she was not only going to let me live, she was also going to leave the human race out of her plans to destroy the Universe with a death ray. And the fact that the earth is still here is a testament to the fact that I am telling the truth.

It's a wonderful memory. The only fly in the ointment is my invoice to the BBC, which has still not been paid more than forty years later."

A further £25 bill that has yet to be paid concerns the character of Dr Who's companion Rose, who Dullard maintains was based on one of his own assistants.

"When the series was revived in 2005, I was amazed to see the Doctor's new assistant Rose Tyler, played by Billie Piper, was the dead spit of one of my own assistants, a cracking young blonde piece called Daisy. Well it was obvious they'd simply changed her name to a different flower, but everything else about her was exactly the same. Except, in contrast to the sweet-natured innocent girl on screen, my version was a right dirty goer.

anomaly

I remember this one time, we were in the Tardis, travelling through the fourth Quadrant of the Neptune Nebula when we went through a tear in the space-time continuum and an anomaly happened. Suddenly, instead of just Daisy and me in the Tardis, there was Daisy, me and all my eleven previous incarnations.

My companion's face was a picture, and I'm sure I don't have to explain what happened next, but I will. Licking her lips lasciviously,

Daisy suggested a twelve-way Dr Who gang-bang. Needless to say, all of the versions of me were up for the idea, including the earliest black and white version who was by now very old indeed, and I was soon stripping off my various eccentric costumes ready for the forthcoming orgy.

anemone

All of me pulled a train on her. I was first up ... and second ... and third and so on! It was amazing. Anyone who's had a dozen orgasms all at the same time whilst enjoying their own sloppy seconds, thirds, fourths, fifths ... all the way up to elevenths ... will know what I'm on about. Then we went through another anomaly and all the other versions of me vanished back to their own dimension and it was just me and Daisy again. She told me I was the best twelve shags she'd ever had.

analogy

Needless to say, all twelve television Dr Whos later appeared in an episode of the series. That's another £25 the BBC owe me, but of course they still haven't paid up. How the BBC have the nerve to fine me for not having a television licence after all the money they've made out of me I do not know.

> **Daisy suggested a twelve-way Dr Who gang-bang. Needless to say, all of the versions of me were up for the idea**

I know I could just get in the Tardis and nip back in time to when they sent me my final reminder and get one, but it's the principle of the thing."

A BBC spokesman told us he was aware of Hilton's accusations of plagiarism. He told us: "Dr Who was a successful programme a good thirteen years before this gentleman was born. Our lawyers say we should just ignore him and he will probably just go away."

But Dullard brushes their objections aside. He told us: "Yes, it is true that I was born in 1976 and Dr Who started in 1963. But that can be explained easily as I'm a Time Lord."

"Last week I was invited to a party in Caldicot in 1962, and I nipped along in my Tardis. Ask anyone who was there, if they're not dead by now. Actually, I think they're all dead," he added.

Who's Shoes Are Thoose?

OVER the last 51 years, Dr Who has gone through 12 different incarnations, and each one has had his own eccentric taste in footwear. Can you match these four pairs of shoes to their original Time Lord wearers?

A  These smart hand-made brogues are definitely the real McCoy. But to which short-lived, rather unsuccessful Doctor and former Vision On jester do they belong?

B These wellington boots would have served this ex-Doctor well when he was shoving his arm up a cow's fanny in his previous incarnation as a Yorkshire Dales vet.

C  These sandals are size 13 - that's a Baker's dozen. But to which Baker do they belong? Clue - it's not the one you never watched and won't be able to remember.

D The Tennant who once inhabited these shoes has since moved onto better things, including an acclaimed Hamlet at the RSC and adverts for Virgin Broadband.

Send your completed entry to: Dr Who Shoes Competition, PO Box 841, Whitley Bay, NE26 9EQ to arrive no later than 3rd of November.

Who Do You Think You Are?

A MYSTERY man found wandering alone along Brighton Beach with no memory of who he was or how he got there has been identified as the sixth *Dr Who* **COLIN BAKER.**

The actor, 71, who had spent the last 18 months at Brighton General Infirmary, was identified after a porter recognised him on the cover of a 1985 *Dr Who* annual in a charity shop.

driftwood

Doctors believe that Baker, who played the time-travelling character between 1984 and 1986 - may have banged his head on the pier whilst collecting driftwood on the beach back in summer 2013. "His injuries brought on an attack of amnesia," said a hospital spokesman. "He simply had no recollection whatsoever of his previous life."

Mystery beach man identified at last

Baker was later re-united with his wife and family, who hadn't realised he was missing.

SOFA, SO GOOD

Scary sci-fi series sets settee sales soaring

FURNITURE retailers are reporting booming sales as TV viewers flock to buy sofas to hide behind whilst watching *Dr Who*. Since the BBC began broadcasting the new series, with *Peter Capaldi* taking over the title role from Matt Smith, many stores have been forced to take on extra staff to cope with the hugely increased demand.

"For the first time in our history, we're not having a sale," said DFS chairman Humphrey Draylon. "We're not offering interest-free credit with nothing to pay until 2016, and we're actually having to put our prices up just so we'll be left with some stock in the shop."

"I've never known anything like it. Our sales have gone through the roof," he added.

barker

Meanwhile there were ugly scenes at Barker & Stonehouse in Gateshead as shoppers fought over the last three-seater Chesterfield in the store. Police were forced to call in mounted officers in an attempt to quell violent scuffles as prospective settee purchasers

EXCLUSIVE!

battled over the buttoned leather couch. 16 people were arrested and 20 taken to hospital with minor injuries following the riot. Prime Minister David Cameron appealed for calm as panic buying began to spread throughout the country, with the Twitter hashtag *#NoSofasLeft* trending throughout the UK. Following an emergency meeting of the Downing Street COBRA committee, the government advised the public to keep their heads.

hazlehurst

"There is no need to panic. There are plenty of sofas to go round, but demand is exceptionally high at the

moment, leading to minor supply chain problems," said a No.10 spokesman. "Until stocks can be replenished, a very serviceable sofa for hiding behind whilst watching Dr Who can be made by putting three kitchen chairs in a line and draping a blanket over them," he continued.

But his words seemingly fell on deaf ears, as public anxiety over settee

Settee limits: Sofa stocks are running out fast, say experts, whilst PM David Cameron (left) appealed for calm.

levels continued to grow. In Basildon, Essex, a large furniture warehouse was looted and set on fire by a mob of *Dr Who* fans after rumours that there was a sofa in it proved to be groundless.

And in Wiltshire, a removal van was chased along the A354 by a gang of leather-clad mutants with mohican haircuts driving a motley assortment of stripped-down military vehicles. The truck was eventually driven off the road and ransacked just outside Blandford St Mary, from where the whooping bandits carried off their prize - a 2-seater sofa in an orange and brown velour with teak arm-cappings and Queen Anne-style feet.

Who Do You Who?

WITH A DOZEN different Whos to choose from, it's often difficult to decide just which one is our favourite Doctor. But we all know exactly what we want when we go to McDonalds. And according to TV shrink Dr RAJ PERSAUD, *the two things are inextricably linked*. "The area of the brain which decides what you order at Maccy-Ds is directly connected by a neural pathway to the bit of the hypothalamus responsible for deciding which Dr Who you prefer," says Dr Persaud. "Believe it or not, a trained psychiatrist - even one who's temporarily struck off for plagiarism - can tell you your favourite Doctor simply by finding out what you order at your favourite fast food restaurant."

Large Big Mac Meal with Strawberry Thick Shake and Smarties McFlurry

"The person who ordered this meal has a big appetite. Not for them a small grilled chicken salad, a cup of tea and no pudding. They eat to the max and they prefer their Dr Who just the same - big and brash and with plenty of sauce. And nobody fits the bill better than the fourth Doctor - TOM BAKER."

Cheeseburger, Medium Fries and a Coke

"It's an everyday, run-of-the-mill order. Those who buy this uninspiring, unimaginative lunch will similarly like an everyday, run-of-the-mill, uninspiring, unimaginative Dr Who. This meal's eater would undoubtedly choose the Dr Who with the most adequate, sparkle-free and ultimately forgettable performance - PETER DAVISON."

Filet-O-Fish, Medium Fries, Oasis and an Apple Pie

"By ordering this unusual selection - and opting to wait for ten minutes whilst their seafood burger is removed from the back of the deepfreeze - this person is really thinking outside the box. Their favourite Dr Who would therefore be a similarly left-field, bizarre and inexplicable choice; the sixth Doctor - COLIN BAKER."

Happy Meal

"The eater of the Happy Meal - a gaily coloured cardboard box containing a simple hamburger, a small bag of chips and a cheap plastic toy, is a person who yearns for the innocence of childhood. Therefore their favourite Doctor Who is the first one they remember from when they were young - WILLIAM HARTNELL."

WITH *Peter Capaldi* just starting his stint as the Doctor, it's already time to start speculating about WHO will be his successor. And for the first time it's possible that the next inhabitant of the Tardis might be a Time Lady rather than a Time Lord. BBC bosses are reported to be keen to sweep away the glass ceiling that has prevented women from becoming Dr Whos for more than half a century. But which actress should be cast in the iconic role as the first female Dr Who. We've asked Boyd Vacuous, showbiz editor of *Take a Shit* magazine, to take a look at the Top Five lady contenders for the most coveted role in television and speculate...

Just Who will be the First Lady Doctor?

Angela Lansbury ~ *Happy Shopper Miss Marple*

THE VETERAN *Bedknobs and Broomsticks* stalwart is already a seasoned Time Lady, with an impressive 88-years of time travel - albeit all in the same direction - under her belt. Lansbury's decades of solving daytime TV crimes as *Murder She Wrote*'s amateur sleuth Jessica Fletcher would also stand her in good stead when it comes to facing up to murderous foes such as Cybermen, Daleks and the Master. But at nearly 90, her days of running round spaceship corridors may well be numbered. One slip whilst being chased by an angry Sontaran and she could easily fall and break a hip.

Young Male Companion: *Harry Styles*
Who Potential: *61%*
Who rating: *7/10*
Whoability: *****
Overall Who Quotient: *Medium*

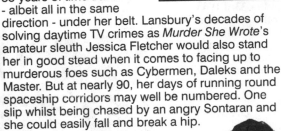

Madonna ~ *Pointy-titted popster*

THE QUEEN OF POP famously sang "Who's That Girl". Little did she know it at the time, but this question would one day turn out to be a statement of fact. For many believe that Madge could well be in line to take over from Peter Capaldi as the thirteenth Dr Who. Already an accomplished movie actress, with roles in such hit movies as *Desperately Seeking Susan*, *Body of Evidence* and *Evita*, the *Like a Virgin* singer would undoubtedly make the move to the small screen with aplomb. The BBC costume department would also save money, as her typical stage outfit of fishnet tights, thigh-length boots and pointy-titted basque already look like something cooked up for a low-budget TV sci-fi series. Also, just like the Doctor, she has hardly aged in the last 50 years. Were she to bring the same charged eroticism to the series that she does to her sexually-charged stage shows, perhaps simulating oral sex with her sonic screwdriver or straddling Davros's wheelchair with her legs akimbo, she could bring a whole new audience of frustrated, masturbating middle-aged men to the Saturday teatime favourite.

Young Male Companion: *Jellybean Benitez*
Who Potential: *25%*
Who rating: *9/10*
Whoability: *******
Overall Who Quotient: *Severe*

Lady Di ~ *Former Princess of Hearts*

CONTRARY to what you might think, being dead should pose no obstacle to the tragic England's Rose becoming the Dr Who of Hearts, as she could simply take a Tardis trip back in time to before that fateful 1997 day in Paris and decide to put her seatbelt on before being driven through a narrow tunnel at 90mph by a pissed-up Frenchman. Once in the role, the qualities that made her such a marvellous princess would stand her in good stead as a Time Lord. When faced with a menace such as a Menoptera, an Ice Warrior or a Quark, she would merely have to look at them with her big doe eyes from under her fringe and simper, completely disarming them with her charm and elegance. As in life, she would ask for nothing in return except for a lavish lifestyle, several stately homes and millions of pounds tax free.

Young Male Companion: *Paul Burrell*
Who Potential: *74%*
Who rating: *5/10*
Whoability: ******
Overall Who Quotient: *Moderate to High*

Lily Savage ~ *Scouse comedian and dog lover*

WHEREVER the gravel-voiced leggy lovely travelled throughout the Cosmos, she would bring the character of Dr Who down to earth. Plain-talking no-nonsense Dr Lily would give monsters a taste of their own medicine, using her acid Scouse tongue to send the Slitheen slithering back where they came from and scaring the Daleks back to Skaro. Also, she also already owns a dog - Bullseye - which could appear in the show as a K-9-style robot companion wrapped in foil, saving the BBC trick photography department a fortune in special effects.

Young Male Companion: *Wee Jimmy Krankie*
Who Potential: *4%*
Who rating: *8/10*
Whoability: ***
Overall Who Quotient: *Low to Middling*

White Dee ~ *Benefits Queen of Hearts*

THE REALITY television benefits queen isn't afraid of anybody on this planet or the next, and would thus make a formidable adversary for any alien life forms attempting to colonise our planet. However, her weakness is spiders - White Dee goes even whiter at the thought of them - so if she ever finds herself on the notorious spider planet Metabilis 3, her comapnion will have to be first out of the Tardis with a large glass and a birthday card to remove any of the offending creatures lurking outside. Another drawback to the *Benefits Street* star taking on the role is that no matter where she was in the fabric of the space-time contiuum, she would have to return to present day earth every Thursday morning to sign on at her local DSS office in Winsom Green, Birmingham.

Young Male Companion: *Anton du Beke*
Who Potential: *99%*
Who rating: *3/10*
Whoability: ********
Overall Who Quotient: *Moderate with rainy spells later*

HE'S BEEN ON OUR SCREENS for more than half a century and he's as familiar a part of our childhood Saturday teatimes as the classified football results, beans on toast and a light entertainment show hosted by a sex offender. *Dr Who* enthusiasts - so-called "Whovians" - claim to know every detail of the doctor's amazing adventures through space and time, from his birthdate on the Planet Gallifrey to what sort of batteries his sonic screwdriver takes. But how much do these tragic sci-fi anoraks REALLY know? Here are...

10 time-travelling tit-bits that 'Whovians' never Knewvians about...

DOCTOR WHO

make-up to create hideous toothy alien monsters for the Doctor to battle against. However, in 1987 production budgets were slashed and producers were forced to cast Ken Dodd instead.

8 **THE** series is watched and loved by everyone all over the world... except by the Amish people of Pennsylvania. This is because every Doctor, from William Hartnell to Peter Capaldi, has had buttons on his coat, and the Amish people don't believe in buttons.

1 **LIKE** his legions of fans, Dr Who is a loner, although unlike them he doesn't still live with his mum. However, back in 1963 when the series first aired, his companion was his own granddaughter. This shows that at some point he must have had a son or a daughter and therefore, on at least one occasion, the Doctor has achieved an erection and ejaculated into a lady's vagina.

of giant spiders. However a quick phone call to Brain Cox, Professor of Astrophysics at Manchester University, confirmed that no such planet exists. "The BBC must of simply made it up to boost ratings," he told us.

5 **DESPITE** having a sink plunger on their heads, Daleks are unable to unblock sinks. That's because their evil overlord Davros created them without waists. Consequently, if

their plugs get blocked up with fat, hair and vegetable scraps, they have to put Mr Muscle down.

6 **DR WHO** was first broadcast on November 23rd 1963. However the programme's reception was muted coming as it did just a day after a momentous event across the Atlantic - the release of the album *A Christmas Gift For You* by Phil Spector.

7 **OVER** the years, the BBC Secial Effects department spent a fortune on prosthetic

9 **OTHER** cloth fastenings that the Amish don't believe in include zips, velcro, toggles and press-studs.

10 **PRESS** studs were invented by German inventor Heribert Bauer, who first marketed them in 1885 as the "Federknopf-Verschluss."

2 **AT 7'3"**, Tom Baker is the tallest man to have played the Doctor. Ironically, the world's shortest man Calvin Phillips has never played the role. But if he had of done, he would have criss-crossed the space-time continuum in a Tardis no bigger than a shoebox.

3 **IRONICALLY**, on the inside, a Tardis no bigger than a shoebox would be the size that a normal Tardis is on the outside.

4 **IN ONE** of his adventures, the Doctor landed on a planet called *Metabilis 3*, where he was attacked by a race

WHO LETS THE DOGS OUT

Leading man: Dr Who actor McCoy hopes to use fame to pick up dog business.

FORMER *Dr Who* actor SYLVESTER MCCOY has set up a mobile dog walking service in his home town of Chelmsford. For £4 per hour-long walk, the seventh Doctor promises to exercise any breed from a chihuahua to a great dane.

"For that, your pet gets a three-mile walk whatever the weather, and I pick up their turds and everything," McCoy, 73, told his local paper *The Chelmsford Glans & Prostate*. "And it's only £5 if you want me to walk them as Dr Who."

success

The former Time Lord expects his business - Dr Who's Real McCoy K-9 Dog-Walking Services - to be a roaring success. He told the paper: "There are

Ex-Doctor launches pet walking service

thousands of dog owners in Chelmsford and there must be just as many Dr Who fans."

"Where those two demographics overlap is my target clientelle," he continued. "Especially busy people who go out to work and don't have time to take their dogs out during the day."

And McCoy says that if his business booms, next year he'll be introducing a Premium Service where pampered pooches will be exercised by both Dr Who and a glamorous assistant. "I'm in talks with Billie Piper, Bonnie Langford's agent and Richard Dawkins's wife," he said. "They're all happy to hold the leads as long as I promise to scoop up all the shits."

LETTERBOCKS

Viz Comic P.O. Box 841 Whitley Bay NE26 9EQ : letters@viz.co.uk

ST★R LETTER

PEOPLE often blame all the ills of the world on war or religion, but personally, I blame sex. There have been endless murders because of it, not to mention STDs and crabs. If people stopped having sex, then I think the world would be a much better place. If couples want to have children, then there's always adoption.

Morgan Ironballs, Chester

WHAT a swizz these tortoises are. When I was a kid, everyone had a tortoise in their back yard. Now I'm 42 and I don't know anyone who's got one. So much for them living for 200 years.

Fortescue Twelves, Hull

IF the security services are serious about protecting the public from terrorist attacks, why don't they simply monitor people who buy clocks that tick backwards?

Kendal Mintcake, e-mail

LAST week my 7-year-old son broke his ankle whilst at school. The nurse who took care of him wasn't bad looking, mind you.

Neil Stewart, e-mail

GIVEN all the recent historical sex cases, I would like to apologise in advance to any women at Tiffany's nightclub in the 1970s if I ogled your tits whilst off my head on snakebite.

Richard Knox, e-mail

I MAKE elephant's foot umbrella stands for a living, and I usually get four of them out of each elephant. However, because of the ban on the ivory trade, I can't sell the tusks any more and have to throw them away. It's madness.

Frank Sunblest, Exeter

I DON'T know why everyone bangs on about the ice caps melting. I bet the Eskimos are delighted. When I consider how much I hate gritting my drive during the winter, I can only imagine how bad it is for those poor bastards.

Trevor Doogan, Wales

CATS are supposed to reduce their owners' blood pressure and prolong their life expectancy. Well my granny tripped over her moggy coming out of the bathroom and shattered her pelvis. I don't know how that's going to make her live longer.

Sue Botolphs, Truro

THERE is no such thing as a free lunch, or so the saying goes. But I gave away my crisps at lunchtime today. What do the so-called boffins make of that?

Jimmy Boogaloo, e-mail

I DON'T know why electric lawnmowers always have orange cables on them. They are invisible in the grass to colourblind people, who are likely to run over them and electrocute themselves. Like the nazis, perhaps the manufacturers of these machines are practising eugenics, trying to rid the world of what they see as 'defective' people.

Lester Pylons, Cromer

OKAY, moving the Sabbath to a weekday might improve church attendance (*Letterbocks, page 22*), but not to a Tuesday, please. That's our vicar's day off and the only opportunity me and him have for our regular spot of nookie in the vestry.

Claire Wilson, e-mail

THESE supermarkets get my goat, selling you food and then cashing in by selling you lavatory paper as well. The ruddy cheek of it.

Ada Nevis, Glasgow

DURING *Songs of Praise* this afternoon, I coughed so hard that I followed through. Can any of your readers beat that?

Harriet Kempton-Park, e-mail

MY mum used to say "what makes you bad, makes you better". But the other day I was hideously constipated after eating a 12-egg omelette, and the second one just made things worse.

Tarquin Balls, Luton

BROS sang "When will I, will I be famous? I can't answer. I can't answer that." I can. 1987-1988.

Dave Benson-Backflips, e-mail

WHAT'S the point of Norway? They haven't invented anything since the metal hat with horns 2000 years ago, and that could have been Sweden.

Peter Alexander, e-mail

MICHAEL Gove is a stuck-up, toffee-nosed cunt and I've wanted to give him a fat lip for ages. However I recently noticed that he already has a fat lip. Two in fact. Would anyone mind if I just kicked him in the bollocks instead?

Pak Choi, e-mail

THEY say that "A Watched Kettle Never Boils." This is particularly true if you buy it from Argos, in my experience.

Walter Peachtree, Croydon

I KNOW that the international weapons inspectors never actually found any WMDs in Iraq, but in my experience things have a habit of turning up when you're not looking for them. I lost a pair of underpants ages ago but found them down the back of

YOU Ask...? WE Answer?

WHY is it that when an animal dies they go all stiff, yet a piece of steak is all floppy?

Frampton Golightly, Luton

• **BOTH** animals' bodies and pieces of meat are made of molecules which move with what is known as Brownian motion, named after the soul singer James Brown who was well known for moving on stage. Cold things have less Brownian motion than hot things and so are stiffer - think of a block of ice and a glass of warm water. When something dies it gets colder and so goes more stiff, whilst a piece of steak is all floppy as it warms up in the frying pan.

* **DO YOU** have a question about the world around you? Write to **You Ask, We Answer**, Viz Comic, PO Box 841, Whitley Bay NE26 9EQ, and we'll explain all.

CONMAN THE BARBARIAN

SIGH...

PUNT

WHAT TROUBLES THOU, TRAVELLING KNIGHT?

...BUT IF TRUTH BE TOLD, I AM SHITTING MYSELF!

HA HA HA! I DO LIKE AN HONEST MAN!

OH, I AM ON A QUEST TO SLAY A DRAGON TO WIN THE HEART OF A BEAUTIFUL DAMSEL...

MY FRIEND, I MAY HAVE SOMETHING IN MY CHEST TO DEFEAT YOUR DRAGON!

AH, HERE IT IS - THE SHIELD OF INVINCIBILITY! PROTECTS AGAINST FLAME, MAGIC BLASTS AND THE BLOWS FROM GRABTHAR'S HAMMER!

WOW! HOW MUCH DOTH IT COST?

BECAUSE I LIKE YOU, ONLY 50 GOLD COINS!

DONE!

SO....

THERE'S THE FOUL BEAST UP YONDER!

EASY DOES IT....

GADZOOKS! ON CLOSER INSPECTION, THIS SHIELD IS NOTHING BUT CARDBOARD WRAPPED IN TIN FOIL!

SHRRIP!

SORRY NO REFUNDS....

GULP!

-Tayler-

You couldn't make it up... BUT YOU HAVE!

Your clearly fabricated stories you're trying to pass off as true

● I SENT my grandson in London a birthday card last week. I put a first class stamp on the envelope and popped it in the post box. As I did so, I realised that I hadn't written an address on the front... I'd left it blank! Imagine my surprise when it was delivered to his house the following morning. Well done the Post Office, I say.

Edna Liar, Edinburgh

● MY HUSBAND was shot 100 times during the war, and on every occasion, the bullet struck the metal cigarette case he carried in his jacket pocket and saved his life. He still has the case today. 200 times, actually.

Ada Dissemble, Hull

● WHEN MY 8-year-old grandson came over to stay last week, I cooked him some Alphabetti Spaghetti on toast for his tea. But walking from the kitchen to the dining room I tripped over my cat and spilled it. When I looked at the mess on the floor, I was astounded to see that the spaghetti letters had done the entire works of Shakespeare.

Doris Falsification, Rye

ME AND my wife went to see Michael McIntyre in concert last week at The Pavilion Theatre, Bath, and he was really good. We didn't stop laughing all night.

Frank Perjury, Bristol

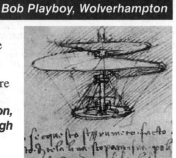

I NOTICE that Frank Sinatra sang about Chicago being his kind of town and then in the next breath he's singing about how brilliant New York is. I think this is really patronising to the audiences concerned.

Bob Playboy, Wolverhampton

I ONCE poured a glass of milk and the bubbles on the top looked like a pair of tits, but I wasn't able to take a picture in time. Do I win a fiver?

Jake Cuthbertson, Middlesbrough

* *Pull the other one, Jake, it's got bells on. Everyone knows that the bubbles on the top of a glass of milk could never look like a pair of tits. You must think we were born yesterday. Anyone else trying to get money out of us by fraudulently claiming to have witnessed £5 worthy events will have their e-mails sent directly to the police.*

I FEEL extremely lucky to come from a country where I can say the Queen sucks tramps' cocks without fear of prosecution. If I lived in North Korea and insulted Kim Jong-un in a similar way, I'd be executed and fed to some dogs. I'm not saying that the Queen does suck tramps off, I'm just glorying in our marvellous constitution that allows me the freedom to say it.

Hampton Cromwell, Luton

I AGREE with Mr Cromwell *(above)*. Nowhere else in the world could I accuse the country's leader of participating in watersports with prostitutes and avoid prosecution. But our centuries old constitution gives me the freedom to say I think that Prince Philip does a Cleveland Steamer on the Queen's tits. Hooray for Britain.

Marjory Fforbes, Surbiton

I DON'T know why monks still insist on wearing long, drab robes and sandals like they did in medieval times. Surely they can still dedicate their lives to God and wear a shirt and trousers and a nice pair of shoes.

Hector Vaudeville, London

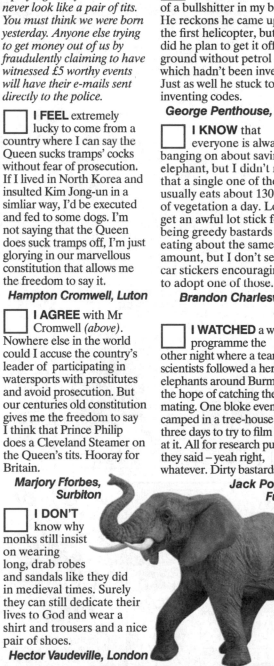

THAT Leonardo da Vinci bloke was a bit of a bullshitter in my book. He reckons he came up with the first helicopter, but how did he plan to get it off the ground without petrol – which hadn't been invented? Just as well he stuck to inventing codes.

George Penthouse, Settle

I KNOW that everyone is always banging on about saving the elephant, but I didn't realise that a single one of them usually eats about 130 kilos of vegetation a day. Locusts get an awful lot stick for being greedy bastards and eating about the same amount, but I don't see any car stickers encouraging us to adopt one of those.

Brandon Charlesworth, Leeds

I WATCHED a wildlife programme the other night where a team of scientists followed a herd of elephants around Burma in the hope of catching them mating. One bloke even camped in a tree-house for three days to try to film them at it. All for research purposes they said – yeah right, whatever. Dirty bastards.

Jack Popkiss, Fulham

---

the settee when I was looking for a custard cream which had also slid down there. I'm betting that if Hans Blix went back now he'd find the chemical weapons in a matter of minutes and have a right old chuckle to himself into the bargain.

Albert Bremner, Rugby

I'LL tell you what, when the Queen dies, we'll never hear the bloody end of it. You won't be able to open a sodding paper or turn the bloody telly on without it being Her Majesty the Queen *this* and Her Majesty the Queen *that*. I mean, stroll on! Give it a bloody break.

Hampton Mortimer, Lowes

JOHN Lennon was criticised in 1966 for saying that The Beatles were more popular than Jesus. But they did have 20 number one hits in the USA between 1964 and 1970, which is 20 more than Jesus had. So maybe he had a point.

Gavin Roche, Pembrokeshire

I RECKON that if those Hari Krishnas wore proper uniforms, they might do a bit better with their recruitment drive. I have recently joined the RAC, and I have to say that it was in part because of their smart and businesslike appearance.

Arthur Peasgood, Bradford

SEEING as flooding is, according to religious people, a direct result of gay marriage being legalised, shouldn't same sex marriage be encouraged in those countries affected by drought?

Mark H, Liverpool

HOW come a Johnny-come-lately pop star like Bruno Mars gets a whole planet named after him, yet a cross-eyed 1950s rock icon like Bill Haley can only manage a comet? It seems all so unfair and fucked up to me.

Reg Dulcimer, Oswestry

LOOSE CHIPPINGS

I'D GET A TOY BOY... ONLY I'D WEAR HIM OUT!!!

HAAR! HAAR!

NA-A-A-A!!

SCREECH!!

CACKLE!

MY UNCLE KEN IS GETTING MARRIED TODAY, READERS, AND I'VE MADE HIM A SUPER WEDDING PRESENT...

DING-DONG DING-DONG

SAINT GREAVSIE'S CHURCH

THIS PISTON-POWERED "YOU-MUST-BE-FUCKING-JOKING-O-MATIC" WILL ENABLE THE HAPPY COUPLE TO SHOVE THEIR HIGH-PRICED JOHN LEWIS WEDDING GIFT LIST RIGHT UP THEIR ARSES!

HOORAY! HERE COME THE BRIDE AND GROOM!

LET'S THROW RICE OVER THEM!

THROWING THOSE GRAINS OF RICE LOOKS LIKE HARD WORK.

I'LL BUILD A RICE FLINGING MACHINE TO DO IT FOR ME.

OOPS! MY RICE-FLINGER HAS GOT A GLITCH...

CRACK

OH CRIKEY!

SPROING!

IT HAS THROWN THE FAMOUS LYRICIST **SIR TIM RICE** AT THE NEWLYWEDS!

THE ACADEMY AWARD WINNING SONGSMITH HAS SMASHED THE BRIDE'S SKULL IN!

YOU BIG DAFTY, GILBERT! YOU'VE GONE AND KILLED MY WIFE!

THAT'S TAKEN THE SHINE OFF MY WEDDING DAY, SOMEWHAT!

NOT TO WORRY, UNCLE KEN...

TIP

I'LL BUILD YOU A REPLACEMENT WIFE OUT OF BITS AND PIECES FROM THE COUNCIL TIP NEXT DOOR

THERE!

BLEEP! NAG! NAG!

MY "MARITAL-BLISS-O-MATIC" WILL BANG A VACUUM CLEANER AGAINST YOUR FEET AND TELL YOU TO PUT UP A CURTAIN RAIL IN THE SPARE ROOM WHILE YOU TRY TO WATCH 'BOTTOM' ON UKTV GOLD.

WELL DONE, GILBERT! YOU'VE SAVED MY MARRIAGE!

COME ON, EVERYONE - LET'S HEAD OFF TO THE WEDDING RECEPTION!

COME ON EILEEN TOO-LOO RYE-AYE...

DISCO

YUM! THOSE HOT BUFFET SAUSAGES LOOK TASTY!

I'M AFRAID THEY'RE GOING TO BE **COLD** BUFFET SAUSAGES

THESE DRATTED HOT PLATES DON'T SEEM TO BE WORKING!

WE'LL SOON GET THESE SAUSAGES WARMED UP!

FIRST WE CONNECT UP THE BROKEN HOT-PLATES TO THE CHEEKS OF MY TWO TEENAGE COUSINS...

NEXT WE ENSURE THAT UNCLE REG'S PINT GLASS IS CONSTANTLY TOPPED UP.

WATNEY'S RED BARREL

THE BOOZE SHOULD START TAKING EFFECT ANY MOMENT...

THERE! NOW MY TEENAGE COUSINS ARE FORCED TO WITNESS THEIR PISSED DAD THROWING SHAPES ON THE DANCE FLOOR

HI HO SILVER LINING

THEIR BURNING EMBARRASSMENT WILL HEAT THOSE BANGERS UP IN NO TIME!

DJ '14

UH-OH! UNCLE REG IS ATTEMPTING 'GANGNAM STYLE'...

HIS TEENAGE KIDS' MORTIFICATION IS TURNING **RED HOT!**

HISSS SPIT

LOOK OUT!

THE SAUSAGES ARE GOING TO **EXPLODE!**

WHEEEE

BANG! POP!

WOW! THAT'S GREAT, GILBERT!

YOU'VE ORGANISED A LOVELY FIREWORKS DISPLAY IN HONOUR OF MY WEDDING!

UNCLE KEN WAS SO IMPRESSED WITH MY SAUSAGE FIREWORKS, HE GAVE ME THIS SCRUMMY WEDDING CAKE!

CHOMP! MERRY NUPTIALS, READERS!

OH, LORDY! IT'S THE FAT SLAGS

New Star Charity Scheme Hits Road

On the Abuses: The keys to the specially-adapted celebrity sex offender coach were handed over by orphan Timothy Cratchitt (left).

BRITAIN'S big-hearted underprivileged kids have pulled out all the stops and raised £80,000 to fund a specially-equipped minibus to take disgraced 1970s showbiz personalities on day-trips from prison.

Minibus will provide day-trips for celebrity sexcases
EXCLUSIVE!

Orphans' charity the **Kiddies' Organisation for Stars** held a series of raffles, bring and buy sales and sponsored events to fund the brand new vehicle, the keys of which were yesterday presented to Fulton Barraclough, governor of Strangeways Prison, by street urchin Timothy Cratchitt at a waif-studded ceremony.

seaside

"The Yewtree Sunshine Bus will provide much-needed trips to the seaside for many of the country's most disgraced stars," said Mr Barraclough. "Many of them are locked in their cells for up to twenty-three hours a day. Often, the only time they come out is to be taken to court is to be charged with more sex offences."

"A nice trip to the seaside would make such a difference to their lives," he continued. "I can't thank the underprivileged children enough for all their tireless efforts."

And the charity's endeavours won't stop with one Sunshine Bus. As the police widen their investigations into historic offences, the charity now intends to raise half a million pounds to buy a dozen 55-seater Yewtree coaches for disgraced celebrities, and is already planning a series of fundraising picnics and a pro-orphan golf tournament.

The coaches will be adapted with ramps to enable elderly stars to get aboard more easily, along with extra-strong child-abuser-proof locks to prevent them getting out.

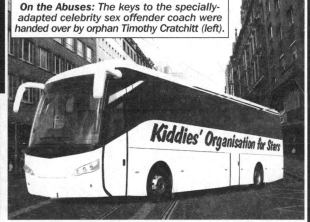

ROY'S DAD OF THE ROVERS

Football team Parkbridge Rovers had made it through to the final of the Fulchester & District Under 11s Cup. On the morning of the big match, the players took to the field along with their proud parents...

...and no dad was more proud than Colin Trumpton, whose son Roy was on the subs' bench.

You've done so well to get picked for the team, Roy. Remember, it doesn't matter whether you win or lose as long as you enjoy yourself.

Yes, dad.

Rovers coach Billy Brown interrupted the pair...

Come on Roy, let's go. Team talk!

Okay, Mr Brown.

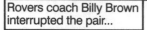

Right everyone, we all know this lot are shit and we can beat them easily.

Yeah!

Woo!

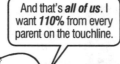

But we don't want to just **beat** them, we want to **destroy** them!

Come on!

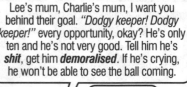

The ref's only young, sixteen, so I want everyone screaming at any decision he makes that doesn't go our way. We've got to keep at him - Pressure, pressure, pressure for the full ninety minutes.

And that's **all of us**. I want **110%** from every parent on the touchline.

Josh's dad, you take the left wing. Callum's dad, you take the right wing. I want you both on the linesmen's backs - screaming abuse - "*Our ball! Our ball! Come on! Are you fucking blind?!*"

You got it, Billy.

Don't let up... Jockey them all the time, okay?

Lee's mum, Charlie's mum, I want you behind their goal. "*Dodgy keeper! Dodgy keeper!*" every opportunity, okay? He's only ten and he's not very good. Tell him he's **shit**, get him **demoralised**. If he's crying, he won't be able to see the ball coming.

Leave it to us.

Alfie's dad, I want you on the pitch two inches from the ref's face every time one of our lads trips on his laces. You know what to say?

Again. Louder! Closer!

Yeah! *You having a fucking laugh, eh ref? He's got to go off for that, the dirty bastard!*

YOU HAVING A FUCKING LAUGH, EH REF? HE'S GOT TO GO OFF FOR THAT, THE DIRTY BASTARD!

That's it. he'll shit himself. It's his first season...

...and his last. Poor sod.

What would you like me to do, Billy?

Erm... you just look after the kit bag, eh?

...if we're far enough ahead at the end, I'll put you on for five minutes laughing theatrically at their back four.

This is our chance to make history. We've never scored thirty in a match before... but today's the day.

Let's destroy them!

No prisoners!

The more we score, the louder we shout.

Woo!

PHEEP!

The game got underway and the Rovers' parents were soon on the attack...

One-nil! Here we go! Here we go! Here we go!

Get the fuck in!

Haaar! Haaar! See that?! What a fucking spanner!

Give it up, son! You're shit!

You fucking big girl's blouse!

The coach's tactics paid off as the score rose higher...

What's up with you, man, doesn't your fucking flag work? He's a fucking mile off!

Get your fucking flag up, you dozy bastard!

Erm ... offside?

...and higher...

Fuckin' hell, ref. Come on. High foot, dangerous play. Fuck's sake, get a grip!

Y' don't know what y' doing!... Y' don't know what y' doing!

Taxi for the ref!

PHEEP!

...and higher.

Last man, ref! Last man! Red card! Red fucking card! The bastard's got to go.

Er ... yes, off you go ... sorry.

With less than half a minute of the match left to go, Parkbridge Rovers had put twenty-nine goals past their demoralised opponents when suddenly...

Handball!

Okay, Alfie's dad. Get out there and do your stuff.

Leave it to me, boss.

But...

Aargh! My ankle!

I've twisted it!

Bloody hell. It's come up like a balloon.

There's no way he can go and berate the ref in this condition.

Ow!

Roy's dad! You're on!

Wha..?

But I haven't had a chance to warm up...

There's no time. This is our last chance to get thirty. We need that penalty.

Get out there and give that wanker in the black what-for. Get right up to his face, question his eyesight, tell him he doesn't know the rules...

...Pressure, pressure, pressure! Okay?

Continued over...

And you don't give up until he gives that spot-kick, okay. I want his glasses covered in your spit, understand?

B-but I haven't done this before...

Well it's going to be a baptism of fire. Now get out onto the park, step up to the plate and do the business for the Rovers Under 11s.

Roy's dad had never got a penalty before, but with every step he took towards the spot he could feel his confidence growing...

I can do it! This is my big chance!

Hey, fucking four-eyes! Have you lost the pea from your fucking whistle?

No, I ...

That was a fucking penalty! *They* saw it! *I* saw it!

Every cunt on the fucking park saw it except you! Plain as fucking day, it was, plain as fucking day!

Erm ... I think it was accidental...

Accidental?! Are you having a fucking giraffe?! It was hand to ball, son, hand to fucking ball! You don't know the fucking laws of the game!

You're a joke, sunshine! A fucking joke!

Wow! What a debut!

Get that badge in a fucking jumble sale, did you?!...

Erm... was it ...?

...It was a cast iron penalty, that. Fucking cast iron, all day!

Yes it fucking was. Now are you going to fucking blow or are you going to fucking bottle it?!

PHEEP!

That's what I'm talking about!

Yessss!!!

Result!

Well done Roy's dad. You really showed class out there.

Yes, you came through for the team!

And...

Thirty-niiil, to the cham-pions! Thirty-niiil, to the cham-pions!

THE END

SCROOBY POO

OH NO! THE MYSTERY VAN HAS RUN OUT OF PETROL, GUYS!

SPLUTTER!

T-WIT! T-WOOO!

GEE! THIS PLACE SURE IS SPOOKY! IT GIVES ME THE CREEPS!

...AND IT'S GIVEN SCROOB THE CRAPS!

LAY BY

LOOK!

YIKES! I CAN SMELL IT FROM HERE!

DON'T WORRY ABOUT THAT...

THERE'S A LIGHT ON IN THAT OLD HOUSE. LET'S GO AND SEE IF THEY'VE GOT A CAN OF GAS FOR THE MYSTERY VAN!

CREEPVILLE MANOR

NOT SO FAST...!

YOIKS! A RHOST!

HO-HO! IT'S NOT A GHOST, SCROOB. IT'S A RANGER!

YOU KIDS CAN'T LEAVE THAT DOG-DIRT THERE! IT'S AGAINST STATE BY-LAWS!

...BUT WE'VE GOT TO GO UP TO CREEPVILLE MANOR TO GET SOME GAS FOR OUR VAN.

YES. AND WHEN WE GET THERE, THERE MIGHT BE SOMETHING FISHY GOING ON!

THAT'S AS MAYBE. BUT FIRST YOU'LL HAVE TO PICK UP THAT DOG SHITE.

THERE'S A FIFTY DOLLAR FINE IF YOU ALLOW YOUR MUTT TO FOUL THE SIDEWALK.

YIKES! LIKE, DOES ANYONE HAVE A POOPER-SCOOPER?

NOT ME, SCRAGGY.

NOT ME.

ROT REE!

I'VE GOT AN EMPTY CRISP PACKET, FRANK.

GREAT, THELMA! PICK UP THE TURD... AND QUICK! THE CREEPVILLE MANOR JANITOR COULD BE USING A PROJECTOR AND FAN-TYPE MOTOR TO SIMULATE PARA-NORMAL ACTIVITY!

EURGH! I'M NOT PICKING IT UP. IT'LL STILL BE WARM AND I'LL BE ABLE TO FEEL IT THROUGH THE PLASTIC.

WHY DON'T WE FLICK IT INTO THE BAG WITH THIS BIT OF CARDBOARD.

HURRY, GUYS! THE JANITOR IS PROBABLY DRILLING SOME HOLES IN A PAINTING SO HE CAN LOOK FROM SIDE TO SIDE THROUGH IT!

LIKE, HOLD THE BAG OPEN THELMA!

OKAY SCRAGGY.

FLICK!

SCRAPE!

OH NO! I'VE DROPPED MY GLASSES!

MY GLASSES! MY GLASSES! WHERE ARE THEY?

AARGH! I'VE PUT MY HAND IN IT NOW...! RETCH!

LOOK, QUIT FOOLIN' AROUND, YOU GUYS!

SHORTLY...

THERE! IT'S IN THE BAG AT LAST, SCRAGGY!

GREAT!

NOW PUT IT IN THE BIN AND, LIKE, LET'S GET OUTTA HERE!

WHERE'S THE BIN?

THERE'S NO DOG WASTE BINS IN THESE PARTS.

WHAT?!

BUT WE'VE GOT TO GET TO CREEPVILLE MANOR! THE JANITOR MIGHT BE CONSTRUCTING A FALSE BOOKCASE WHICH SPINS AROUND WITH A LOUD GRINDING NOISE WHEN SOMEONE SELECTS A PARTICULAR BOOK!

I DON'T CARE ABOUT THAT. ALL I KNOW IS, YOU GOTTA DISPOSE OF THAT CRISP BAG OF FOULAGE PROPERLY. AND THE NEAREST DOG SHIT BIN IS IN DEADWOOD COUNTY... TEN MILES AWAY!

COME ON, GUYS. LOOKS LIKE WE'VE GOT A TWENTY MILE WALK AHEAD OF US!

MEANWHILE, IN CREEPVILLE MANOR...

HMM... I WOULDN'T HAVE GOT AWAY WITH IT TOO IF THOSE MEDDLING KIDS HAD EVER TURNED UP.

Ghosties and Ghoulies and Long-legged Beasties and...

THINGS THAT GO BUMP AT THE BEEB!

By our Paranormal TV correspondent
Bo-Derek Acorah

What a grey day: See-through shade of Saturday night light entertainment favourite Larry Grayson still stalks studios.

BBC Director General *George Entwhistle* hit the headlines in 2012 when he resigned after being in his post just 54 days, following the broadcast of a controversial *Newsnight* report which falsely implicated Lord McAlpine in the North Wales child abuse scandal. Or so the corporation would have you believe.

For now, two years later, Entwhistle has sensationally revealed the real reason he quit his post at TV Centre: *The building is FULL of ghosts!*

According to George, the Grade II-listed studio complex, opened in 1960, is home to more than 1000 terrifying phantoms, wraiths, poltergeists and spectres - that's more than twice as many ghosts as in all the haunted castles, stately homes and lighthouses in Britain put together. But what is even more remarkable is that many of the spectres and phantoms that walk the corridors of the iconic Shepherds Bush building are the restless spirits of showbiz stars!

"These people made their name at the BBC before moving to the other side," says Entwhistle. "And believe you me, I'm not taking about ITV."

teeth

The former DG's teeth chatter with fear and the blood drains from his face as he recalls his first paranormal experience whilst at Television Centre. "It was my first day in the job and I was in my office, arranging some pot plants on the windowsill when somebody walked through the door."

"Nothing unusual about that, you might think, until I tell you that the door to my office was firmly shut and that the figure who floated before me was none other than disgraced DJ Jimmy Savile... who had been dead for nearly a year! And I could see right through him."

"He was making an unearthly

Ex-DG George lifts lid on hauntings at BBC

gurgling noise and seemed to be imploring me to help him clear his name. As I looked at him, he simply vanished into thin air, leaving nothing behind but an unmistakeable smell of cigar smoke and sweaty tracksuit trousers."

Earlier that day, Entwhistle had attended a champagne breakfast meeting with the BBC board of governors, a five-star bonding lunch at the Ivy with senior administrative staff and a high-powered afternoon tea at the Savoy. "I put my spooky experience down to stress caused by overwork," he told us. "And I thought no more about it."

But the very next afternoon, the Director General was lying on the sofa in his office, thinking about the upcoming Autumn schedule, when a sudden clicking noise woke him up. "When I opened my eyes, I saw that the Newton's cradle on my desk had started to swing of its own accord."

"Not only that, my executive sand picture was turning over and over all by itself and my miniature basketball was repeatedly flying through its hoop, thrown by an unseen hand. At first I thought I must be dreaming, so I pinched myself to see if I was still fast asleep, but there was no mistake. This was all too real, and the haunting of my office was about to take an even more horrifying turn."

"Suddenly, my putting machine started firing golf balls across the carpet and my r/c helicopter took off. It was as if some malign supernatural entity had taken control of my office and was working all my executive equipment."

"I froze as I became aware of two grey figures manifesting in the corner of the room. At first they were wispy, like smoke, but gradually their outlines became clearer and clearer until I was able to identify them as the late *Record Breakers* presenters Roy Castle and Norris McWhirter. Or Ross."

breasts

"McWhirter carried a clipboard and a stopwatch, whilst Castle was waving his ghostly arms about and almost seemed to be conducting the mayhem which had enveloped my office."

"Then suddenly it stopped as quickly as it had begun, and McWhirter's eerie voice announced that his spectral companion had just beaten the world record for the

> **Castle's spectre was attempting to set a new tap dancing speed record**

most poltergeist activity in a single room."

"Once again, I put my hair-raising experience down as an hallucination due to overwork following a particularly long, stressful day playing Angry Birds. But when I recounted the episode to my secretary the following day, her face went white."

"She explained that my office was built on the site of the old *Record Breakers* studio, and previous Director Generals had reportedly seen Castle's spectre attempting to set a new tap dancing speed record, whilst his ghostly performance was monitored by by the phantasm of Norris McWhirter. Or Ross."

Over the coming weeks, the spooky goings-on in Entwhistle's office grew in frequency. In a single week he witnessed:

● *A hideous grey lady, thought to be the late Les Dawson dressed as his gossip character Cissy, silently mouthing words whilst hitching up her enormous see-through bosom.*

Water Waste!

£3.6 BILLION
holy water

BEEB insiders are warning that the TV licence fee may have to rise next year to cover the mounting cost of battling ghosts at Television Centre. The Beeb currently spends nearly 10% of its £3.6 billion budget on exorcists, holy water and mediums in an attempt to rid the building of its supernatural presences.

"The main problem is that the price of holy water has gone through the roof," BBC governor Lord Patten told us. "The church is charging us two hundred pounds per ampule, and we're having to use gallons of the stuff every day just to

Auntie Spunks Licencepayers' Cash on Holy H₂O and Exorcists

keep the infestation at TV Centre at a manageable level."

But Archbishop of Canterbury Dr Justin Welby dismissed accusations that the church was profiteering at the licencepayer's expense. "It's supply and demand. Simple as, end of," he told us. "If the beeb don't want to cough up for our holy water, that's up to them."

"Nobody's making them buy it. If they can get the stuff cheaper from some other religion, good luck to them," he continued. "Doesn't bother me. I couldn't give a fart."

- A chain-covered *That's Life* stalwart Cyril Fletcher manifesting in a chair, laughing maniacally and holding a radish that looked like a man's penis and testicles.

- A troop of Black and White Minstrels with burning, red eyes sauntering through the wall singing "I wish I was in Dixie" and pushing a ghostly woman in a big dress on a swing.

After eight weeks of constant visitations, Entwistle's nerves were shattered and he decided to resign.

"I couldn't take any more and I handed in my notice," he told us. "Luckily, *Newsnight* had run a made-up story about a bigwig bumming some kids, and I was able to use that as an excuse for why I was quitting so soon. And I think everybody bought it. But a year on, I finally feel able to reveal the real reason for my departure."

bottom

Immediately after Entwistle's departure the hauntings stopped. And a BBC spokesman refused to confirm that his successor, caretaker Director General Tim Davie, was later arrested after being found in possession of film projector, a fog machine, several rubber masks and a fan-type motor.

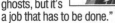

DG Lord Hall told us: "Of course, we do realise that this is a lot of money to be spending on ridding the BBC of ghosts, but it's a job that has to be done."

"We are first and foremost a broadcaster, and we look forward to the day when licencepayers' cash can be re-allocated to where it is needed," he continued. "For example, renting the Royal Festival Hall for departmental bonding sessions, buying iPads for middle managers and paying six-figure golden handshakes to people who are resigning because they've been offered a better-paid job at ITV."

Terrorvision Centre

BBC TV Center is officially the most haunted building in Britain, home to over 1,000 celebrity spooks, star spectres and A-list apparitions. So it's time to wrap up warm for a spine-chilling ghost hunt round the studio complex's most famous phantoms, haunted-household names and wrell-known wraiths...

Studio 1a
...Largest in the building, Studio 1a was the home of the *Generation Game*. Following host Larry Grayson's death in 1995, backstage staff have repeatedly seen Grayson's headless ghost carrying its head under its arm, dragging a chair behind it, shutting doors and limply running its fingers across surfaces as if checking for "muck". Eerily, when later examined, the dust on these surfaces is undisturbed and shows no trace of the "what a gay day" funnyman's fingermarks.

Studio 3
...The *Blue Peter* studio, where Lulu the elephant famously disgraced herself during a live broadcast of the show in 1969, repeatedly urinating and defecating on the set. Every year, on the anniversary of Lulu's death, it is said that a big brown and yellow stain appears on the floor of the studio which, no matter how thoroughly the cleaners scrub it, can never be washed away.

Studio 5b
...In 1976, studio 5b was used to shoot the epic series *I, Claudius*, set in ancient Egypt. Several prop mummies were brought in to dress the set, but unbeknownst to studio staff, one of them was real. Not only that, but it carried a curse, one which promised death to any TV executive that disturbed its eternal rest. Almost 40 years later, the bandaged figure is still seen walking around the studio looking for the drama's director Herbert Wise and its stars Derek Jacobi, George Baker and Chris Biggins.

The Canteen
...Everyone in the BBC goes to the canteen at least once a day, but nobody spends more time there than the ghost of Fanny Cradock. The former TV chef's restless spirit manifests each morning at ten o'clock, already drunk on cooking sherry, and harangues diners and kitchen staff. "Fanny's phantom has a high-pitched shrieking, wailing voice and mad, staring eyes," says Radio 4 presenter Eddie Mair. "But she's still nowhere near as horrific as she was when she was alive."

Studio 8
...For many years home of Saturday afternoon sports magazine *Grandstand*, Studio 8 is one of the most haunted parts of Television Centre and now hosts the popular *Match of the Day* programme. But as well as Gary Lineker, Alan Hansen and Alan Shearer, the set is also home to another malign presence - the skeleton of late presenter David Coleman. The bony ghost, which is doomed to wander the studio for ever, looking into the wrong camera and muddling its words up, has never been seen on screen. "David's skellington usually turns up when we're showing a game," says Lineker. "But if he manifests during the post-match analysis we just cut to a replay of a disputed offside incident until he disappears through the veil to his own realm."

Weather Centre
...The ghost of an un-named BBC weatherman can often be glimpsed in this studio, attempting to stick old-fashioned weather symbols onto the map of Britain. However, because the BBC now uses a computerised "green screen" map, the symbols keep falling off, so the spectral presenter will never achieve release from his eternal torment. Current weatherman Tomas Shavenknackers is so scared of the phantom that he refuses to go in the studio alone. Every time he broadcasts, his mum and dad - Les and Ada Shavenknackers - are standing just out of shot.

Broom Cupboard
...The CBBC Continuity Booth, or the Broom Cupboard as it is affectionately known, is reputedly haunted by the terrifying ghost of Dickie Mint - one of Ken Dodd's Diddy Men. The grinning marionette was killed in a treacle mine collapse in 1973, and his restless spirit now wanders the studio from where the tickling stick funnyman's show was introduced each week, looking for his shirt. In 1992, Phil Schofield and Gordon the Gopher spent the night in the studio for a dare and paid a hefty price. By the morning, Schofield's hair had turned white and his puppet sidekick had been driven completely and hopelessly mad.

Make-up
...Many BBC employees avoid using Dressing Room 13 at all costs, as it is reputedly haunted by the ghost of a make-up artist who hanged herself after spending two hours working on Nicholas Witchell. In 2003, *Changing Rooms* presenter Carol Smillie dismissed production staff's warnings about the cursed room as "mumbo jumbo" and went in to remove her make-up. She was never seen again.

Prop Store
...The prop storeroom at TV Centre was built on the site of an old Red Indian burial ground, and is consequently one of the most haunted areas of the building. "We've seen it all in here," said one BBC employee. "Hands coming up through the floor and grabbing at your legs as you walk past, cockroaches forming themselves into words on the wall, mute twins and tidal waves of blood coming out of the lift doors. It's all in a day's work. In fact, we barely give it a second thought these days."

TOUR de TIPTON!

Saddle do nicely: Tipton cycle race will be a spectacle to rival the Tour de France.

THE BOSS of a West Midlands local authority has announced his intention of taking on the French at their own game by launching a cycling race that will rival the world famous Tour de France. And *Hugo Guthrie*, a former mayor of Tipton who is now head of the borough council's Leisure and Tourism sub-committee, says that the "Tour de Tipton" is set to put its 100-year-old counterpart well and truly in the shade.

Ready, steady, Hugo: Guthrie yesterday

According to Guthrie, the spectacular success of the Tour de France's recent Grand Départ in Yorkshire showed the British public's appetite for competitive cycling. "The people of this country are bike mad, and none more so than Tiptonians," he told a sparsely-attended press conference at the Steve Bull Leisure Centre.

"There are three cycle shops in Tipton alone, four if you include the big Halfords on Moat Farm Retail Park, so it's clear that the people of this area have a passion for the sport."

top

During the competition, the world's top riders will race

Guthrie announces sporting spectacle for Midlands town

Sprocket and Cogwheel: Tour de Tipton's cheeky, loveable mascots designed by Guthrie's brother-in-law's son Callum.

around a course taking in many notable landmarks and historical sites around Tipton, including Tibbington Estate, where the borough's 2000th council house was opened in 1936, the Angle Ring factory in Princes End and the former site of Great Bridge railway station, which was sadly demolished in the 1970s.

"Unlike our French counterparts, we are not blessed with challenging mountain stages like the Pyrenees and Massif Centrale," said Mr Guthrie. "But we've got some pretty steep slopes around the town, I can tell you, including Ocker Hill which is a one-in-twelve."

finger

Mr Guthrie says merchandising, featuring the Tour's mascots Sprocket and Cogwheel, is very much at the centre of his business plan to ensure that the event pays for itself from day one. "My brother-in-law has just been laid off from a large bakery, and he has sunk his entire redundancy money into a rubberised film heat transfer machine off eBay," he said. "We have awarded him the exclusive contract to produce all the jerseys and T-shirts at a knock-down price for cash."

And Guthrie had this warning for anyone out to make a fast buck from unofficial Tour de Tipton memorabilia: "Just like the London Olympics we will be coming down very hard on anyone who infringes our intellectual property."

bath

But no stranger to controversy, Guthrie is courting criticism by staging the inaugural Tipton cycle race to coincide with the 2015 Tour de France.

"We're coming out fighting. We're going all out to attract the biggest names in world cycling - your Lance Armstrongs, your Chris Hoys, your Bradley Walshes," he said.

bob squarepants

"We're still waiting for permission to close off all the roads in the town for a month, but if that doesn't come through they'll have to ride on the pavement," said Mr Guthrie. "One way or another the race is on."

"The riders and spectators will have to make a straight choice in 2015: Will it be the Alpe d'Huez, Mont Ventoux, Provence, the Col de Tourmalet and the Champs Elysées? Or Tipton," he added.

Tipton Tops

JUST like its rival Gallic pretender, competitors in the Tour de Tipton will wear special jerseys to show their progress during the gruelling twenty-seven-day event.

The Yellow Top
At a special ceremony on the town hall steps at the end of each day's competition, the Tour de Tipton's *current leader* will be presented with the Yellow Top, a bunch of flowers and a kiss from the reining *Miss Tipton* Shania Bartram and *Miss Angle Rings 1993* (the last year that the competition took place) Janice Endercott. "Janice has assured us that she can lose four and a half stone by this time next year and will be back to her glamorous 1993 self," said Mr Guthrie.

The Polka-dot Top
Awarded to the *"King of Ocker Hill"* - the first rider to make it to the top of the notorious strength-sapping 300-yard, one-in-twelve climb each day.

The Green Top
This is awarded to the *"King of the Sprints"* - the fastest rider along a timed 100-yard section along Toll End Road between Evans Outsize Ladieswear and the zebra crossing outside the Pound Bakery.

The White Top
This is reserved for the *"King of the Peloton"*. Guthrie admits that this one has got him a little foxed. "I'm not entirely sure what a peloton is," he told reporters. "But whatever it is, we've definitely got a lovely white top reserved for the king of it."

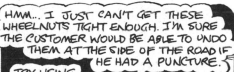

61

HEY, I WISH I'D BROUGHT A BIGGER CASH BOX, TOM! I'M FUCKING **CREAMING** THE STUFF IN HERE

ROGER MELLIE "DALEK OUT OF DR WHO"

THERE MUST BE TWO AND A HALF LARGE HERE, AND I'VE NOT GIVEN OUT A SINGLE RECEIPT...

AND WE KNOW WHAT **THAT** MEANS

NEXT! HURRY UP... TIME IS MONEY

WHAT EPISODES WERE YOU IN?

WHAT!?

IT'S TWENTY QUID, SON

WHAT EPISODES WERE YOU IN?

CYBER MEN

STAR WARS

BECAUSE I DON'T RECOGNISE YOUR NAME FROM ANY OF THE CREDITS OF DOCTOR WHO, AND I DON'T THINK YOU WERE EVER IN IT

WELL, I FUCKING WELL **WAS**, SON

WELL WHICH EPISODE?

ERM... IT WAS THE ONE WHERE HE GOT INTO A PHONEBOX WITH SOME BIRD AND WENT TO ANOTHER PLANET OR SOMETHING

WHO WAS PLAYING THE DOCTOR?

I DON'T KNOW, I COULDN'T SEE... I WAS IN THIS FUCKING COSTUME, WASN'T I? IT WAS PROBABLY HIM WITH THE SCARF

AH! TOM BAKER, THE FOURTH DOCTOR. THEN YOU MUST MEAN SERIES SIXTEEN, EPISODE NINE - THE POWER OF KRULL

THAT'S THE ONE...

THERE YOU GO... THAT'LL BE A HUNDRED QUID

HMM... BUT THE DALEKS IN **THAT** EPISODE WERE PLAYED BY GRAHAME MALLARD, TERRY WALSH, PHILIP BIRD AND MARK HARDY

DID YOU HEAR THAT?.. HE WAS NEVER IN 'WHO'

WHAT!?... HE'S AN IMPOSTER!?

OI! WE WANT OUR MONEY BACK!

YES! YOU CONNED US...THAT'S NOT FAIR

SORRY.. IT'S STRICTLY NO REFUNDS SO YOU CAN ALL **FUCK OFF!**

I'M GOING TO WRITE TO THE DR WHO FAN CLUB BLOGOSPHERE

AND TELL MY MUM

ROGER MELLIE "DALEK OUT OF

TEN MINS LATER...

WELL, THE MORAL IS 'DON'T RIP OFF DR WHO FANS

FUCK ME, TOM. THAT TURNED UGLY PRETTY QUICK DIDN'T IT? AND THEY WERE PRETTY TASTY WHEN THEIR BACKS WERE UP

NO, YOU CAN RIP THEM OFF ALL YOU LIKE, TOM

IT WAS WHEN I CALLED THEM A BUNCH OF PASTY-FACED, SPOTTY, VIRGIN **TREKKIES** THAT THEY GOT THE RED MIST...

...THEY'RE **WHOVIANS**, APPARENTLY...

I WON'T MAKE THAT MISTAKE NEXT YEAR

PLAYTIME FONTAYNE

DON'T DAWDLE, PLAYTIME. YOU DON'T WANT TO BE LATE ON YOUR FIRST DAY BACK AT BANK AFTER THE SUMMER HOLIDAYS.

MU-UUM..!?

WOULD YOU WRITE A NOTE FOR THE AREA MANAGER AND SAY THAT THE DOG ATE MY QUARTERLY AUDIT RETURNS..?

≡SIGH≡ HOW MANY MORE TIMES, PLAYTIME? NO, I WILL NOT.

I'M NOT GOING TO LIE TO MR TURPIN. YOU SHOULD HAVE SAT DOWN AND FINISHED THEM AT THE START OF THE HOLIDAYS LIKE I TOLD YOU.

BUT HE'LL KILL ME IF I DON'T HAND THEM IN!

PLEEEEASE!

WELL YOU SHOULD HAVE THOUGHT OF THAT BEFORE YOU SPENT THE WHOLE TWO WEEKS PLAYING SKYRIM AND PAINTING IRON MAIDENS EDDIE ON YOUR BRIEFCASE.

BANK

CHEER UP, PLAYTIME. HAVEN'T YOU HEARD? FARTY-BREATH TURPIN'S HAD A HEART ATTACK!

?

...WE'VE GOT A SUPPLY AREA MANAGER IN FOR THE NEXT SIX WEEKS!

PLEASE! PLEASE! EVERYONE JUST GET ON QUIETLY WITH YOUR WORK! DON'T MAKE ME GO AND FETCH THE BANKING OMBUDSMAN...!

COR! I LIKE YOUR BRIEFCASE, FONTAYNE! IT'S MINT!

LetterBOCKS

**Viz Comic P.O. Box 841
Whitley Bay NE26 9EQ
letters@viz.co.uk**

STAR LETTER

I DON'T know why tradesmen put "Free Estimates" on their adverts. If they think I'm going to pay them to tell me how much a job would cost they can fuck off before they start.

Manfred Mansell, Notts

I REALISE that Roy Horn out of Siegfried and Roy was extremely experienced in dealing with big cats, but in my experience rubbing their nose in their own shit usually sorts them out and shows them who's boss. Maybe if he's reading this, he's thinking "Now you tell me," but I've only just read about the savage mauling he got off his tiger in 2003, and I can hardly be blamed if my paper boy is a lazy little bastard can I?

Frank Baelish, Blackpool

THIS morning I woke up at 08:57 for a doctor's appointment at 09:00 - and I live half an hour's drive from the surgery. Luckily I'm the doctor, so I just made all my patients wait.

Dr R Jessop, e-mail

I NOTICE that in horror films, whenever someone turns up at a local inn and asks for directions to Dracula's or Frankenstein's castle, everyone in the place goes deathly quiet and looks away. It seems blatantly obvious to me that they have both been barred. I'm guessing that some kind of late-night scuffle was involved in Dracula's case and perhaps being unsuitably dressed in the case of Frankenstein.

C Treadworthy, Tooting

YESTERDAY I saw the International Space Station go across the night sky and I was astonished to see how incredibly bright it was, far brighter than everything except the moon. It got me thinking that perhaps it was this object that the Three Wise Men saw in the heavens on that very first Christmas night. I don't want to shake anyone's faith, but it is something worth considering.

George Dury, Tyne & Wear

IT'S very true that porn gives distorted views of what sex is really like. I have never seen a bongo film where the woman complains of a headache or tells him to 'keep it down a bit' because the kids are still awake. And despite selflessly devoting hours and hours of research to the matter, I have yet to see a porn star fall asleep as soon as he has chucked his muck up some bird's wizard's sleeve.

Dalcome Mixon, e-mail

I TELL you what, I'd like to "Only Connect" with Victoria Coren. By that I mean I would like to have penetrative sex with her, just in case she's reading this and isn't as clever as she's been making out.

Peapod Manure, Glasgow

WHY do documentary makers insult their viewers when showing an expose on Göering or Himmler by showing footage of them in slo-mo grainly black and white with *Jaws* music in the background? We're smart enough to figure out who the baddies of the story are.

Jimmy Fuck, e-mail

DID I send you an email about Sandra Bullock's tits last night? I know I meant to but I got a bit hammered and everything after 9 o'clock is a bit of a blur I'm afraid.

Nick Lyon, Truro

* No, Nick, we didn't receive a letter about Sandra Bullock's tits. Perhaps you simply dreamt you sent it, or indeed, you may have sent it to the wrong e-mail address. Did any of our readers receive an e-mail from Nick Lyon regarding Sandra Bullock's tits? If you did, please forward it to letterbocks@viz.co.uk.

I NEARLY stacked my car on the way home from work, dancing to S-Club 7's *Reach for the Stars*. Has anyone else had a near fatal accident to a worse song?

Steve Kilner, e-mail

I RECENTLY invited the neighbours over for a few drinks. Whilst the wife kept them entertained, I nipped over the back wall and burgled their house. I can't stand the bastards.

RR Rasputin, e-mail

THEY say absence makes the heart grow fonder. But Michael Winner's not been around for over three years now and I think of him as just as big an arsehole as I did before he died.

Dom Whitehouse, e-mail

IT'S pissing down with rain, and all the cows in the field opposite me are standing up and walking around. So much for these so-called 'experts'.

Dr Heather Jenkinson, e-mail

CAN I just say how disappointed I am with Dr Heather Jenkinson *(above)*. A perfectly good letter about cows standing up in the rain has been spoilt by the gratuitous use of the 'p' word. The fact that a lady, and a doctor at that, cannot get two words into a letter without resorting to foul language is shocking.

Ada Stoolage, Barnton

ARE there any *Dr Who* fans who can explain to me why the Tardis doesn't disappear when it travels back in time to before it was built?

Peter Busby, e-mail

* Can any Dr Who fans explain that one? If you can, keep it to yourself as we're not interested, and we assume Mr Busby's question was rhetorical.

IN an attempt to ensure I get the recommended amount of sleep at night I now use a stopwatch, stopping it everytime I wake up during the night, and I don't get up till it hits the 8 hour mark. I feel great but the downside is I have been late for work every day for the past six months. Fortunately I'm a train driver so no-one has noticed.

Simon Hoffmann, e-mail

Desert Island Dream Dinner Party Alans

Each week, we ask some famous Alans to pick 4 people, living or dead, who they'd invite to their desert island dream dinner party.

Alan Titmarsh *TV gardener*
I'm interested in gardening, Christianity and writing mucky stories. So I'd invite *Capability Brown*, *Jesus* and the *Marquis de Sade*. For my final guest, I'd like to invite Judas Ischariot to ask him why he betrayed Jesus in the Garden of Gethsemane, but with the Big man sat at the other side of the table, there'd probably be a pretty awkward atmosphere. So I'd probably just go for *Albert Einstein* or *Joe Swash*.

Alan Davies *QI ear-nosher*
I once bit a tramp's ear off outside the Groucho Club, so for my desert island dream dinner party I'd invite people who were also famous lug-nobblers. On my guest list would be heavyweight boxer *Mike Tyson*, artist *Vincent Van Gogh*, *Reservoir Dogs* actor *Michael Madsen* and 14-year-old *King Henry II* who cut off a peasant boy's ear for not showing him enough respect. We could chat about our various careers in sport, acting, art and history, with particular reference to removing ears.

Alan Bennett *playwright*
Oh goodness me, with all the people in history to choose from it's very hard to narrow it down to just four. But to my desert island dream dinner party I'd probably invite Motley Crue drummer *Tommy Lee*, *Gene Simmons* out of Kiss, *Ted Nugent* and *Dee Schneider* out of Twisted Sister. However, I'd be so intimidated at the prospect of going out for a meal with four of the wildest men in rock, I'd probably lose my nerve, and just stay at home and have a poached egg.

Alan Hansen *football pundit*
As viewers of *Match of the Day* will be aware, I'm a very dull person with no imagination. So to my desert island dream dinner party I'd probably invite *Gary Lineker*, *Alan Shearer*, *Mark Lawrenson* and *Robbie Savage*.

ASK any angler what he is doing this weekend and the reply will invariably be "I am off for a bit of fishing." Why don't they do all the fishing? I am sure they would catch a lot more. It seems obvious to me and I am no angler.

Steve Adams, e-mail

YOU have to wonder about Captain America. As far as I'm aware, he's held that same rank since 1941 and has never been promoted. Was there perhaps some scandalous indiscretion with a young recruit or inappropriate behaviour in the NAAFI? I don't suppose we'll ever get to know.

Bradley Cheese, Leeming

HOW come people say something is 'below par' meaning that it is bad, yet to be 'below par' in golf is good? Once again, it's one rule for golfers and another for the rest of us.

Matthew Clarke, e-mail

WHEN will the BBC stop using MILFs to present the weather forecast? I get enough of that on the internet.

Mike F, e-mail

UP THE ARSE CORNER

O Bhaji, Banbury

I A Nortcliff, e-mail

G Reuland, e-mail

RECENTLY I slogged my guts out for nearly five hours to run a marathon and yet all the fuss was made over some chap that ran for a couple of hours and didn't even collapse at the end. Once again, the red carpet is rolled out for idle foreigners while us hard-working native Brits are overlooked.

Mike Tatham, e-mail

THOSE scientists proclaiming graphene to be the thinnest black material ever developed have obviously never bought Aldi value bin liners.

Kermit Biro, e-mail

YOU'D think, given that we are cutting down all their trees and building nice big roads for them, the least some of these indigenous natives in the Amazon could do is put on a pair of trousers when one of our documentary crews turns up to film them.

Brady Bunch, Carlisle

A LOT of people get up in arms about airport expansion, especially when they hear plans for a new runway. One way around it would be simply to scrap the one-way system and use both lanes of the existing runways rather than one plane hogging the centre as they do now.

Morgan Oaktree, Cardiff

IRONICALLY, 'strap on' spelled backwards is 'no parts'. I don't want a fiver or a pencil for sending this in, I just thought I would mention it.

Ross Kennet, e-mail

I WISH critics like Paul Morley and Germaine Greer on *The Review Show* would just get to the point instead of spending twenty minutes

PAYDAY loan companies. Enforce a strict repayment scheme by using victims in neck braces, plaster casts and on crutches in your television adverts.

Hapag Lloyd, Runcorn

KIM Jong-Un. When throwing your family or enemies of the state to hungry dogs, stop western governments from frowning on you by dressing in a smart red jacket, blowing a bugle and shouting "Tally-Ho." The west will think you are a good egg and jolly good sport.

Peter Bagge, e-mail

WIGS
1 FOR $35
2 FOR $50

I THOUGHT some of your cheaper slap-head readers might be interested in this shop in Alicetown, Bimini. Its a long way to go for a rug, but the weather is nice there and you can drink in the street.

Fat Dan, Pieland

describing why a book, film or play is so bad. Why not just say, "It's fucking shit," and then move on and stop wasting licencepayers' money.

Hector Nicelybig, Truro

HOW come ghosts in films are always right scruffy buggers? Surely there must be a few

A PEELED boiled egg cut in two lengthways with the yolk removed makes an ideal urinal for hamsters

Ross Williams, e-mail

STOP your iPod earphones from falling out whilst running by smearing them with No More Nails and then pushing them into your ears as hard as you can.

Hapag Lloyd, Runcorn

LOCKED out of your house at night? They are many techniques you can employ to survive. A plastic bottle from the recycling bin makes an ideal pillow and gathering fallen leaves into a plant pot makes an ideal fire pit to cook the neighbour's cat over.

Bear Grylls, e-mail

smart-looking ghosts out there wearing a trendy three piece suit or perhaps a nice jumper and sporting a decent haircut? The majority of people get buried in their best gear anyway.

Ada Chelstrom, Stockport

SAVE hours of time wasted trimming toe nails by simply pushing a sheet of sand paper into the end of your socks. Hey presto! Neat nails as you walk to work.

The Scarlet Fang, e-mail

RADIO commentators. Don't get hysterical every time a horse wins a race or someone scores a goal. Just tell us what's happening and we'll decide if we want to get fucking excited about it.

Arigato Ian Hughes, e-

toptips@viz.co.uk

PEOPLE always assume that because ants are forever on the move, they're working hard. For all we know they could be running from work and trying to hide under those leaves they're carrying. A bloke who works with me hides under a stack of pallets when a lorry turns up for unloading.

Richard Thomas, Nottingham

Clarissa Dickson-WRONG!

One Fat Lady "regretting move to other side"

BBC chef *Clarissa Dickson-Wright* "bitterly regrets" making the move to the other side, according to close pals. The *Two Fat Ladies* star had been a fixture a the Beeb for nearly twenty years, but took the risky decision to pass over to the other side after suffering congestive heart failure three months ago.

"Clarissa, 66, thought dropping dead was the right thing to do, but now she's not so sure," said an insider. "Moving around and existing in the world was always such a big part of her life. Now she's six foot under and struggling to come to terms with the upheaval."

nosedive

Dickson-Wright's move mirrors that of her former on-screen partner Jennifer Paterson, whose

Cook-up: TV chef Dickson-Wright fears that move to other side was biggest mistake of her career.

career took a nosedive following her decision to have a fatal pulmonary infarction in 1999.

DOG TRAINING

I WANT TO STOP MY DOG POOING ALL THE TIME

HEY BABY. WANT TO COME BACK TO MY PLACE?

YEAR
the
Take a Shit...

WINNER!
MAGAZINE of the YEAR
~Take a Shit Magazine of the
Year Awards

Take a Shit...

Dyer Straits

Mockney Hard Man's Mum and Dad Tell of their Despair

COCKNEY actor **Danny Dyer** has found himself in hot water yet again - after coming home late **3 times in the same week!** The *Football Factory* star returned home after his 9.30 pm curfew on Tuesday, Wednesday and Friday of last week, and his mother, Dolly, 61, said the stress was causing her health issues.

"Daniel knows his father and I worry terribly when he is out late," she told her hairdresser Sue. "There's all sorts of people on the streets these days. My nerves can't take much more. I am at my wits end."

Sue sympathised with Mrs Dyer's feelings, but had these words of comfort: "Danny's a sensible lad. I'm sure he won't come to any harm."

Meanwhile, quizzed by his father on his reasons for arriving back after the agreed time on Tuesday, Dyer proclaimed his innocence. "I was out filming a low-budget British gangster movie with **Vinnie Jones** and **Guy Ritchie** and my watch must've stopped," he said. But Dyer's father Stan was unmoved. "We bought him that expensive mobile phone and he never turns it on," said Mr Dyer.

After a stern talking-to, the dust seemed to have settled over the affair, but incredibly just 24 hours later Dyer was at it again – this time a full 20 minutes late coming home.

"His Dad has been up and down the street looking for him, knocking on doors. Lord knows what the neighbours think of us, " Mrs Dyer told Mrs Hetherington who works in the Post Office.

"All we ask is for a call to let us know how he is. Is that too much trouble?" said the *Straightheads* star's clearly exasperated mother. Mrs Hetherington, 72, agreed with Mrs Dyer that it wasn't too much trouble.

> *Since he's been hanging around with that Vinnie Jones and Guy Ritchie, we don't know what he'll be like from one day to the next.*

Worried sick: Danny's mum and dad (with cat Mr. Pookey) are at their wits' end over wayward son's antics.

"We're at our wits' end with the bugger" ~ Dolly and Stan Dyer

Off the rails: Dirty stop-out actor Dyer has been repeatedly coming home at yon time.

However the 37-year-old actor had his excuses at the ready, claiming he had been for dinner with his agent to look over a couple of scripts he had been sent, before meeting his accountant to discuss his tax affairs. "I don't see what all the fuss is about to be honest," he stormed, insisting that he hadn't asked to be born and that his mother and father were not the boss of him.

However, Mr and Mrs Dyer responded that while the *Vendetta* star was living under their roof, he should abide by their rules, and if they said he should be in by nine-thirty, he should be in by nine-thirty, and no excuses. They also accused the *7Lives* actor of treating their house like a hotel.

Dyer's father told pals: "It's a liberty, it really is. His mum was going spare and then he comes waltzing through the door at 10 to 10 like he hasn't got a care in the world. And you could smell the smoke on him straight away. I just dread the day I get a call from the police."

There was some respite for the *Britain's Hardest Men* host's parents on Wednesday, when he returned home at 9pm. Mr Dyer was quick to acknowledge his son's good behaviour, but added a note of caution. "He can be as good as gold sometimes," he told fellow allotment holder Stan Crabtree. "But since he has been hanging around with that Vinnie Jones and Guy Ritchie we just don't know what he'll be like from one day to the next."

"They're a bad influence on him," said Mr Dyer. "I look at his angelic little face in his old school photographs and I could weep, I really could."

Mr Crabtree commiserated with Mr Dyer, commenting that his son Ian was just the same.

And true to form on Thursday the actor was up to his old tricks, arriving home at past 9.45pm whilst his harrassed-looking mother looked on. "I hope you're satisfied with yourself," said an angry Mr Dyer. "Your mother's been up at them curtains since nine o'clock, worried sick about you."

Unsuitable friends: Dyer is being led astray by ne'er-do-well pals Vinnie Jones and Guy Ritchie

As usual the ex-*Hollyoaks* star had an excuse at the ready, claiming he had been to the *GQ* awards where he was presenting the prize in the Best Dressed Male category, before taking longtime girlfriend **Joanne Mas** for dinner at the Ivy.

But Dyer's tall stories cut no ice with his parents. "We've heard them all before," his mother told next-door neighbour Mrs Finch over the back fence. "He's like a bloody broken record."

Last night, Dyer's agent Becky Thompson told us that the *Age of Heroes* star was unavailable for comment as he had had his phone taken off him and been confined to his bedroom for the next two weeks.

OH NO! it's the PATHETIC SHARKS!

AT THE PUB... ...WELL THIS IS NICE! VERY RUSTIC, I MUST SAY.

WAHEY! A LADS' NIGHT OUT! WHAT'S EVERYONE HAVING?

HALF A LAGER SHANDY PLEASE.

JUST A GLASS OF TAP WATER FOR ME...

QUIZ TONIGHT

...I'M DRIVING.

YOU'RE NOT DRIVING.

WELL I MIGHT HAVE TO DRIVE IF YOU HAVE TOO MUCH TO DRINK TONIGHT.

HE'S RIGHT. ONE OF US HAS TO STAY SAFE.

BUT WE HAVEN'T GOT A CAR.

MIND YOU, FRIEND OF MINE IS A POLICEMAN, AND HE SAYS YOU'RE ALRIGHT UP TO 2½ PINTS.

FIVE PINTS OF BEER, PLEASE. AND A BAG OF PORK SCRATCHINGS.

I DON'T WANT ANY. I HAD ONE ONCE AND IT STILL HAD HAIRS ON IT.

I HAD A WHOLE NIPPLE ONCE.

YOU DOING THE QUIZ?

A QUIZ! HOW EXCITING! COME ON EVERYONE- LET'S FIND OURSELVES A TABLE.

HAS ANYONE GOT A PEN?

HERE WE GO... PICTURE ROUND, NUMBER ONE... WHO'S THAT A PHOTO OF?

OOH! IT'S ON THE TIP OF MY TONGUE...IT'S THAT GOLFER...

IS IT TOBY ANSTIS?

I CAN'T TELL. IT'S UPSIDE DOWN.

NO, IT'S HIM OFF THAT THING. OH, YOU KNOW..."WHOO WOOULD LEEVE IRN A HOOURSE LAARK THEEESE?"...

WHAT? LLOYD GROSSMAN?

NO. SHUT UP. IT'S THAT GOLFER.

IT'S THAT GOLFER.

NO, NOT LLOYD GROSSMAN. THE OTHER ONE OFF THAT PROGRAMME.

LLOYD GROSSMAN DOES PASTA SAUCES NOW.

THEY'RE QUITE EXPENSIVE THOUGH.

WELL, YOU GET WHAT YOU PAY FOR, I ALWAYS SAY.

YOU DO.

OH WHAT'S HE CALLED?

I USUALLY MAKE MY OWN PASTA SAUCE, BUT SOMETIMES, IF YOU'VE JUST COME IN FROM WORK, YOU KNOW, AND YOU HAVEN'T TIME...

IS IT KEITH LEMON? I LOVE KEITH LEMON.

I KNOW WHAT YOU MEAN. THEY'RE JUST SO CONVENIENT AREN'T THEY.

IT'S THAT PROGRAMME KEITH LEMON DOES NOW, BUT IT'S THE MAN WHO USED TO DO IT. HIM.

ARE YOU SURE IT'S NOT TOBY ANSTIS?

NO. I DON'T THINK TOBY ANSTIS EVER DID IT.

WELL, WHAT AM I THINKING OF, THEN, THAT TOBY ANSTIS USED TO DO?

LIVE AND KICKING?

NO, THAT WAS ANDY CRANE.

NO IT WASN'T. YOU'RE THINKING OF ANDI PETERS. HE DOES THAT QUIZ NOW, WITH THE CHAIRS, BUT IT'S NOT AS GOOD AS POINTLESS.

WHO USED TO GO "HEWOW GOODEEVE NINAAAND WEWCOOM", LIKE THAT?

...ALWAYS HAD A NICE BLAZER ON?

A...N...D...Y... SPACE...C...R...A...N...E...

WHAT'S HE DOING?

SHH! HE'S GOOGLING IT ON HIS PHONE.

RETURN.

HE'S LUCKY HE CAN GET A SIGNAL. MINE SAYS "NO SERVICE".

I TELL A LIE...I'VE GOT ONE BAR THERE NOW.

MY DATA PLAN SAYS IT'S UNLIMITED BUT IT'S NOT REALLY.

MOTORMOUTH?

'ERE! THEY'RE LOOKING THE ANSWERS UP, LOOK.

?!

OI FISHFACE! THERE'S NO CHEATING ALLOWED.

LET'S GET 'EM!

BIFF! GRIP PUNCH! BAWALLOP!

...AND FUCKIN' STAY OUT!

DOF!

SHORTLY... ...AND HERE ARE THE ANSWERS TO THE PICTURES ROUND...PICTURE ONE: JOHNNY DEPP. HALF A POINT FOR EDWARD SCISSORHANDS...

GROAN

BIG VERN

KNOCK-KNOCK!

HELLO THERE VERN.

WOTCHA ERNIE. I'M COLLECTING FOR CHARITY.

IT'S THE ROYAL SOCIETY FOR THE REHABILITATION OF EXTREMELY VIOLENT CRIMINALS, ERNIE.

WELL THAT SOUNDS LAUDABLE, VERN.

TOO RIGHT IT IS, ERNIE. TURNED MY 'OLE LIFE RAHND, I 'AVE, FANKS TO THESE GEEZAS...

BEFORE I WAS ON THE PROGRAMME, I WAS A PARANOID 'OMICIDAL MANIAC - PRONE TO SUDDEN SHOOTIN' SPREES...

BUT NOW I'M A DIFFERENT MAN.

THAT OTHER VERN FROM THE BAD OLD DAYS... I DON'T KNOW 'IM NO MOWAH.

WELL THAT'S GOOD TO HEAR, I MUST SAY.

SO, IF YOU'VE GOT ANY LOOSE CHANGE KICKIN' RAHND IN YER GAFF, ERNIE...

OF COURSE...

CHING! CHING!

ACTUALLY, THERE'S A FEW COPPERS IN THE KITCHEN. I'LL JUST GO AND GET THEM...

COPPERS IN THE KITCHEN!? IT'S A FACKIN' TRAP!

YOU STITCHED ME APP, YOU BARSTAD!

BLAM! BLAM!

BLAM!

Grease is the Word for Cost-Cutting Osborne

Current favourite: The wattage generated by Olivia Newton-John's charged performance in the final scene of Grease could cut UK bills in half, says Osborne.

CHANCELLOR of the Exchequer GEORGE OSBORNE today announced new plans to cut household energy bills **IN HALF** within just a matter of weeks. And this incredible feat won't be achieved by raising income tax or spreading costs over a longer period – but instead by harnessing the electrical charge emitted by *Olivia Newton-John* in the final scene of *Grease*.

Osborne, 43, outlined the origins of his unorthodox cost-cutting scheme to journalists outside the House of Commons this morning.

"Last Sunday, I was sitting on the sofa when Grease came on Channel 5. The remote control was out of reach so I was forced to watch it," he told reporters.

Osborne explained that he sat through the popular 1978 musical patiently, until the final scene suddenly made him stand up and take notice.

EXCLUSIVE!

"In the last bit at the fairground, Olivia Newton-John comes in and she's wearing all tight leather and with a perm and that, and John Travolta says, and I quote, 'I've got chills, they're multiplying/And I'm losing control/Because the power you're supplying/It's electrifying'."

shock

He continued: "Such is the potency of the invisible current Newton-John is emitting, Travolta

"You've got bills, they're multiplying, but I'm taking control," says Chancellor

literally convulses with shock and collapses to the ground. The power of that image struck me to my very core and I realised that if we could harness the immense charge Newton-John supplied at that moment, we'd save the British homeowner a fortune on energy bills."

eel

Osborne Googled Newton-John's agent, and within seconds had fired off an e-mail requesting the actress's urgent help.

"I explained that I was the British Chancellor of the Exchequer, and I

desperately required Ms Newton-John's assistance in a vital government matter", claimed Osborne. "I said we would pay her the market rate to spend a few weeks hooked up to a generator inside number 10 whilst smoking a fag, wearing a leather cat-suit and repeating the phrase 'Tell me about it, stud' over and over again.

The subsequent electricity she would supply could be used to provide heat, light and power for hard-working British families," he explained.

Osborne revealed that he received a near-instant reply to his email, informing him he had been blocked from the addressee's mailbox.

However, he informed reporters that the plan was still on track and he is currently arranging for Downing Street to be re-decorated to resemble a 1950s fairground, as well as casting the additional supporting roles required for Newton-John's performance.

boogaloo

"Myself and various high-ranking members of the Conservative Party will play the T-Birds", Osborne confirmed. "I'll be John Travolta obviously, since it was my idea, and Cameron's already bagsied Kenickie. But the other three shit ones are still up for grabs."

THE ULTIMATE FIGHT FOR THE MO[...]

BOY vs BOBI[...]
WHO IS THE REAL KIN[...]

IT'S THE DEBATE that's splitting the country down the middle in three. In every pub, club, factory, office and shop from Land's End to John O'Groats, there's only one topic of conversation on everyone's lips: Just who is the best George? Is it 80s gender-bending pop star **BOY GEORGE**, jewel-bedecked maestro of the nine dart finish **BOBBY GEORGE**, or is it **BARRY GEORGE**, whose false conviction for murdering TV star Jill Dando was overturned in 2007?

Only one of them can take his rightful place on our country's throne as **BRITAIN'S BEST GEORGE**. And to decide once and for all which should reign supreme over us, we're going to pit them against each other head to head to head. And this no-holds-barred Battle of the Millennium will award points for their

---

BOY

BO[...]

ROUND 1 GENDER

WHEN Boy George first appeared on *Top of the Pops*, singing with his band Culture Club, the British public was thrown into confusion by his long hair, lady's makeup and frock. Nobody could tell what sex he was, and so the term "Gender Bender" was born. Several months later, he finally came out of the closet and revealed that he was a sort of man, although he would rather have a cup of tea than sex.

9

THIS is a particularly low-scoring round for the Cockney ace of the oche, as there is surely no more manly occupation than drinking beer and playing darts. However, George's two Christian names, Bobby and Francis are also girls' names, a fact which could eas[...]

ROUND 2 B[...]

AFTER seeing him dressed like a woman and wearing girls' makeup, you might expect Boy to have a taste for draping himself with feminine jewellery too. But nothing could be further for the truth, for the Karma Chameleon singer eschews bijouterie of all kinds, preferring big daft hats and all rags tied in his hair to rings, necklaces, tiaras and bracelets.

4

EVEN if he doesn't win this competition to become monarch of the B Georges, Bobby will always be the undisputed 24 carat King of Bling. Dripping with his trademark "luvverly jubberly" gold ingots and sporting

ROUND 3 PSEU[...]

ON HIS passport, birth certificate and when he is being charged with various offences in court, the former Culture Club frontman goes by the nickname of "George Alan O'Dowd". However, this not-particularly-snappy monicker has never really caught on with the public and to his legions of ex-fans he'll always be best known as Boy George.

5

BOBBY George's roll call of alternative appellations reads like an A to Z of nicknames, including "Bobby Dazzler", "the King of Darts", "the Earl of the Nine Dart Finish", "the Duke of One-Hundred-and-Eighty", "Doc-

ROUND 4 TIME I[...]

IN 2008, Boy was sentenced to fifteen months in prison after being convicted of assaulting and falsely imprisoning a naked man whom he believed to have been tampering with his computer. When this is added to the eight weeks jail term and five-year driving ban of his namesake pop star George Michael, Boy George's total time behind bars comes to over six years!

7

A CURSORY internet search and half-arsed skim-read through his Wikipedia entry turn up no evidence that darts star Bobby has ever served time at Her Majesty's pleasure. However, that is not to say that he isn't guilty of many serious crimes for which a custodial sentence would be the only appropriate punishment. Scotland Yard's files are ful[...]

ROUND 5 BEING IN[...]

IN A 1986 episode of *The A-Team*, Boy appeared as an androgynous British pop star who was called upon to solve a crime or something. You might expect this fact to secure him full points in this round, but sadly his fellow members of Culture Club - Jon Moss, Mikey Craig and the other one - also appeared in the show, so by the rules of the contest Boy's score has to be reduced pro rata.

2½

LIKE Boy, Bobby also starred in an episode of *The A-Team*, when he appeared as BA Baracus's long-lost darts-playing twin brother "BG" Baracus. Blacked up and resplendent in dunga-

ROUND 6 JUMPING OVER 4 DOUBLE DE[...]

WITH five gold discs, five platinum discs and a string of almost three UK Number One singles to his name, Boy George has had a successful pop career by any standards. However, at the time of going to press, the *Time (Clock of the Heart)* singer had yet to announce any plans to perform a roller skate jump over four double decker buses.

0

EVEN though he no longer competes in the top flight of international darts, Bobby nevertheless keeps himself busy commentating on the BDO World Championship for the BBC, running his

HOW DI[...]

HEY THERE, Georgie Boy! We really don't want to hurt him, but there isn't "O'Dowd" in our minds that the Culture Club vocalist has failed to make the grade on this occasion.

27½

BAD ARROWS! It's a frustrating score of thirteen, one, treble-seven for the former darts Bobby Dazzler as he narrowly misses the Bull and has to be contented with the runner's up

T COVETED C OWN IN T E LAND!
Y vs BARRY
GEORGE OF ENGLAND?

BECAUSE YOU'RE GEORGES: Boy, Bobby and Barry, yesterday.

ndividual attributes and qualities before totting up their final scores to decide which one comes out on top.

Three contenders will enter the Viz Georgedome, but only one will emerge victorious. Which one will it be? Only time will tell.

BY		BARRY

NDERISM ROUND 1

ly throw his gender into question. To muddy the water still further, he enters the darts arena to the sound of We Are the Champions by Queen, whilst carrying a candelabra like Liberace.

8

BARRY George has proven time and time again that he is a 100% red-blooded male. Marrying a woman for a while, performing daredevil stunts and loitering in a balaclava amongst the bushes outside Lady Diana's house armed with a fifty-

foot length of rope are only things that a real man's man would attempt. Only his obsession with flamboyant gay singer Freddie Mercury prevents him from scoring nothing at all in this round.

1

G ROUND 2

sovs on every finger, the 1980 World Championship runner-up has truly earned his reputation as the Tutankhamen of Darts.

6

BARRY performs poorly in this round, as he has rarely been seen wearing jewellery in public. In any case, any items of bling he may have owned would probably have been traded with his fel-

low prisoners for "snout" or hardcore pornography during the years he served in stir following his wrongful conviction for the 1999 murder of *Crimewatch* presenter Jill.

3

NYMS ROUND 3

tor Double-top" and "Emeritus Professor of the Bullseye". The list is literally endless.

8

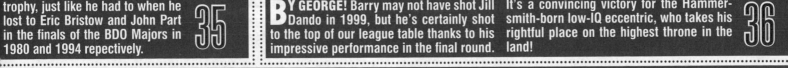

THROUGHOUT his thirty-year career as an obsessive loner, the London-born 53-year-old has assumed a number of alternative identities, such as "Paul Gadd",

"Steve Majors" and "Tom Palmer". In the 1980s, he changed his name by deed poll to "Barry Bulsara", after which he took to using the alias "Barry George".

7

RISON ROUND 4

of unsolved cases whose perpetrators, perhaps including George, have got away Scot free. But the British legal system says he is innocent until proven guilty in a court of law, and this technicality secures him a low score in this round.

5

FANTASIST George famously spent eight years banged up in the nick for a crime he didn't commit. Less famously, in 1982 he also was also sentenced to two-and-a-half years for a crime he did commit, on top of a three month

suspended sentence for another bit of mischief the year before. All told, it's an impressive tally of nearly a decade of porridge for the self-styled former British karate champion.

8

E A-TEAM ROUND 5

rees and his own Mr T-style bling, Bobby's performance sadly hit the cutting room floor after producers had second thoughts about the appropriateness of their casting decision. The part was eventually played by Burt Kwouk.

5

BARRY spent much of the 1980s making outlandish claims about his identity. At various times he declared he was the first SAS man into the Libyan Embassy, that he was a session musician for ELO and that he was a Hollywood stuntman called Steve Majors. Although many of his boasts have

since proved to be fabrications, it is just possible that he was telling the truth on this last occasion, and if so he would almost certainly have appeared in *The A-Team*, perhaps driving that van off a ramp or jumping out of a helicopter flown by "Howling Mad" Murdock.

7

ER BUSES ON ROLLER SKATES ROUND 6

own tinned apricot importing business and appearing on a 2009 episode of *Cash in the Attic*. Sadly, this packed schedule leaves him little time for jumping over anything on roller skates, least of all four double decker buses.

3

IN 1982, hundreds of people crammed into Derby County football ground to watch Barry George leap over four double decker buses on his roller skates. In becoming the first person to successfully perform this incredible feat, he joined an elite pantheon of Great Britons who

have achieved an historic first, adding his name (whichever one he was using at that time) to an illustrious roll call of national heroes that includes astronaut Neil Armstrong, Arctic explorer Roald Amundsen and mountaineer Sir Edward Hillary.

10

HEY DO?

trophy, just like he had to when he lost to Eric Bristow and John Part in the finals of the BDO Majors in 1980 and 1994 repectively.

35

BY GEORGE! Barry may not have shot Jill Dando in 1999, but he's certainly shot to the top of our league table thanks to his impressive performance in the final round.

It's a convincing victory for the Hammersmith-born low-IQ eccentric, who takes his rightful place on the highest throne in the land!

36

NEXT WEEK Nat vs Old: *Who's the best King Cole?*

"MY GOVERNMENT and I are often accused of being elitist and out of touch with you, the ordinary working classes. But let me tell you, nothing could be further from the truth. Just like Great Britain itself, my Cabinet is made up of people from every conceivable background - Eton, Harrow, Oxford, Cambridge... the list goes on.

And just like ordinary working class people, we know what it is like to "graft" for a living. At school I used to spend prep every Wednesday serving cream teas in my house buttery, and my Chancellor George Osborne once spent a gruelling week at Selfridges, re-folding towels.

So you see, we are truly ordinary salt of the earth, working class people just like you. And just like you, after work we enjoy relaxing in exactly the same ways that ordinary salt of the earth, working class people do. A night out at the local Bingo parlour, a trip to the whippet racing circuit and eating delicious fish and chips and mushy peas out of a filthy old newspaper are just a few things that we have in common with you lot.

And believe me, we understand the problems you face on those nights out only too well... because we face them too. Where do I keep my Bingo pen? Which pocket did I put my betting slips in? Where can I keep this sachet of salt to season my "chip butty" on my way back from the "rub-a-dub"?

That's why we at Number 10 have teamed up with our pals at Viz to bring you this fantastic Multi-purpose Working Class Requisites Hatband. It's the handy organiser that keeps all the things you sort of people care about within reach at all times whilst you're out and about. Suitable for any sort of hat, from opera topper to Henley Regatta straw boater*, it's yours FREE to cut out and keep.**"

*Not suitable for flat caps

Rt Hon David Cameron MP
Working class
Prime Minister of
Great Britain and
Northern Ireland and
direct descendant of
His Majesty King William IV

Eeeh! By gum and Gaw Blimey! It's super!

BINGO

BETTING

BENEFITS

SAVE! 50%OFF! £££ BOGOF! 3 for 2

Fish 'n' Chip Shop Condiments

BETTING SLIPS, SCRATCHCARDS, ETC

BINGO PEN

BETTING SHOP PEN

SIGNING ON PEN

FISH AND CHIP SHOP CONDIMENTS

SUPER MONEY-OFF

BUS TICKETS

VIZ

LOOK AT ALL THESE FEATURES!

1. Betting Slip and Scratchcard Pocket
2. Bus Ticket Holder
3. Retaining loops for Bingo, turf accountant and signing-on pens
4. Fish & Chip Shop Condiments Larder

8 HANDY HOLDERS IN ONE!

5. Supermarket money-off coupon wallet
6. Pub Darts repository
7. 'Baccy' pouch
8. Receptacle for cigarette ends picked up out of the gutter

You can use it ANYWHERE!

At the soccer game...

...down the public house...

...in court.

Instructions

Cut out and assemble your David Cameron Multi-purpose Working Class Requisites Hatband as shown in the diagram, adjusting it to suit your hat size using the measurement scale provided (*if you don't know your hat size, simply ask your milliner*). Put it round the hat of your choice and Hey Presto! Being Lower Class just got a whole lot easier!

Bull's Eye

Double Top

180

I ♥ BACCY

It really is remarkable, guv'nor, make no mistake!

Rt Hon George Osborne MP
Heir apparent to the Osborne Baronetcy

You fucking plebs will love it, you verminous proles!

Rt Hon Andrew Mitchell MP*

*Testimonial may have been fabricated by members of the Metropolitan Police

GAME of LOANS

"The HBO hit fantasy series stars are queueing up for payday subs," says Bolton moneylender

Credit where credit's due: The rollcall of Game of Thrones stars who have borrowed money from Baz reads like the cast list of HBO hit show Game of Thrones. Tyrion Lannister (inset) and a combi boiler (below) similar to the one owned by Daenerys Stormborn.

NEITHER a borrower nor a lender be, or so the saying goes. But as the recession continues to bite and the country's mountain of debt climbs ever higher, we often have no option but to borrow a few pounds to tide ourselves over till payday.

But you might be surprised to learn that it's not just the skint man in the street who typically finds himself needing a quick cash injection to pay off his final demands. For, with their expensive jet-set lifestyles, many of the biggest names in showbiz also often find themselves caught short and looking for a high interest, short term loan. And none more so than the cast of hit HBO drama *Game of Thrones.*

One man who knows this first hand is independent credit broker **Baz Barron**. Since 2008, the Bolton-based entrepreneur's company Barron's Hard-Up Loanz has given cash advances to many of the historical fantasy series's stars who have found themselves temporarily in Queer Street.

" I started out mainly lending money to unemployed, single mums who play too much bingo and alcoholics who've put all their jobseekers' allowance in the fruities down the pub," Barron told us. "But then actors from Game of Thrones started coming in for subs, and

EXCLUSIVE!

eventually that side of the business took over completely.

"Not many people know that the series is shot on the moors near Bolton," he added. "I suppose I was just handy, being nearby.

Apparently HBO handed out the wages on a Friday afternoon after filming finished. The actors were on good money too, make no mistake. But like all Hollywood stars, they've got expensive tastes and more often than not, about half way through the week they'd not be left with two ha'pennies to scratch their arses with.

I remember one Wednesday morning, I turned up at my office above a chip shop to find the bloke who plays Lord Baelish stood outside. I recognised him as he was wearing his long black cloak and his gauntlets out the series. He explained that he had come straight from the set because he was desperate for a payday loan.

Apparently a bearing had gone in his Saxo and ATS had quoted him £140 to fix it. He told me he was on the bones of his arse and they wouldn't let him have the car back until he paid the bill. Obviously, as a big fan of the show, I was a little starstruck and also flattered that such a big star would come to my company for a short term cash advance.

squeeze

I quickly sorted out the paperwork and Littlefinger, as he is known in *Game of Thrones*, was soon happily on his way to the garage with £140 in his back bin and instructions to come back on Friday with £430 to pay off the loan plus interest. It felt good to have helped one of my favourite stars out of a tight squeeze. It's moments like this that make this job worthwhile.

But that feeling didn't last. Friday morning came and there was no sign of Lord Baelish with my Nelsons. That wasn't too serious in itself; it just meant he'd have to cough up the thick end of a grand before next weekend. But at half past five, just as I was closing up the office, he knocked on the door and came in. This time he wasn't alone; he had two of the prostitutes from his brothel at King's Landing with him.

brinsley schwarz

He explained that he hadn't brought my money, but he'd come to settle the debt in kind. What happened next was like an X-rated scene from the Emmy-nominated show itself. Littlefinger casually undid a clasp from the back of each of the prostitutes' capes and their clothes fell to the ground. Giggling, the naked courtesans made their way towards me and began to take turns performing sex acts upon me right there in my office above a chip shop.

When I'd finished, Lord Baelish clapped his hands twice and the girls gathered up their clothes and ran out. 'I believe the debt is now settled, Baz,' he told me in that icy voice that is familiar to millions of Game of Thrones viewers. And I had to agree that it was. I have to admit, I am a hard-headed businessman but I had broken my own golden rule; I had allowed myself to mix business with pleasure. I may have been sucked off by two full-breasted lovelies, but I was £140 out of pocket.

WORD must quickly have got around on the GoT set that Barron's Hard-Up Loanz was a good place for actors in a tight spot to

> *Littlefinger casually undid a clasp from the back of the prostitutes' capes and their clothes fell to the ground...*

Bearing straits: Cash strapped Baelish needed money for work on Saxo.

get hold of money in a hurry. Over the next few weeks Baz found his office besieged by a succession of famous faces from the cast.

❝ This one time I'd just collected eight grand from a single mum who'd borrowed two hundred quid to buy her kiddies a trampoline for Christmas, so I was feeling pretty flush. I was putting my baseball bat back in the cupboard when the door opened and in walked her who plays Daenerys Stormborn. She explained that the blow-off valve on her combi boiler had gone tits up and she wasn't on the British Gas Homecare scheme so she couldn't get it mended.

brinsley ford

She needed two hundred quid before a plumber would even come out and look at it, and meanwhile she was having to go round her mum's twice a week for a bath. Queen Targaryen is a really good character who has freed thousands of slaves in Game of Thrones, so I offered her a specially reduced interest rate equivalent to 2,560% APR. She bit my hand off and happily left with the money.

She was back next day asking for another two hundred. Apparently, when the plumber had taken the front off the boiler, the bleed valve had been dripping water through the circuit board on the timer, and that was buggered as well. I figured that, as supreme monarch of the Targaryen race, Queen of the Andals and the First Men, Khaleesi of the Great Grass Sea, Breaker of Chains and rightful heir to the Iron Throne she was good for the money.

gillian bailey

A week later, she came in my office carrying a leather bag. 'I've come to settle up, Mr Barron,' she told me. But instead of slapping fifteen hundred nicker on the desk, she reached in the bag and pulled out an oval shaped, scaly rock and placed it down on the blotter. I knew what it was immediately; one of three petrified dragon's eggs given to her as a gift on her wedding to Khal Drogo. 'This egg is priceless,' she intoned. 'It is worth far more than mere money.'

It may well have been priceless, but as I explained to her majesty, the only use I could make of it would have been as a paperweight. And now that I've got a laptop my office is virtually paperless these days anyway. I was half tempted to take her up on her offer, but in the end

I decided not to. I thanked her politely, but said it was a cash only deal. Without argument, she handed over £1586.50 as full settlement of her £400 debt.

Turns out I made the right decision, as I was watching the DVD a few nights later and all three of the dragon's eggs hatched when they were placed into Drogo's funeral pyre. The thought of one of those fire-breathing monsters flying round the office while I'm trying to run a business doesn't bear thinking about. And who knows how big it would have got by series five. Also, the lease off the chip shop downstairs specifies no pets. ❞

ANOTHER *Game of Thrones star who found himself in temporarily straitened circumstances was Peter Dinklage, who plays Lord Tyrion Lannister in the series. It was a rainy Monday when there was a knock at the door of Barron's office and the 4'5" actor walked in.*

❝ In the programme, Tyrion is the dwarf uncle of mad King Joffrey Baratheon, but I was surprised to see that he was also a dwarf in real life. He needed five hundred quid in a hurry and he was flat broke. I made a rather amusing, light-hearted play on words about his lack of height and his financial status, but he clearly didn't get it and just stared at me angrily.

He explained that due to his busy filming schedule, he was always out at work when the gasman came round, and as a result they'd been estimating his consumption for the last four years. They'd finally got in to read the meter a month earlier and sent him a proper bill. It was a whopper! Tyrion said he didn't have the cash to hand and now they were threatening to cut him off.

Daenerys explained that the blow-off valve on her combi boiler had gone tits up and she wasn't on the British Gas Homecare...

Old boiler: Daenerys Stormborn needed cash to pay plumber.

As a keen viewer of the show, I knew that the motto of his family was *'A Lannister Always Pays his Debts'*, so I had no qualms about sorting out the dockets and advancing him the lolly there and then. However, it turned out that my faith in him had been misplaced, because the next Monday he came back and told me he needed a bit more time to settle up. There had been a family emergency, he explained. His granny needed an eye operation and the upshot was he wouldn't be able to pay me back for another week.

peter firth

I gave him the benefit of the doubt that time, but seven days later he was sat in front of me again with another tall tale about his granny needing an operation on her other eye. Alarm bells started ringing; I regard myself as a responsible lender and I don't like to think of my clients getting in over their heads. And with the frankly extortionate interest rates I charge, that can happen very easily. For his own sake, I didn't want to let his Lordship roll his repayment over again. It was time to call in my expert debt recovery man - Lennie Two-Boots

When Tyrion knocked on my door the next Monday with another excuse at the ready, Lennie was already waiting for him. At 6'8" in his steel-toecapped dealers, Lennie is known in the trade for being ambidextrous: he can kick equally nastily with either foot. He's quite capable of kicking cash out of anyone, so watching him set about the diminutive Lord Lannister was a dreadful scene to behold. It is something that will haunt me for years, but in this game you can't afford to make exceptions. My terms and conditions are there in the small print: If you're not prepared to pay me back with Interest, don't take out a loan in the first place.

whipped nougat

In the show, Lannister is shadowed everywhere he goes by his bodyguard Bronn. Why this sword-wielding man-monster wasn't with him that day I'll never know. As it was, he took the pasting of his life and - surprise surprise - was back later that afternoon with six grand in a carrier bag to settle his debt in full. Where he got the money from I don't know and frankly I don't care. He famously said that he wanted to die at the age of eighty, in bed with a belly-full of wine and a woman on his cock. But as I told him, that's not going to happen if he goes on trying to welch on his payday loan payments. ❞

ALTHOUGH *the independent loans business is still unregulated, there are nevertheless strict rules that must be adhered to if lenders are to stay on the right side of the law. And one of those is that money cannot be advanced to anyone who looks like they might be under the age of about sixteen.*

❝ Youngsters are always coming in here trying to muster enough cash to buy an X-Box or a Playstation

4, but I operate under a strict moral code so instead of money, I usually give them a clip round the ear and the bum's rush. As a result, I didn't bat an eyelid when young Bran Stark, Prince of Winterfell, turned up in my office. I felt really sorry for the kid; he'd had a hard start in life, getting crippled as a kid when he was pushed out of a window by the Kingslayer, whom he had caught having incestuous sex with his sister Cersei, so he was sitting as usual in a basket on the back of his feeble-minded servant Hodor.

The youngster wanted £100 to buy an electric guitar and an amplifier off Theon Greyjoy, who had lost interest in playing after getting being emasculated by Ramsay Snow. Bran explained that he and some of his mates were going to start a band, so he was really disappointed when I told him that I couldn't lend him the money due to his age; he was only fourteen at the time. But there was a way round the problem; *Hodor could borrow the money on his behalf.*

Master plan: Servant Hodor took loan for Prince Bran

I quickly prepared the paperwork; of course the giant simpleton couldn't understand the complex terms and conditions of the loan he was taking out, nor was he able to sign his own name at the bottom of the docket. But those are mere formalities and a simple, scrawled 'X' in triplicate sufficed. Bran was soon the proud possessor of the hundred notes he needed to buy the shiny red Telecaster copy of his dreams.

Watching Lennie Two-Boots set about the diminutive Lord Lannister was a dreadful scene which will haunt me for years...

It was only after the pair had left that I began to question the wisdom of my decision. Hodor wasn't the sharpest tool in the shed, but he was a hulking seven-footer and I doubted even Lennie Two-Boots would be able to make much of an impression on him were he to default on his repayments. I prepared to kiss my money goodbye and made a mental note not to let my heart rule my head in future.

cereal crispies

I couldn't have been more surprised when, a week later, the little prince and his giant dullard companion turned up to pay off their loan in full. All the money was there, every last penny. And along with it was an invitation to Bran's group's first gig at Riverrun Castle. They were playing at the reception after the wedding of Edmure Tully and Roslin Frey.

As it happened, in the end I was unable to attend as I had a dental abcess flare up that night. But it's a good job I didn't go, as by all accounts it was a massacre and all the guests got their throats cut by Roose Bolton, Lord of the Dreadfort, and his men. I definitely dodged a bullet there. ❞

NEXT WEEK: *The time Prince Joffrey Baratheon came in and threatened to cut off my head and feed it to my wife unless I lent him £150 to buy some designer jeans from Jack Wills.*

MiLLiE TANT

I'M MAKING A STAND FOR WIMMIN AND COVERING UP SOME OF YOUR STOCK AS PART OF THE "LOSE THE LADS' MAGS" CAMPAIGN.

I'M RECLAIMING THESE SHELVES.

AND BEFORE YOU START WITH YOUR MISOGYNISTIC RANTING, THIS IS NOT CENSORSHIP... I AM MERELY PREVENTING PEOPLE FROM SEEING THINGS THAT I DO NOT AGREE WITH.

NUTS AND ZOO OBJECTIFY WOMEN. WELL I AND MY SISTERS ARE MORE THAN MERE OBJECTS FOR YOUR MASTURBATORY FANTASIES, MISTER.

I'M COVERING THEM UP.

NEW STATESMAN!? IS IT ANY WONDER THAT THIS COUNTRY HAS NEVER HAD A FEMALE PRIME MINISTER WHEN THE TITLE OF ITS LEADING POLITICAL MAGAZINE EXCLUDES 50% OF THE POPULATION? WHEN THEY RE-NAME IT NEW STATESWOMAN IT WILL BE UNCOVERED.

PRACTICAL WOODWORK..? WHY DON'T THEY JUST PRINT AN ERECT PENIS ON THE FRONT AND HAVE DONE WITH IT?

COVER IT UP!

TOP GEAR MAGAZINE? PETROL-DRIVEN ADOLESCENT PORNOGRAPHY FOR MEN WITH REALLY SMALL DICKS WHO JUST WANT TO TIE WOMEN UP AND ABDUCT THEM IN THE BOOTS OF THEIR CARS!

?

NEWS AGENT

NYMANS STATION:RY STORE

EXCHANGE AND MART..!? WIMMIN ARE NOT TO BE BOUGHT, SOLD OR SWAPPED LIKE PIECES OF MEAT. COVER IT UP!

SEXIST!

PORNOGRAPHIC!

TRANSPHOBIC!

PHALLOCENTRIC!

DOMSOGYDECAHEDRANISTIC!

THE BEANO.?! FLICK THE BEANO, MORE LIKE. ANTI-CLITORAL PROPA-GANDA! COVER IT UP!

THERE! NOW BROWSE THE SHELV ISSUE OF BIG FA MAGAZINE

THE LOST VALLEY!

It was the end of another busy day on the Snowdon Mountain Railway as train driver Ifor Idris pulled into Llanberis Station and his now penniless passengers piled onto the platform...

Wow! What a spectacular trip to the gift shop at the sunmmit. Well worth thirty-five quid a head, I must say.

Yes. Let's find the station gift shop.

End of the line! Everybody off, look you!

With the tourists gone and the train to himself, the half-hour ride to the engine shed was Ifor's favourite part of the day...

Come on, old girl. Time to get some rest. You've got another busy day ahead of you tomorrow, hauling more sightseers up the mountain.

Suddenly, a small landslide clattered down the mountainside...

The points!

RUMBLE!

KER-CHUNK!

CLANK!

Ifor knew he should turn back and re-set the points, but a strange force compelled him to keep going...

I've never seen this piece of track before. Where am I going?

Wow! I can't believe what I'm seeing!

It's a giant city - a whole civilisation hidden between Llanberis and the Go Ballistic Snowdonia Paintballing Centre!

Greetings, O rider of the small gauge iron horse. Welcome to the city of Cwm Llostopia.

Who are you?

We are the elders of the Hidden Valley.

CWM LLOSTOPIA

Come with us. We have much to show you.

We are a civilisation founded on the principles of trust, fairness and equality.

The people of Cwm Llostopia have never heard of workplace sexual harrassment, Operation Yewtree or internet chatroom grooming. These to us are alien concepts.

We have no crime, no weapons, no war.

Next Week: Myfanwy ~ the Wicker Sheep of Death!

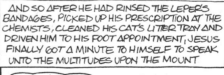

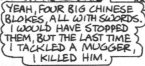

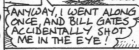
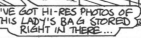

Floody Hell!

Britannia Rues the Waves as UK Set to Become New Atlantis

THE recent floods which devastated vast swathes of the country came as a wake-up call for us all. Nowhere was safe from the rising waters as a conveyor belt of storms lashed Britain from Land's End to John O'Groats. Record high tides smashed coastal defences into matchwood and low-lying areas were left counting the cost as the relentless barrage of stormy weather continued unabated.

The desperate battle to stem the inundation was matched only by the bitter war of words that erupted between government and the Environment Agency, as politicians rushed to the scenes of the worst flooding to witness the terrible devastation at first hand. But as the arguments raged and the Westminster blame game moved into top gear, the flooded-out British public had more important matters on its mind: *Just which MP had the best wellies?*

Sandbags at thirty paces: War of wellies erupted as Chris Smith (top), Boris Johnson (middle) and Eric Pickles (bottom) toured sites of terrible flooding (below).

In Penhaligon Bay, Cornwall, 85-year-old resident Ada Crumbhorn lost everything when local sea defences were overwhelmed. Record high tides breached the sea wall and swept away her 2-bedroom seafront cottage. The following day, Prime Minister **David Cameron** arrived to offer support to the devastated villagers.

"Mr Cameron turned up with a TV crew in tow the next day, and I was going to give him a piece of my mind," she told us. "I wanted to know why money hadn't been made available to reinforce the inadequate sea wall."

lovely

"But he was wearing such a lovely pair of wellingtons that I ended up asking him where he got them," said Mrs Crumbhorn. "He told me they were Le Chameau Chasseurs, and they cost £340 a pair from Harrods."

"He even let me feel the leather lining. Ooh, it was soft," added Mrs Crumbhorn.

EXCLUSIVE!

"I'd love to get a pair for myself but unfortunately I lost everything when my home was swept into the sea."

Meanwhile in the Somerset Marshes, Environment Agency boss **Lord Smith** arrived at the village of Moorside to inspect the devastation wearing a pair of Hunter Original Wellingtons, in Cocoa Gloss finish. "They're quite expensive at £85 a pair, but if you buy cheap you always end up buying twice, that's what I say," he told local resident Edna Yclept, 78.

lucky

Speaking from an upstairs window due to the lower floor of her 3-bedroom semi being awash with untreated sewage, Mrs Yclept told Lord Smith that the boots looked very stylish.

No nonsense Local Government Minister **Eric Pickles** wore a suitably down-to-earth pair of Wellington boots when visiting the now shattered Somerset

community of Burrowbridge. "I'm a Yorkshireman, and where I come from wellies are wellies," he told residents who were being temporarily housed in the waterlogged village's sports centre. "They don't have to look good, they just have to keep the water out."

robin

"I bought them half a size bigger than my shoes so they don't pull my socks off when I'm walking around," he assured shell-shocked families whose homes had been destroyed.

London Mayor **Boris Johnson** chose a pair of blue Barbour Country Classics for his outing to survey flood damage in the village of Sunbury. Local residents Hilda and Frank Jissholm,

77, who had abandoned their riverside home of fifty years to the rising floodwaters and had spent the night sleeping on a school floor, were delighted by the tousle-haired tory's choice of footwear.

"They were lovely boots, sturdy and well-made," said Frank, who believes that dredging the Thames could have alleviated flooding caused by a combination of heavy rainfall and high tides. "And of course, being made in the UK, by wearing them Mr Johnson is showing his support for British industry."

darren

"They looked lovely in the blue too," said Hilda. "But Boris joked you could also get them in red, but they'd have been more suitable for his socialist predecessor as

mayor, Ken Livingstone. We had to laugh."

Mr Johnson looked dazzling in the wellies, which he paired with puce moleskin trousers, a tattersall country-check shirt and lambswool sweater, offset with a a fetching olive gilet by Gant, featuring suede epaulette detailing, double back vent and roomy poacher's pocket.

Bags to Riches

WHILST THE REST of Britain counts the cost of the recent floods, one West Midlands business man is counting himself lucky. For Colin Beeswax, chairman, managing director and sole employee of Empire Flood Defences Ltd., the UK's biggest supplier of sandbags, has never had it so good.

"These sandbags are flying off the shelves as quick as I can fill them," he told us from the Tipton Portacabin where he operates his business. "Every drop of rain that falls means another pound in my pocket, and I'm as happy as a pig in shit."

Colin has been accused of profiteering from other people's misery after the recent floods saw him raise the price

Sandbag magnate on raincloud nine

of his sandbags from 10p to £15 each -a whopping 15,000% hike. But he is unapologetic and remains adamant that it's a simple case of supply and demand. "If people don't like my prices, they're quite

GOD TO BLAME
says Archbishop of Canterbury

By our Biblical Flood Correspondent

MANY crackpot theories have been put forward in an attempt to explain the recent catastrophic flooding. Everything from climate change and rising sea levels to increased sun-spot activity and building on flood-plains have been held responsible for the recent spate of disastrous weather. But one man who knows at whose door the blame really lies is Archbishop of Canterbury *JUSTIN WELBY.* "It's all God's fault," he announced in a recent sermon. "Simple as. End of."

"Think about it for a moment," continued Dr Welby. "He made the Sun, the Moon and the whole of creation, He made Adam and Eve and all the animals that crawl upon the face of the Earth, so I'm sure He could have stopped it bloody raining if he wanted."

"No, the truth of the matter is He just didn't want to. And worse than that, it would have been Him what sent the bloody floods in the first place," he added. "Let's face it, it's not the first time He's done floods. There's three of the buggers in the bloody Bible to my certain knowledge."

consternation

Welby's words have caused embarrassment and consternation amongst his fellow members of the General Synod. Dr Rowan Williams accused the Archbishop of intemperate language and warned him to consider his pronouncements more carefully in future. "Welby's full of shit," Williams stormed. "It's not God's fault."

"And if He has sent the floods, He'll have had a very good reason for doing so. He's probably just punishing us for doing something wrong, such as women bishops, bumming or supermarkets opening on Sundays," he added.

And Dr Williams's criticism was echoed by Archbishop of York Dr John Sentamu. "Everyone feels frustrated by the floods, but blaming God in

Welby in a bishop's hat (above) and God, yesterday

the face of a natural disaster is simply an easy way out," said Sentamu.

"Rather than blaming the Lord we should be praying to Him to help us in our hour of need," he added.

Dr Sentamu yesterday held a midnight service at York Minster, where he led the congregation In prayers for sand-bags, high-visibility jackets, 200 heavy duty diesel-powered water pumps and 10km of 8" diameter vulcanised canvas-backed hose.

constipation

Meanwhile Welby was standing by his controversial outburst. "It's alright for God. It's going to be a long time before the water level rises high enough for Him to get His bloody sandals wet," he stormed.

"You mark my words. Once untreated sewage starts seeping under the Pearly Gates, you see how quick the bloody sun comes out," he added.

PM Pledges 'Unlimited Funds' for the Posh

Piles: Big houses set for stately hand-outs from government.

BRITAIN'S TOFFS were breathing a sigh of relief yesterday after the Prime Minister pledged that taxpayers would foot the bill for all repairs to flood-damaged mansions.

"The money will be found," says Cameron

Speaking in Parliament, **David Cameron** promised that cash would be found to fund restoration work on stately homes belonging to the country's richest people whatever the cost.

"It's a tragedy when any house is flooded," he told MPs. "But some pleb who only pays £2.50 a roll for wallpaper from B&Q can't begin to imagine the grief experienced by a higher class person whose water-damaged wallpaper costs at least £120 a roll from Barnaby & Gates."

rats

"We have to be realistic. The lower classes probably have very damp little houses at the best of times. Most of them live like filthy rats along a canal so a little water in their house is neither here nor there and they take flooding in their stride," he continued. "But for people like my friends, who have been to Eton, Oxford and Cambridge and are used to the finer things in life, such as Chippendale furniture, Pre-Raphaelite oil paintings and fine wine, a flood can be truly devastating."

"At such a time of nationwide emergency, it is the responsibility of the government to prioritise where financial assistance must go," said Mr Cameron. "That means sending it to posh people so they can repair their lovely houses, damaged art treasures and valuable antiques."

"It would be a national disgrace if that money ended up in the hands of vermin who want it to replace their water-damaged flat-screen televisions, video games and tasteless sofas," he added.

But Labour MP **Tristram Hunt** hit back, accusing the Prime Minister of having an out-dated "Hooray Henry" attitude, and being out of touch with the needs of ordinary people.

"David Cameron is living in cloud cuckoo land," he told *Newsnight*'s Jeremy Paxman. "His attitude to the lower classes is out of date and offensive. I met some working class proles once and they were absolutely super, salt-of-the-earth types."

cocks

"When their little homes are flooded, they deserve government financial help to get them back on their feet just as much as normal people do," he continued.

"Even if they do decide to spend the money on ghastly things like mass-produced prints, garden decking or those dreadful nylon carpet remnants you buy from a warehouse on some odious trading estate, it is simply not our place to pass judgement," he added.

Cough up or fuck off: Beeswax (inset) is laughing all the way to the (sand) bank.

free to let their houses fill with water," he told us. "Fuck them. Doesn't bother me."

deal

However, TV money saving expert Martin Lewis accused Mr Beeswax of unfair price-fixing. "This is just another example of rip-off Britain," Lewis fumed. "Charging fifteen pounds for a simple sandbag is extortionate.

I would encourage anyone who is flooded to shop around for the best deal on sandbags."

"For example, a few minutes' searching on the internet and I found a stockist in Guangdong Province, China, who was charging less than five pence for an identical product, with a delivery time of less than two months."

sandwich

Meanwhile Channel 4 make do & mend expert and Duke's daughter Kirstie Allsopp insisted that a perfectly serviceable "sandbag" can be crafted for as little as £5. "Simply go to your local charity shop and buy a pair of men's trousers for about a pound," she said. "Then tie a knot in the bottom of each leg and fill them with the cheapest rice you can find at your local cash and carry. Then thread ribbon through the belt loops and tie the trousers closed with a pretty bow."

"For a healthier option, use brown rice," Allsopp added.

"My wet tyre HELL!" ~Sting

FORMER Police frontman Sting was last night being comforted by his servants after floodwaters inundated the drive of his Wiltshire mansion and lapped around the wheels of some of his luxury cars.

Following several days of heavy rain and high tides, the nearby River Bourne burst its banks, flooding hundreds of homes in nearby villages and drowning livestock on local farms. But tragedy struck when the floodwaters began lapping at the gravel drive of Lake House, the *Roxanne* singer's 50-bedroom Elizabethan manor house, threatening to wet the tyres on his collection of expensive luxury cars. The alarm was raised as fears grew that the wheels on dozens of Sting's top-of-the-range Rolls-Royces could end up standing in almost an inch of water.

habitats

The Tyneside-born eco-campaigner famously does not believe in sandbags, as he maintains that they deplete the county's natural coastal defences and destroy habitats for endangered shore-dwelling species such as crabs, seaweed and natterjack toads. He told British Airways *VIP Lounge* Magazine: "I immediately ordered five thousand of my domestic servants to lie three-deep around the perimeter of the estate to form a protective barrier against the rising waters."

The human flood defences held for ten minutes, until one employee - thought to be a junior assistant to the man who is employed to

Singer's luxury cars in flood tragedy

fold the end of the singer's toilet paper into a V-shape - turned his head slightly to take a breath. "His ear only left the ground for a couple of seconds, but it was long enough for the water to break through and get my car tyres a little bit wet," said Sting.

ikeas

Fortunately, a detachment of Royal Engineers was in the area, pumping water out of a flooded operating theatre at nearby Salisbury Children's Hospital. "They dropped everything and came straight round when I raised the alarm," the cod-reggae singer turned jazz lutinist continued. "They were marvellous, jacking the cars up about an inch-and-a-half in a bid to keep the bottoms of their tyres out of the water."

"Unless you own a hundred Rolls-Royces like I do, you could never understand the pain of having to stand by and watch as their tyres get slightly wet, knowing that there's nothing you can do to help them."

"It's every multi-millionaire's nightmare," he added.

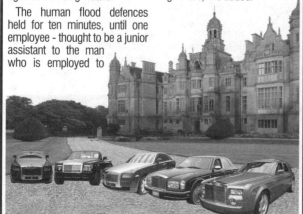

Have Your Say

THE RECENT FLOODS in the south of England and Wales have divided the nation. Some say that they were a natural disaster on an unprecedented scale causing misery to thousands and disruption to the country's travel network and infrastructure. Others thought they were great. We went out on the streets to find out exactly what you, the British public had to say...

...I don't know why the news keeps making all this fuss about the flooding in the south-east. I live in Manchester on top of a hill.

Bez Vulpine, Urmston

...I spilled a glass of water on the kitchen floor the other day and my wife just mopped it up. It took her five minutes. These flood victims should stop whining and simply get their wives to get the mop out. Honestly, it will take them five minutes.

Frank Vesperidae, Oswestry

...Somerset residents whose home floods once or twice a year don't know they're born. I grew up in a house that had been built at the low tide mark on the beach at Whitby, and it used to flood twice a day, every day, up to the living room ceiling and you never heard us complain. We just got on with it. You had to in them days.

Kathleen Ferrousmetal, Staithes

...These old people who've been flooded out of their homes on the news make me sick. They whine on about how there was no running water in the house when they were kids, and in the next breath they start complaining because there is. For God's sake, make your mind up, you moaning Minnies.

Brian Twatt, Leeds

...Vicars have a ruddy nerve, coming round to offer their sympathy to flood victims when it's their company CEO that's caused this Act of God in the first place. If you ask me, the Church of England should be made to pay to put all the damage right. And if a vicar came round here offering me a shoulder to cry on, I'd hold his head under the water till he either paid up or drowned.

Audrey Ffistula, Somerset

...There's a simple solution that's staring everybody in the face. When they get their repairs done, people whose homes flood should simply get the builders to replace the floorboards four foot higher up the wall. Then, next time the waters rise, they'll be sitting high and dry. What's more, in between floods they'll have a handy four-foot high cellar to store bottles of wine and their lawnmower etc.

Jack Churchill, Newcastle

...We should take a tip from the people of Venice, and turn our waterlogged towns into tourist attractions. The locals could buy some gondolas and vastly overcharge for a sightseeing trips that are half as long as promised, and then demand hefty tips before pinching the women's arses as they climb out of the boat.

F Muir, Bridgnorth

It's King Cam-Ute!

IN A BOLD move, Prime Minister *David Cameron* yesterday announced his intention to sit on a throne on the beach and personally command the waves to stop rolling in.

The PM's plan is seen as a desperate "last resort" after other proposed anti-flood schemes, such as improving sea defences, providing householders with sandbags and dredging waterways to improve drainage, proved prohibitively expensive. Cameron hopes to succeed where his predecessor, 11th Century Danish-born English monarch King Canute, failed.

pilot

During his party's spring party conference in Brighton, the Prime Minister intends to sit on an elaborate gilded seat at the water's edge and order the tide to remain out and not get his feet and robes wet. "It's just a pilot scheme at the moment," a Downing Street spokesman told us. "But if it proves successful, it will be rolled out countrywide by the Environment Agency."

"As soon as the Met Office issues a flood or high tide warning, Mr Cameron will

PM's plan to rule the waves

race to the nearest beach and drive back the rising waters using his God-given dominion over the elements," he added.

racey

It's a brave move that could, if successful, shave many millions of pounds from the country's emergency flood defence budget. However, some commentators see it as a risky political gamble that could leave the coalition government with egg on its face and the Prime Minister with wet socks and turn-ups.

"Mr Cameron is trying to make up for his government's lack of investment by overcoming the forces of nature," said Shadow environment secretary Maria Eagle. "He should learn from history. This crackpot idea didn't work a thousand years ago and it's not going to work this time either."

Wavey Davey: *Cameron to sit on beach.*

And Ms Eagle set forth her own party's three-point plan to deal with any future threat of flooding, which includes:

• **AN EXTRA** £50 million contingency fund to reinforce pre-existing flood defence infrastructure.

• **A WIDE-RANGING** public enquiry to look into the long term effects of increased development on greenbelt flood plains.

• **ED MILLIBAND** to grow a beard, wear a robe and sandals, and to command floodwaters in the Somerset Levels to part allowing local residents to get to the shops and back.

88

So you THINK you want... a Goldfish?

EVERYBODY dreams of winning a goldfish at the fair. One of these iridescent aquatic creatures is a perfect memento of success at the Hook-a-Duck stall or Coconut Shy. Properly cared for, a goldfish can be a friend for life ...*but are you really ready to take on such a long term commitment?* There is far more to goldfish ownership than occasionally changing the water in its bowl or feeding it a few ant eggs. Getting a goldfish is a life-changing decision and not one to be taken lightly. So, before you take your shimmering prize home in its plastic bag, take a few moments to STOP and THINK of the real cost of your new pet...

LIKE ALL pets, goldfish need to be looked after seven days a week, so arrangements have to be made to care for them properly when you go on holiday. Most people leave a key under a plant pot to allow a neighbour to pop in whilst they are away and check that the fish is alright. But a hidden key is an open invitation to burglars, and you could find that your decision to own a fish leads to your house being ransacked and all your valuables stolen. And remember, it's a sad fact that many thieves also defecate on their victims' carpets.

GOLDFISH don't need much in the way of accommodation. A simple round bowl will suffice to keep your new pet happy. But wait - filled with water, that bowl effectively becomes a powerful lens, and if it is kept on a windowsill there is a chance that it will focus the rays of the sun into a powerful, white hot point of light, reaching upwards of 2000°c. This will set fire to soft furnishings, which will burn and give off thick clouds of black, choking fumes. On a sunny summer's day, that harmless fish you won at the fair could quickly turn your home into a raging inferno.

LIKE ALL animals, your goldfish will soil his environment, which will need regular cleaning. This will involve pouring the old water down the sink whilst catching the fish in a sieve, before topping up with a fresh supply. But with wet hands, a fishbowl can easily slip and break in the sink. If one of these jagged shards of glass should stick in you, you are looking - at best - at a painful cut that may require stitches. At worst, the razor sharp edge could sever one of the main arteries in your wrist. Unless treated quickly, such an injury could cause massive blood loss and lead to death.

GOLDFISH suffer from a variety of minor ailments which can become serious if left unchecked. Fin rot, mites and gill fungus all need to be treated by a qualified vet. Whilst the treatment is not expensive, many vets are young and good looking. Combined with their high income and status, they may prove irresistibly attractive to your wife, and the result may be a torrid affair and an acrimonious divorce. A small swim bladder infection in your goldfish that could be sorted out with a couple of crystals of potassium permanganate could well end up costing you your marriage.

THERE ARE many ways of livening up your goldfish's environment. Novelty items such as plastic deep-sea divers, little castles and brightly coloured gravel are all readily available to purchase on the internet. But before you type in your order and click on your mouse, stop and think. Is that website checkout as secure as it appears? In purchasing a small bubbling treasure chest, you may have inadvertently had your credit card details stolen and your identity cloned by criminals in another country. Before you know it, your bank account could be being used to buy sickening illegal pornography.

So you think you want a goldfish?...
Think again!

Next week: So you think you want... a Stick Insect?

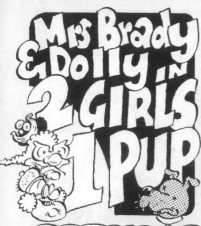

LETTERBOCKS

WHATEVER happened to those halcyon days when railway porters were affable old cockneys who called you "guv'nor" and would doff their caps as they lugged your heavy cases for a couple of pence? I spent an absolute age looking for one at Euston Station the other day. So much for progress.

Marston Pedigree, Wells

THEY often say that people laughed at Christopher Columbus when he said that the world was round. But I saw a picture of him recently, and I reckon they were more likely tittering at that noncey hat he used to wear.

Bartram Twelveacres, Hull

I KNOW the famous 'bunny boiling' scene from *Fatal Attraction* is viewed with horror and repulsion by many. But if I'd been on a long day out with my wife and children and then returned home to find my bit on the side had rustled up a nice rabbit stew and then fucked off, you wouldn't hear me complaining.

Frank Pyrimidine, Leeds

I ONCE read that grey and red squirrels hate each other so much that naturalists have to make sure that they don't even cohabitate the same areas in case they wipe each other out. Bill Oddie, Chris Packham and that Michaela Strachan bird are always telling us how great they are, but they can hardly be held up as role models for our children with that type of behaviour.

William Beehive, Pudsey

**Viz Comic
P.O. Box 841
Whitley Bay
NE26 9EQ**
letters@viz.co.uk

STAR LETTER

IN HER 6th decade as our country's monarch, Queen Elizabeth II must have been photographed getting out of a limousine a million times, and not once have the paparazzi got a flash of her gash. If only these so-called supermodels and 'IT' girls took a leaf out of Her Majesty's book and showed as much decorum when they exited a car, we'd be saved all these sordid beaver shots in the gutter press every day.

Tarquin Bingedrink, Kew

SAW the image of our lord and saviour Biffa Bacon in a water leak in Goole Methodist Church.

Nofty, e-mail

I READ a magazine article at the dentist the other day entitled *Mary Berry's Secret of Good Baking*. I have to say, with her own TV series and a load of books to her name, not to mention all the radio and TV interviews she's done, she's not very good at keeping secrets. I certainly won't be confiding in her, that's for sure.

George Plumbago. Cardiff

DOES the Tardis have a toilet on board, or does the Doctor just travel back in time to when he didn't need a shit?

Larrs Bandeet, e-mail

I DOUBT very much if the Clanton Gang would have described the OK Corral as "OK" after Wyatt Earp and his brothers shot them all to death during a gunfight at it. But that's just my opinion.

Charles Aerstryk, Chester

WHAT is all this nonsense about looking for a needle in a haystack? I lost a needle the other day and the last place that sprang to mind to look was a haystack. In fact, I found it on the floor in the hallway when I trod on it.

Jack Goldust, Newstead

I THINK the writers of the satirical film *Mutiny on the Buses* missed an excellent opportunity to chronicle the political changes that were transforming Britain at the time it was made. The ever-widening chasm between the unions and the Wilson government could have been much more profoundly exemplified other than with the occasional "I 'ate you Butler" from Blakey. Moreover, Jack persistently looking up clippies' skirts and saying "Cor," as they ascended the stairs may well have been symbolic of women's rise on the political stage, but somehow detracted from the overall picture.

Gordon Cottonsocks, Hull

TWENTY years ago, I committed a murder which fortunately I got away with. I was never a suspect and wasn't even questioned by the police. Now I'm terrified that if I catch the flu, I might develop a high temperature and begin to ramble incoherently and say something that might incriminate me. As a result, I will take the precaution of having a flu jab this winter, and suggest that all other murderers who have gotten away with with their crimes do likewise.

Hampton Plywood, Cheam

THEY say it's always sunny in Philadelphia. But *Rocky* was filmed on location there and a large proportion of scenes take place at night.

Mal McGinley, e-mail

I THINK the makers of the recent *24: Live Another Day* series could have made Jack Bauer's escapades in London a lot more realistic if he had gotten a few frustrating PPI spam calls on his mobile. As well as being true to life, receiving one of these, just as he was awaiting important instructions about saving the president's life, would have really built up the suspense.

Bradley Tungston, Woking

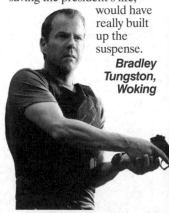

IS IT SAFE TO GO?

YES, THAT MAN IS FLASHING YOU

I WAS always good at maths as a child but shit at English. Then they really fucked me up by introducing algebra, which contained numbers AND letters. I reckon I probably could have been a quantum physicist if they hadn't moved the goalposts on me.

Max Gangplank, Basle

I CAME home unexpectedly the other day and was shocked to find my husband parading around the bedroom wearing my underwear and looking at himself in the mirror. He said he had put it on by mistake, but I did not believe him and stormed out of the house. What a fool I felt when I remembered that we are a married gay couple, and he might well have put on a pair of my underpants thinking that they were his.

A Greaves, e-mail

WHEN I visit my local Sainsburys supermarket and use the self service checkout, the assumption seems to be that I'm some kind of thief since I am always asked if I have 'swiped my Nectar card.' I must have an honest face as the staff on the other checkouts take it for granted I acquired it by legitimate means.

Graham Flintoff, Gateshead

I RECENTLY told my husband that I liked carrots more than he did, but he told me that I was wrong. Needless to say, I don't like carrots as much now.

Edna Spuds, e-mail

I'VE just done a fart in the lift at work that lasted 17 floors. It would have lasted longer but I had to finish with a flourish as I approached the ground floor. Can any of your readers beat that?

Botty Burp, e-mail

MY wife just binned one of our Morissons 'bags for life' because it was 'getting in the way'. Put that in your pipe and smoke it, Greenpeace.

Gentle Ben, Medway

WATCHING several WW2 films recently, it occurred to me that whenever British forces were dropped into France behind enemy lines, they always looked an utter disgrace. Their faces were smeared in muck, and all their clothes were covered in leaves. It's hardly the sort of impression one wants to create when arriving as liberators on foreign soil. I myself went to France on a "Booze Cruise" recently, and I have to say that I was rather well togged out and even the wife remarked on it.

Brian Nicelybig, Croydon

EARLIER today I saw an old man pushing his wife down the road in her wheelchair. He was really

DAVID Icke. Hold a locust 10 feet away from the Queen and if a long sticky tongue snatches it out of your hand, you're right.

Tam Dale, e-mail

IF your oven keeps burning things, then it's probably too hot. Placing a bag of ice cubes at the bottom will help to cool it off, I should imagine.

Nick Wesley, e-mail

CEREAL manufacturers. Boost sales of flagging brands by putting pictures of Emma Watson's fanny in every box.

Reinhold Messner, e-mail

NEXT time the police raid your house for possession of contraband, simply tell them that you're wrapping their Christmas presents, so they can't come in.

Gladys Spume, e-mail

struggling, but the old love in his heart was giving him the strength to carry on. It got me thinking, when I'm that old, I hope my wife is long dead. There's no way I'm shoving her all the way to Morrisons like that.

Gareth Alan, e-mail

A BLOKE I work with rang up the other day to say he couldn't come to work because he reckoned

TOP

IF you find that your fridge is too cold, then I would imagine that starting a small fire in one of the vegetable compartments would warm it up nicely.

Nick Wesley, e-mail

FAILED hotel proprietors. Get your own back on Alex Polizzi by planting a pair of soiled knickers in her room once she's checked out and then bring the camera crew up to film it.

Toby Jugsworth, Newcastle

OFFICE workers. Save desk space by simply resting all your paperwork on a colleague's head.

Nobby Shaft, e-mail

IF your microwave is too powerful and making soup boiling hot, I would have thought putting a big big block of lead in there would somehow absorb up all the X-rays, making the soup just right.

Nick Wesley, e-mail

he had "brain sweats", the idle cunt. Can any other readers claim to have heard a more lame excuse for bunking off work?

Jason Penny, e-mail

I DON'T know why the staff and pupils at Hogwarts School celebrate Christmas like you see them doing in the *Harry Potter* films. The Christian world would have had them all

CONVINCE friends and neighbours that you are running a 1920s-style speak-easy by fitting a sliding viewing slot to your front door.

Terry Astatine, Atherstone

CHANGE the order address on your parcels to that of your next door neighbours. That way, if they aren't in, the delivery driver will bring them to you and ask if you can take them in for them.

Terence, e-mail

AVOID being bothered by Jehovah's Witnesses by becoming one and then having a blood transfusion, after which they will shun you and leave you in fucking peace.

Marcus Chipboard, Nottingham

TIPs

toptips@viz.co.uk

burned at the stake a few years back.

Hector Trimble, Goole

WHEN *Viz* dropped through my letterbox, it hit my 2-year-old, son who was sitting on the other side of the door, on the head. Thanks *Viz* for an extra laugh this month.

Ross Kennet, e-mail

You're welcome, Mr Kennet. It's all part of the service.

George Bestial

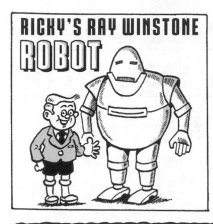

RICKY'S RAY WINSTONE ROBOT

Young Ricky Doohickey was the proud owner of a remarkable robotic actor - built by his Father: a brilliant inventor with a troubling history of mental illness...

GREAT! THEY'RE HOLDING AUDITIONS FOR THE SCHOOL PLAY TODAY

THERE ARE BOUND TO BE A COUPLE OF PARTS FOR ME AND MY INCREDIBLE ACTING AUTOMATON.

'SCHOOL PLAY'

BZZZT...SHAT YAW FACKIN' MAARFF, YEWW CANT..CLICK....

Ricky and his steel-plated sidekick hurried to the drama class - but..

HEY THERE, FELLOW THESPIANS - WHY THE LONG FACES?

SIGH! WELL RICKY, I SIMPLY SUGGESTED THAT THIS YEAR WE MIGHT PERFORM THE POPULAR ALL-KIDS GANGSTER MUSICAL: 'BUGSY MALONE'.

BUT WILKINS HERE SPOILED EVERYTHING BY SAYING THAT THE WHOLE PRODUCTION COMES ACROSS LIKE SOME CREEPY PROHIBITION-ERA THEMED PAEDOPHILE WANK FANTASY.

YOU'RE A NASTY PIECE OF WORK, WILKINS!

Suddenly ZZZT...YEWW CANTS ARE GIVIN' ME THE RIGHT OLD STEAMIN' HUMP...BLEEP!

LOOK EVERYONE! RICKY'S LUMBERING ANDROID ACTOR HAS SPRUNG INTO ACTION.

HEY! THERE'S SOMETHING EMERGING FROM ROBOT RAY'S BUILT-IN LASERJET PRINTER.

BZZT... FACKIN' 'AVE IT! ...KLUNK!

BY JOVE - IT LOOKS LIKE A SCRIPT - WITH THE STORYLINE SET IN SOME BRUTALLY OPPRESSIVE SEVENTIES BORSTAL.

DOES IT HAVE ANY NICE MUSICAL NUMBERS, SIR?

IT'S CALLED 'SCUM' AND THERE ARE WONDERFUL PARTS FOR EVERYONE: SADISTIC SCREWS... ANTAGONIZED AFRO-CARIBBEANS..

MY GRACIOUS! SOME CHAP EVEN GETS ROGERED IN A GREENHOUSE!

WOW RICKY! THAT CLANKING TYPECAST COCKNEY TOUGH-GUY CONTRAPTION OF YOURS HAS REALLY COME UP TRUMPS!

During rehearsals, Robot Ray provided a master-class in automated acting skills...

BZZT... WHERE'S YER TOOL? ...BLEEP!

ERM... WHAT F... FUCKIN' TOOL?

BZZT... THIS FACKIN' TOOL...!!! BLIP!

WHACK! THUD! SMACK!

ARRGH!

COME ON WILKINS, YOU'RE SUPPOSED TO BE PORTRAYING A BIG BALD BASTARD FROM B-WING BEING BRUTALLY BEATEN

LET'S TRY TO BE A TAD MORE CONVINCING NEXT TIME, BOY.

GROAN..!

Soon it was opening night, and the assembled cast waited nervously backstage...

IT'S A PACKED HOUSE OUT THERE TONIGHT. EVEN THE LORD MAYOR HIMSELF HAS TURNED UP TO SEE US PERFORM.

SO THAT MEANS THERE'LL BE NO ROOM FOR SLIP-UPS; STAGE FRIGHT; MISSED-CUES OR METAL-FATIGUE.

But the anxious drama Master needn't have worried...

BZZZT! RIGHT BANKS, YOU BASTARD! I'M THE DADDY NOW!... KLANK!

YESS!! THAT'S HOW YOU FUCKIN DO IT! GIVE THE CUNT SOME MORE!!

And so the school's production of 'Scum' turned out to be a smash-hit...

INCREDIBLE - AN HOUR-LONG STANDING OVATION! AND IT'S ALL THANKS TO OUR MARVELLOUS MECHANICAL LEADING-MAN.

I DON'T KNOW HOW WE'RE GOING TO TOP THIS ONE NEXT YEAR, SIR.

OH, I RECKON YOUR METAL MATINEE-IDOL ALREADY HAS A FEW IDEAS UP HIS CYBERNETIC SLEEVE, HO! HO!

SCRIPT: SEXY BEAST

BZZZT! BZZZT!

And so, twelve months later... ...IT'S HOT! ...BOILIN'!

...YOU COULD FRY A FACKIN' EGG ON MY STOMACH ...BZZT!

Dial Shhhh! for SEX!

On the shelf: Spinster Maureen looking for romance in the Large Print section of Walsall Public Library yesterday.

Maureen Owlpellet lives up to everyone's stereotypical idea of a librarian. Small, bespectacled and mousey, when she is sat behind her desk in her buttoned-up cardigan and tweed twinset, you would never give the 48-year-year old West Midlands spinster a second glance. But, says Maureen, beneath her dowdy, prudish exterior there beats a heart that is every bit as full of red-blooded passion as the racy romance novels she spends her days arranging on the shelves of Walsall Lending Library.

"THERE'S something about the sexually-charged atmosphere in a municipal lending library that just brings out the animal in me,"** she says, coquettishly nibbling the arm of her sexy horn-rimmed bottle-bottom specs. "And believe you me, that animal isn't a mouse, it's a tiger."

"And not just any tiger... it's a man eater!"

According to Maureen, what she gets up to in the library every day makes saucy bestseller *50 Shades of Gray* look like *The Adventures of Peter Rabbit*. And her steamy sexploits in her blog *Between_the_Covers/blogs/freewebs.net*, are taking the internet by storm. *"My website's only been up for six months and I've already got nearly twenty-three followers,"* she smiles.

"There's an entry for every day, and sometimes multiple entries if you know what I mean," she continues, winking seductively. *"My love life in the library is so full, the only problem is deciding which bits to edit out."*

Maureen's XXX-rated tales certainly turn the old-fashioned stereotype of the frigid, sexually-frustrated, bookworm on its head. *"You might think that all librarians are on the shelf, but I've been taken down and thumbed more times than the latest Harry Potter, I can tell you,"* she says.

Now, in these exclusive extracts from her online library of lust, Maureen lifts the lid on her true-life raunchy adventures amongst the bookshelves. *"Believe you me,"* she says, *"my amazing story proves once and for all that not only is the truth stranger than fiction, it is stranger than fiction, non-fiction and reference all rolled into one..."*

Maureen's blog breaks silence on library sexploits

Between the Covers blogspot

Posted by Between_the_Covers
May 22, 2013 at 23:25

search 🔍 view: full / summary

Wednesday 22 May

The easiest place to lose a book is in a library. When a careless reader replaces a volume on the wrong shelf or in the wrong position on the shelf, it can be gone forever. Today I was checking the Christian Theology section (230 - 239 according to the Dewey Decimal system) and I noticed that a few books of Creeds and Catechisms (238) had found their way into the Apologetics and Polemics section (239). I tutted and began sorting out the mayhem on the shelf in front of me.

Suddenly, I heard a deep, manly voice behind me. "Excuse me, ma'am. Could you direct me to the naval architecture section, please?" he said. I turned to see who had spoken and my heart skipped a beat as I beheld the most handsome man I had ever seen. He was an American Navy captain, and he was wearing his full white dress uniform just like Richard Gere in An Officer and a Gentleman. As I led him to section 359 (Sea Forces and Maritime Warfare), we got chatting.

He explained that he was the commander of a US aircraft carrier that had just docked in a nearby port. As I explained how the books were arranged alphabetically by author, he suddenly took me in his arms, undid my hair and took my glasses off. "To be honest, I don't want to read about naval architecture any more. I just want you. You're the most beautiful woman I've ever seen," he said, kissing me passionately all over.

Soon we were both stripped naked except I was wearing his hat. His strong arms gripped me as were wracked in the throes of animal passion. Roughly but tenderly he turned me round and entered me from behind. I gasped as his girth slid within me, bracing myself against 382 (International Commerce: Foreign Trade). Again and again he thrust powerfully, his manhood driving me to heights of pleasure I had never even dreamt of, giving me ever more intense multiple orgasms, so many of them I lost count. I would have cried out in ecstasy, only it's a library and you have to be quiet, and I bit my lip to stifle my moans.

All too soon it was over, and as we lay amongst the books in the afterglow, he asked me to marry him. He said he was ready to give up the command of his ship and come to live in Walsall, but I said no. True, the sex was mindblowing, but I'm a free spirit and I'm simply not ready for that sort of commitment. As I put my hair back up and replaced my glasses, he put his uniform back on and left. I doubt I'll ever see him again. But I'll never forget the stolen afternoon of passion I shared with my officer and a gentleman.

💬 comments (0) 👍 likes (0) ↪ shares (0)

Friday 7 June

The library was quite busy this afternoon. It always is when it's signing on day, and even more so when it's raining. But the man who walked in this afternoon didn't look anything like our usual rollcall of tramps, job-seekers and pensioners waiting for their wives to come out the hairdressers. Dressed in an immaculately-tailored tuxedo and black tie, with his piercing blue eyes and square jaw he looked like he'd just wandered in off the set of the latest James Bond movie.

My heart skipped a beat as he came over to my desk, where I was stamping "Withdrawn for Sale" in a pile of old Mills & Boons, and asked me if I could direct him to the International Espionage section. His voice was rich and deep and a bit Scottish, like Sean Connery, although he looked more like Pierce Brosnan. I showed him to the Espionage & Subversion shelf (327.12), and he selected a book."Do you have a private reading room?" he asked, raising one sardonic eyebrow quizzically. I took him to one of our study booths, but when I closed the door behind us it became clear that the volume in his hand was the last thing he wanted to study.

He fiddled with his watch and I suddenly found all the metal zips and fasteners on my clothes and underwear coming undone. Soon I was standing before him, completely naked. He undressed too, revealing a pair of tight swimming trunks like Daniel Craig in that picture. He had rock hard abs, but that wasn't all he had that was rock hard, I can tell you. He undid my hair and took my glasses off. What happened next is probably covered by the Official Secrets Act. Suffice to say, by the end of our passionate tryst, my international man of mystery had several endorsements on his Licence to Thrill.

He got up and dressed as I lay on the desk, basking in the afterglow, completely satiated. He told me he had fallen in love with me, but he had to go to Russia to foil an evil international plot. However, he promised, when he got back we would get married. He kissed me tenderly on the lips and left. It was only after he had gone that I realised he had forgotten one of his socks . Pulling on my clothes, I ran after him out of the library, just in time to see him climb into an Aston Martin that he had left parked in the precinct. But I never got the chance to return the sock, as when he turned the key in the ignition, the car exploded in a huge fireball.

The tears of grief stung my eyes as I went back into the library. And, as I sat at my desk and started stamping the withdrawn Mills & Boons again, I clutched that sock close to my heart. Although I know I'll never see him again, I'll never forget the stolen afternoon of passion I shared with the spy who loved me.

Tuesday 9 July

Today we had an unplanned emergency that led to a pair of hunky firefighters giving me a dressing down ... quite literally.

The West Midlands Library Service operates a strict No Smoking policy on its premises. People think that e-cigarettes are exempt from the usual restrictions, but sadly they couldn't be more mistaken, and every time some chancer sparks up an e-cig in the Reading Room it sets off the fire alarm. And that's exactly what happened this morning, as I was sorting out a serious mix-up on shelf 292 (Mythology: Greek & Roman), where Homer had been replaced to the left of Hesiod. Within a few minutes of the bell going off, a fire engine pulled up outside.

Two firemen came over to me. "This is the third time this month we've been called out on a false alarm, miss," they said. "Can we go somewhere quiet to sort this out?" I bit my lip and led them to the Head Librarian's office. I thought I was in for a proper roasting, and I was ... but it wasn't the verbal kind. As soon as I'd locked the door, one of the firemen undid my hair and took my glasses off, whilst the other one stripped me naked. Then it was their turn to undress, but they only took their shirts off, leaving their trousers on, with braces. And also their helmets, like in the calendars.

It is every woman's secret fantasy to be simultaneously pleasured by two muscular firemen in their uniforms. That dream became a reality for me this morning, and believe you me it was every bit as exciting as I'd always imagined it would be. The hose-wielding heroes took turns at each end, ravishing me across the head librarian's desk until I didn't know whether I was coming or going. Fortunately, it was a Wednesday so the Head Librarian was out doing the Redditch run in the Mobile Library.

They may be trained to put out fires, but their emergency service succeeded in igniting the flames of passion deep within my being. I know I may never see them again until someone else lights up an e-cig in the Reading Room, but I'll never forget the stolen morning of passion I shared with my pair of towering infernos.

Monday 24 June

Libraries are supposed to be quiet places, but I spend the vast majority of my working day telling people to shush when they chat, cough or turn pages too loudly. And I was not surprised earlier today to hear a man engaged in a lively mobile phone conversation behind stack 616.1 (Diseases: Cardiovascular system). I hurried round to shush him, but it was me who fell silent when I caught sight of the offender.

He was an eminent heart surgeon with an international reputation, and I felt my pulse quicken as my eyes ran up and down his body. Standing there in his theatre greens with his dark brown eyes, jet black hair and flawless olive skin, he reminded me of a younger George Clooney from when he was in ER. The chemistry between us was instant, and I immediately swooned into his arms. He undid my hair and took my glasses and clothes off, his skilled surgeon's fingers deftly undoing my underwear with a gentle firmness I had never felt from any other man.

He made mad, passionate love to me between the 616.6 (Diseases of the urogenital system) and 616.7 (Diseases of the musculoskeletal system) shelves, and as we reached our simultaneous, shattering climaxes, he whispered words of love into my ear in an exotic foreign language which was probably Egyptian or Persian. As we lay together, spent in the afterglow, I suddenly panicked. What if we were found out? But I needn't have worried. Although the library was busier than usual due to the drains being up in the precinct, the medical books section (610-619) is always quiet and so there was very little risk of us being disturbed.

As we got dressed, he explained that he had come to the library to look up how to do a particularly tricky operation which he was going to perform the next day on a Saudi Arabian prince. In fact he was off to the airport now, to catch a private jet to the Middle East. He told me, in his exotic accent, that if the operation was successful he would be rich beyond his wildest dreams and come back to marry me. But in my heart I know that we can never be together, for we are both married to our professions; me to the library and him to medicine.

Thursday 18 July

Issuing fines is an important part of a librarian's duties. There's no excuse for keeping books out past their due return date, and we take a dim view of it; fines of 21p a week for the first four weeks, rising to 28p a week thereafter are regularly levied against offenders. Today a man strolled in with a book that should have been returned at the end of April.

He cut quite a figure. Tall, athletic and devilishly handsome, his scarlet jacket, tight white jodhpurs, riding crop and shiny black boots told me he was an international showjumping champion. Sheepishly, he pushed a well-thumbed copy of Joe Swash's autobiography King of the Jungle across the counter. "I'm sorry, it's a bit late," he said, and his cut glass upper class accent began to work its magic on me. "Nine and a half weeks to be exact," I smiled.

"A very good film," he said. "My favourite scene was the one where the man covered the woman's body in stuff from the fridge before eating it off her." I felt myself blushing, yet strangely excited. "I've always wanted to try that out for real ... in a library," he said. I pointed out that food and drink are not allowed to be consumed on the premises, but I had a saucy suggestion of my own.

"Why don't you cover me with the date stamp before licking the ink off," I smiled seductively. I was fairly sure the ink was non-toxic. We made our way to the outsize book section, where he undid my hair and took my glasses off. I don't know about his skills in the dressage arena, but when it came to "undressage" he had a clear round with no faults, and I was soon naked before him. For the next ten minutes he stamped away, covering every inch of my expectant, quivering skin with dates. The pleasure was exquisite, as the rhythmic click-thump, click-thump of the self-inking stamper raised me to heights of ecstasy I had only ever imagined dreaming about.Then he blindfolded me and began licking them off, his eager, hot tongue darting inquisitively into every erotic nook and crevice of my flesh, searching out every last drop of ink.

After about two hours of the most intense orgasms I had ever experienced, my skin was clean and his tongue was as blue as a baboon's arse. "Marry me," he said. "As an international showjumper, similar to Rupert Campbell-Black out of Jilly Cooper's Riders, I have bedded thousands of beautiful women such as lingerie models, tennis players, ballerinas etcetera. But you were the best."

But I had to turn him down. As I explained, I am already married ... to Walsall Council's collection of 24,000 books. My showjumper couldn't hide the disappointment in his face as he paid his £2.70 fine and walked out of the library - and my life - forever.

Next week: *The day a dashing Prussian Cavalry officer galloped into the library on a white stallion and whisked Maureen away to the outsize books section for an afternoon of unbridled passion.*

MEDDLESOME RATBAG

CITY HOPPER

FSSSSHH!

UNBOLT UNBOLT

DISMANTLE

WRENCH!

CLATTER!

TYHOPPER

UNBOLT UNBOLT UNBOLT
UNBOLT UNBOLT

DISMANTLE DISMANTLE
DISMANTLE DISMANTLE

CLATTER CLATTER
CLATTER
CLATTER

PANT PANT
GASP

WELL REALLY! HAVE YOU NO MANNERS AT ALL? HERE I AM WITH MY HEAVY SHOPPING BAG AND NOWHERE TO SIT!

WERE YOU NEVER TAUGHT TO OFFER UP YOUR SEAT TO A LADY?

BIG VERN

...THAT WAS MADNESS WITH "ONE STEP BEYOND"... UP TO NUMBER SEVEN IN THIS WEEK'S CHART THIRTY-FOUR YEARS AGO...

I LOVE LISTENING TO 'PICK OF THE POPS' VERN.

YES. IT'S A REAL TRIP DOWN MEMORY LANE.

DO YA ERNIE?

...AT SIX, UP FROM FIFTEEN WAS GARY NUMAN'S TUBEWAY ARMY, AND STRAIGHT IN AT NUMBER FIVE WAS A BRAND NEW ENTRY..!

GIANT STEPS ARE WHAT YOU TAKE... WALKING ON THE MOON...

GET DAHN ERNIE! IT'S THE POLICE!

BLAM!

TAKE THAT, COZZA!

REALLY VERN. I'VE HAD ENOUGH OF THIS SORT OF THING.

DON'T WORRY, ERNIE. I WON'T LET 'EM TAKE YOU ALIVE!

BLAM!

AN' I'M NOT GOIN' BACK INSIDE, I'LL TELL YA THAT, ERNIE.

BLAM!

98

PHEEP! FOUL PLAY

~ Fullback Gary blows whistle on match-fixers who are ruining our game

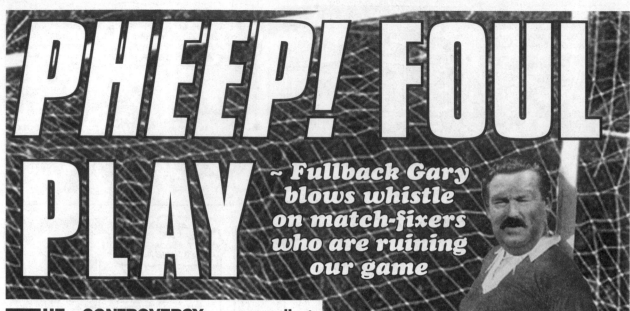

THE **CONTROVERSY** surrounding Qatar's successful 2022 World Cup bid has thrown the subject of international football corruption into sharp focus. Closer to home, several professional footballers have recently been arrested and questioned by police following allegations of match rigging. Online betting has brought vast quantities of dirty money into the heart of the beautiful game, and just like horse-racing, snooker and cricket, our national sport has become tainted by the whiff of sleaze.

And one man who has seen at first hand this rot at the heart of the game is footballer *GARY BIRDLIME*. Throughout his 15-year career in topflight East Nottinghamshire pub football, Gary has witnessed the creeping cancer of deceit that is destroying the sport from the grass roots up.

The first time that Gary came face to face with the ugly side of the beautiful game was in 1997, when his team the Red Lion Barflies were up against their arch

Not defending the indefensible: Fulback Garry Birdlime at his home ground at Clifton Playing Fields yesterday, and (below) a bung similar to the one he accepted.

EXCLUSIVE!

rivals Dynamo King's Arms. "It was an end-of-season mid-table match with nothing riding on it," he told us. "The game was taking place on the other side of Nottingham, and we were going in four cars, so the lads agreed to meet up at half-past twelve in the Red Lion car park."

" By quarter to one only nine of us had arrived, so we went in the bar to see if anybody wanted a game. A couple of the regulars were up for it, so we got a quick round in before setting off," Gary continued. But it was when he went to the gents that he was approached by a shady-looking character.

"He looked far-Eastern and spoke with a strong oriental accent," said Gary. "I was a

£1 Million BUNG

F.A.O. GARY BIRDLIME

bit taken aback because he wasn't the sort of customer you'd usually see in a small local boozer like the Red Lion. He was wearing a white linen suit, a wide-brimmed fedora and sunglasses, and he was smoking a large Havana cigar. We exchanged a few pleasantries about the weather and how I thought the afternoon's match against the King's Arms would go.

"I said that it would be a close game. We were both mid-table clubs, but our opponents probably had the advantage as they were playing at their home ground - the Coppice Rec, and they knew where all the bumps, puddles and broken bottles would be."

What happened next took Gary completely by surprise.

"The mysterious stranger reached into his pocket, took out a thick wad of notes and placed them on the top of the urinal trough," he said "'Here's two hundred thousand pounds,' he told me. 'It's yours if you make sure you lose the game.' It was more money than I'd ever seen in my life. I was so astounded, the my fag dropped out of my mouth and fell in my piss."

"The man explained that he represented a shady Far Eastern betting syndicate based in Singapore, and his clients had £15 million riding on the outcome of our game," said Gary. "With hindsight, I should have told him to sling his hook, but at the time I was working as a brickie's labourer and the money was just too tempting."

trials

As it happened, losing the game proved to be even easier than 14-stone Gary expected. He told us: "The King's Arms had a young centre forward playing on their team who was pretty good; in fact, he'd had trials for Forest. I pretended to be all out of breath and let him run rings round me."

"Meanwhile, our goalie was one of the blokes we'd enlisted in the bar. He was in his late forties and he hadn't played football since he was at school. By half-time we were already eight down and at the end of the game it was fifteen-one to them."

box

"I felt a bit sorry for my team-mates. We'd had a drubbing, and I knew that if I'd played as well as I could have done, I could have prevented all those goals going in. I might be a touch on the heavy side, but I'm still got a fair turn of pace and I'm solid at the back. If I'd given 100% we could have come away from that game with a one-nil away win."

"It's not as though I even benefited from the two hundred grand bribe, because I left the money in the changing rooms at Coppice Rec," said Gary. "I didn't even bother going back to look for it, because I knew nobody would have handed it in."

Birdlime put his brush with the mysterious stranger down to experience, thinking that his first taste of football dirty tricks had been a flash in the pan, but nothing could have been further from the truth.

Unbeknownst to him, he had been snared into a sinister web of bribery and corruption from which it would prove almost impossible to disentangle himself.

The week after we were playing Beeston Building Supplies at home at Clifton Playing Fields on Farnborough Road," said Gary.

"We turned up for the game and I went to see George, the park-keeper, to see which pitch we were on. But before I got to his hut, I was waylaid by three Chinese men in pastel-coloured Armani suits who were loitering by the putting green."

"They were wearing mirror sunglasses and had thin, pencil moustaches and gold teeth. They looked like Triad gangsters out of a Jackie Chan film, and I immediately knew what they wanted."

shoes

"One of them opened a briefcase and showed me half a million pounds. He said it was mine if I could get myself sent off in the first minute of the match. Once again, I gave into temptation; it was more money than I'd ever seen before in my life. I took the cash and went into the changing rooms to put on my kit."

"Getting a red card in the opening sixty seconds proved to be child's play, especially with the ref we'd got, who was a local copper who wouldn't stand for any nonsense. As he blew his whistle for the kick-off, I immediately ran in for an off-the-ball, knee-high, two-footed challenge on their captain, with studs up and everything. The poor sod went down like a sack of spuds with a broken femur."

"When I got the red card, I protested a bit but it was all just play-acting. As I walked off the pitch for my early bath I knew there was every chance the rcf was going to mention my foul on his match report, in which case I'd be looking at a fifteen pound fine.

But that was mere pin money to me now; after all, I had a cool quarter of a million nicker waiting for me in the dressing room."

"I watched the rest of the game from the touchline, fantasising about how I was going to spend my ill-

> ## It was more money than I'd ever seen in my life. I was so astounded, the my fag dropped out of my mouth and fell in my piss

gotten gains. Fancy foreign holidays, exotic supercars, wine, women and song ... my days of mixing mortar on the sites would merely be a bad memory."

"With ten men on the park, we lost the game quite heavily, and at full time I was none too popular with my team-mates as they trooped off the pitch. And the mood didn't improve when we got into the dressing room.

Some kids had been in during the match and been through everyone's pockets. Wallets, watches, car keys... they'd all been pinched, and needless to say the little bastards had also made off with my 250K that I'd hidden in my shoes under the bench.

Word soon got around the Far Eastern betting syndicates that Gary was a reliable match fixer, and the bribes began coming in thick and fast.

Our next fixture saw us taking on the Aircraft Social Club Casuals at their ground in West Bridgford. It was my turn to wash the kits that week, and I was loading it into the boot of my car when I felt a tap on my shoulder."

socks

"I turned to see a tall, oriental-looking man in a flowing, silk kimono. He had a completely bald head, a two-foot long Fu Manchu moustache and his little finger was missing. He also had dragon tattoos burned into his forearms. He told me he represented a big Japanese Yakuza betting syndicate, which had placed a billion dollar bet on the Aircraft Social 11 winning by more than three goals. There was half a million in it for me, he told me, but if I failed they would hunt me down and kill my dog."

handkerchiefs

"Still smarting from the dressing room theft of my quarter of a million the week before, I took the bag of cash and stashed it in the boot. Then I started wondering about how I was going to engineer the result that my sinister paymasters had requested. As it happened, luck was on my side once again. When I reached the ground, which was alongside

the canal in Colwick, I discovered that our goalie had got hammered at his brother's stag-night the previous evening, and nobody could wake him up."

"The lads had been banging on his door for more than twenty minutes and his curtains were still shut."

"Nobody ever wants to go in goal, so the rest of the team were well chuffed when yours truly stepped forward and volunteered to pull on the gloves. Truth be told, I'm a pretty agile shot-stopper, but I certainly wasn't performing to the best of my abilities that day.

soap on a rope

After ten minutes, our opponents had put seven past me and the scoring rate didn't get any lower as the match progressed. The money men had wanted a minimum of a three goal margin after ninety minutes and I certainly wasn't going to let them down."

"My team-mates were calling me all the names under the sun as shot after shot ended up in the back of the net, with me lumbering about, pretending to be unable to get anywhere near them.

At the end of the game, my ears were burning as I got changed and went back to my car. The money was in the boot and I was looking forward to counting it."

wad

"I'm afraid to say it didn't take me long. When I looked at the wad, I was horrified to see that the only real fiver in the bundle was the one on top. All the others were just newspaper! I'd been taken in by the oldest trick in the book. I couldn't go to the police; what would I say? I've taken a bribe for throwing a match and the money was fake?"

Birdlime's next couple of games were bribe-free. The Red Lion Barflies managed a one-all draw against Netherfield Wednesday, although he was taken off after ten minutes to let the sub have a game. But the following weekend, he found himself being drawn back into the shady world of soccer sleaze.

> ## Shot after shot ended up in the back of the net, with me lumbering about, pretending to be unable to get near them

We were playing a team from the packing department at Boots at their Lenton Lane ground by the Trent. With my first touch of the game, I mis-kicked, falling over onto my arse while the ball bobbled into touch for a Boots throw-in. Everybody laughed, including both teams, the referee, all six people who were watching and a man whose dog was doing its business behind the net."

"But the laugh was on them, because just before the match two men wearing sampan hats and Samurai armour had given me a cool million quid to concede a throw-in with my first touch of the game.

stack

This time I'd been a bit more careful and counted the money - twice - before stashing it in my kit-bag in the changing rooms."

"At the end of the game, people were still laughing at my 'mis-kick', but all I could think about was how I was going to spend my million pounds. But just my luck, our centre forward had walked off with my bag because it was his turn to wash the kits."

bolt

"I saw him the next night in the snug at the Red Lion, and told him I'd left some money in the kit bag and had he found it. He said there hadn't been any money in my bag. I knew he was lying, because the next day he packed in his job as a mechanic at the South Notts bus garage, chucked his missus out, married her off that shampoo advert where she has an orgasm in the toilet of a plane and bought a Rolls-Royce.

NEXT WEEK... Gary exposes even more of the sleazy underside of the national game: *"A man dressed in a Samurai warrior suit gave me ten million pounds to trip up and toe-end a penalty ten yards wide in the Nottinghamshire Amateur Club Cup first round knockout."*

Leave it to the Beaver

A YORK millionaire who died last June has angered his wife by bequeathing his entire fortune... *to her fanny!*

Carpet warehouse boss Axminster Wilton left almost £3million when he died following a heart attack in summer 2013, and in his will he specified that every last penny of his fortune should go to his wife's vagina.

comfortable

Ada Wilton, 63, fumed: "I was looking forward to a comfortable retirement, but now it looks like I'll be on the breadline whilst my quim lives it up high on the hog."

Mr Wilton's solicitor Fairburn Disburse said that while he sympathised with Mrs Wilton, the will was legally binding. "My late client was of perfectly sound mind when he formulated his posthumous bequest, which was signed with witnesses in accordance with probate law, so his missus's flaps cop the lot," he told us.

mr. LOGIC

OH, LORDY! IT'S THE FAT SLAGS...

LetterBocks

Viz Comic
P.O. Box 841
Whitley Bay
NE26 9EQ
letters@viz.co.uk

HOW come James Bond never rips the arse of his trousers? Since Daniel Craig took over the role, he always wears those really tight suits, and what with all the jumping off balconies and fights he has, you'd expect to see a bit of arse cheek hanging out occasionally. Unless "Q" has devised some kind of super-strong stitching thread, in which case they should make some kind of reference to it in the script.

G. Lazenby, Gateshead

I THINK the government should buy HRH The Queen seven new golden carriages, each with the first three letters of the day beautifully written on the side just like I have on my socks. It would save the embarrassment of being caught travelling in the same coach two days running.

Olivia Cromwell, e-mail

I WISH the end of a sausage roll didn't look so much like a dog's bottom. I find it very difficult eating one in front of my two Labradors.

Albert Ross, Hull

I REALLY despair of this technology-obsessed generation. In my day, instead of putting something disparaging up on your boss's Facebook wall, we'd stick a spud in their exhaust pipe, piss in their petrol tank or poison their dog. Still, what do I know? I'm just an old-fashioned fuddy-duddy apparently.

Horace Isengard, Tiverton

I'M getting a bit tired of people talking about how strong ants are. I can pick up a leaf too, who gives a shit.

Paige Beauman, e-mail

THERE has been an awful lot of controversy about people hunting lions and driving them into extinction. However, I watched a wildlife programme the other day, and they were doing a pretty good job of it themselves with all the fighting like fuck and killing each other all the time. So to be fair, if they do become extinct, they'll have to put their paws up and shoulder some of the blame.

Dickie Pendleton, Derby

HOW come Alton Towers are always advertising their attractions as "The ride of a lifetime"? Given that the majority of their customers are between 10 and 14, it isn't really saying much is it?

Topline Bradwurst, Staines

I SAW a wildlife programme the other day that said that there are only 3,200 tigers left on earth. ONLY! That sounds like a shit load of tigers to me. Anyway, I'd like to know how they arrived at that conclusion. Surely, most of them were hiding when the bloke was counting them. Either that or because they all look so alike, he may have counted the same ones several times over.

Eddie Bootlaces, Deal

WEETABIX wrote on the back of their cereal boxes that I could win 'the ultimate sports day'. When I wrote to them asking if they could pit an eternally-young Ms Roberts, my old PE teacher, and Mrs Robinson, my old English teacher, in a swimsuit volleyball match, they never replied. Waste of a stamp.

Jim Rustle, Kent

WHILST out driving in the Lake District, I saw a sign at the side of the road that read: 'CAUTION. BADGERS.' I think it was a little over the top as a warning, since badgers are only little and I was in a big 4x4. It was the badgers that should be exercising caution if you ask me.

Billy Mill, North Shields

✳ *Mr Mills' letter wins £1million in gold bars, a thirty minute trolley dash around his local Ferarri shop and a six month holiday in the Playboy Mansion.*

I WENT down to my local last night as I had heard that they held a quiz night every Friday. The first question was "what is the 14th element in the periodic table?" I don't know what the rest of the questions were because I fucked off home after that.

D Tomlinson, Maltby

I ONCE took a lady on a conservation safari in Africa to impress her. However, due to a misunderstanding, I shot a stripey horse and she refused to speak to me for the rest of the holiday. On a positive note, the striped skin really sets off the decor of my bedroom.

Sergeant Vic, e-mail

I SAW a woodpecker in my garden the other day, and my friend identified it as a lesser spotted woodpecker. I did indeed have spots, but there was no need to belittle it. I think he was just jealous because it wasn't in his garden.

Tarquin Verrucca, Hendon

WITH all this hype about the build quality and design of German cars, I was very disappointed to find that when visiting the toilet facilities in my local Volkswagen dealership it took 2 flushes and a brush to even take a dent out of the lamb bhuna I had the night before.

Alun Price, Mold

I CURRENTLY have a dusty rug hanging over my washing line. Can any of your readers beat that? Thank you. I'm here all week.

I Clarkeyus, e-mail

IT occurred to me that, as archaeological digs of old settlements are always several feet below the ground, the earth must be getting bigger like the universe is. You don't hear Brian 'know it all' Cox talking about that do you?

Mike Pope, e-mail

THEY say Rome wasn't built in a day, but how do they know? It might well have been. Archaeologists don't know everything.

Matt Douse, e-mail

APPARENTLY it turns out that 'neck' is just a medical term for where your head connects to your body. Honestly, I'm starting to think doctors invent complicated terms just to make themselves look clever.

Mark Glover, Coventry

I WONDER why bluebottles are called bluebottles? They don't look anything like a bottle, although I'll grant you they do have a blue arse. From now on I'm calling them blue arses.

Tim Briffa, e-mail

JOHN Cleese recently declared that he could no longer perform the silly walk because he has a dodgy knee. Call me stupid, but surely with a dodgy knee it WOULD be a funny walk, and absolutely no effort on his part is required. Some of these so-called celebs are getting a bit too big for their boots if you ask me.

Arthur Pewty, Maidenhead

PEEPING TAM — SCOTLAND'S PREMIER NATIONAL STEREOTYPE

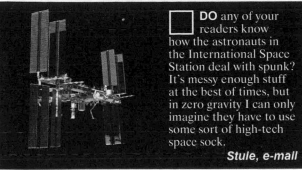

DO any of your readers know how the astronauts in the International Space Station deal with spunk? It's messy enough stuff at the best of times, but in zero gravity I can only imagine they have to use some sort of high-tech space sock.

Stule, e-mail

I THINK that if Hitler had bought his arms from the company that manufactures all those shit air rifles for fun-fairs, then the casualty figures of WWII would have been a lot fewer. I'm not suggesting that we should have given the Germans coconuts or goldfish as an incentive to surrender – that would be just plain stupid.

Dan Broadarse, London

Michael Gove and Penny Mordaunt. Because he looks like a fucking goldfish and she's got absolutely massive tits.

Randy Bob, Normanton

Thank You Very Much...

Your appreciation for the Good Samaritans you didn't have time to thank.

THANK you to the lorry driver who stopped and help me pick up my shopping that I dropped whilst walking home along the fast lane of the M1 between junctions 26 and 27. After other motorists had been very rude, blowing their horns and swerving, you really restored my faith in humanity.

Edna Prolapse, Derby

TO THE kindly tramp who generously offered my a swig from his bottle of Buckfast and some cold chips before putting me up for the night in his cardboard box after I missed the last bus home after working late at my solicitor's practice in Birmingham city centre. You are a true gentleman of the road.

Margot Fforbes, Surrey

A THOUSAND thanks to the police woman strippagram who sucked my fiance off in front of a pubful of his friends and family on his stag do. You made his special night even more memorable, and the fact that you didn't charge extra shows that there are still decent people in this selfish world.

Janice Jaundice, Hull

THANK you to the clairvoyant medium who contacted my late husband on the other side and told me he was happy. I had been very worried that he was in hell because of all the murders he did but you put my mind at rest.

Rose West, Durham

DO you think there is such a thing as beastial paedophiles who prefer kittens and puppies to fully grown cats and dogs over the age of consent? It seems unlikely to me, but you never know these days.

Wolf Warsson, e-mail

I HAD to laugh at something my nephew said the other day. That's because he's a 31-year-old despotic dictator and was cracking a joke, and I didn't want to be torn apart by dogs like my husband was.

Edna Jong-Un, Pyongyang

WHY is it that when the Daleks are about to kill the Doctor do they yell 'exterminate' as loud as they can thus alerting him to the fact they are about to shoot him? Surely Davros could get them to sneak up behind him and shoot him quietly. No wonder he's still alive 50-odd years later.

Findus O'Reilly, Bangkok

IN 1995 I thought I saw the lead singer of The Boo Radleys cycling in Camden. Then my friend Claire pointed out that it was just a bald man on a bike. For argument's sake lets just say it was him.

Sleepy Joe, e-mail

* *SORRY, Joe, we can't just make assumptions like that. Viz comic prides itself on the accuracy of its journalism and we have to get to the bottom of this. Were any Viz readers in Camden in 1995, and if so, did you see the lead singer out of The Boo Radleys on a bike? Perhaps's you were with the lead singer out of The Boo Radleys somewhere else in 1995 and can give him an alibi. Or perhaps you are the lead singer out of the Boo Radleys and would like come clean after all these years and confess to cycling in Camden in 1995. Write to the Viz Comic Incident Room, PO Box 841, Whitley Bay, NE26 9EQ.*

ON BBC *Breakfast* the other day, Paul Weller said that he's not interested in politics any more because politicians are "all the same." The former Jam frontman has clearly never looked at MPs

WHY don't lifts go sideways as well as up and down? It's all very well saving us from having to climb the stairs, but what about when you get out and have to walk along a corridor? Come on boffins! What about getting the job finished?

D Cooper, e-mail

I TOOK my kids along to that *Cirque du Soleil* the other week and what a rip off. I quite enjoyed seeing those women in thongs, getting into all kinds of contortive positions, but they could have thrown in something for the kids like a few lions, tigers or elephants at least. Maybe a clown or two.

Brandon Twelvetrees, Hull

AFTER giving a pint of blood, donors get a cup of tea and a biscuit to help them recover. Why don't they give the patients in accident and emergency a cup of tea and biscuit for every pint of blood they have lost and cut out the middle man?

Daniel Roberts, e-mail

WHY do sausage manufacturers go to all the trouble of filling pigs' intestines with sausage meat and then selling the finished product as sausages? Why not cut out the middle man and just feed the pigs the sausage meat and then remove their intestines?

Hector Bismuth, Bicester

---

the Vape Man

Name of character in this strip obscured on legal advice. If you'd like to know what it is, send a stamped addressed envelope to the usual address.

AAAAYEEAAYEEAAAA!

SKRIEKE!!

I get liquids down the market, save a bomb.

Hard bit is keeping it charged in the canopy.

SKRAYYK!!

NEXT TIME: ___ gets a gum infection

CRIME SCENE INVESTIGATION BOLLOCKS

April 7th. 02:32 EST

What time was he murdered, doc?

Well... judging by the temperature and condition of the body, I'd say sometime between 01:36 and 01:38

VWOOSH!

Hey, keep the noise down. It's 01:37 in the goddam morning.

BANG!

HNNNG!

Over here, Leiutenant.

What is it?

A bit of fluff. It must have fallen from the murderer's pocket when he took the gun out.

VWOOSH!

BANG!

HNNNG!

Let's bag it and get it back to the lab.

April 7th. 02:45 EST

What have you got?

Well from the way the fluff is deformed, we know it fell 38 inches from a right hand pocket...

...which puts the height of our murderer at 5-11.

We sequenced the DNA from the fluff... It's not on our files, but we managed to make an identipic of the guy whose pocket it came from.

So this is him. But who is he? There are 5 million guys in this city.

Wait a minute. What's that on the top of his head? Zoom in.

PING!

It's a scar by the look of things...

...probably caused by a fall from a tricycle on his third birthday.

VWOOSH!

HAPPY

Waaah!

Get up a live satellite feed of Manhatten and look at the top of everyone's head.

You got it.

Clickety! Clickety! Click!

VWOOSH!

Beep! Beep!... Bi..Bi..Beep!

We got him!... He's buying a hot dog on the corner of 25th and Broadway in Times Square.

Let's go!

MATCH FOUND

30 seconds later...

Freeze. You're under arrest.

I admit it. I shot the guy.

Great job, Leiutenant. Another crime cleared up.

Save it for the DA. My kid has a drug problem, I drink too much or my marriage is on the rocks or something.

MORE BOLLOCKS NEXT WEEK

108

Facebook Splashes $40 billion on New Acquisition

FACEBOOK CEO *Mark Zuckerburg* yesterday said he was "delighted and very excited about the future" after snapping up the 'Error 404: Page not found' message for a record $40 billion.

The popular warning, which pops up more than 3 trillion times a day on computers worldwide, is set to be a valuable addition to the internet magnate's portfolio.

expensive

This transaction comes at the end of an expensive 12 months for the specky four-eyed 13-year-old social media entrepreneur. Last July, his company paid more than $1 billion for Instagram, the photo-sharing site where users upload pictures and make them look shit. And in February they shelled out a record-breaking $19 billion on WhatsApp, which allows mobile phone users to exchange text messages exactly as they already do.

dear

Speaking from his bedroom in Silicon Valley, Zuckerburg said he was very

40 billion dollar man: Social media entrepreneur Zuckerburg has added the popular error message to his burgeoning portfolio of electronic will o' the wispery.

pleased with his new acquisition. "Error 404: page not found is set to become the jewel in Facebook's crown", he said. "It's a great opportunity to expand the userbase of our brand to incorporate anyone who follows a broken link or mistypes a URL."

antalope

"Just like everything else I own, I'm not sure how it's actually going to make money, but I'm confident that if we think about it hard enough, we can come up with some way of making a bob or two out of it," he added.

But not all Zuckerburg's buy-outs go as smoothly. In November, he was outgunned by Twitter founder Biz Stone, who paid nearly $100 billion for the spinning beachball and that winking smile thing made from a semi-colon and a bracket.

Posh Spice Named Pipe Smoker of the Year

VICTORIA BECKHAM has been named **Pipe Smoker Of The Year,** it can be revealed.

The coveted title, which has not been awarded since it was bestowed upon *QI* polymath Stephen Fry back in 2003, has been conferred upon Posh in recognition of her work as an ambassador for pipe-smoking.

honour

"It's an honour to receive this accolade and it's an honour to be recognised so publicly as a pipe-smoker," said Beckham, 39, who is the first woman to be receive the award since *Grease* star Olivia Newton-John won it in 1979.

Beckham, whose solo hit includes

Bowled over: Posh Beckham yesterday.

Out of Your Mind, smokes Players Navy Cut Flake tobacco in a quarter bent squat bulldog pipe and previously fronted a controversial £5million *'Bin Your Dottle'* campaign for the Welsh Assembly.

TONY PARSEHOLE

My Tears of Grief for Donald/ Dickie/Robin (ed-pick one)

WHEN I HEARD that Sir Donald Sinden/Sir Richard Attenborough/Robin Williams (*delete as*) had passed on, it was as if a light had gone off in my heart. And I am not ashamed to say that I wept.

I wept and I wept and I wept.

And then I wept some more.

And then I stopped wepting and I smiled. I smiled tears of happiness. I smiled tears of happiness not for the sadness of his passing, but for the joy he had left behind him in his wake.

For Sir Donald Sinden/Sir Richard Attenborough/Robin Williams (*delete as*) was not just an actor. He was a friend. A friend to me. A friend to you. A friend to us all.

A friend to everyone.

For who among us can forget his unforgettable performance in Never the Twain/Jurassic Park/Mrs Doubtfire (*delete as*)? He literally lit up the screen like a Colossus of Rhodes. Like a Belisha beacon. Like a candle in the wind.

But now that candle shines no more. Cruelly snuffed out in the prime of its life at the age of 90/90/63 (*delete as*), Sir Donald/Sir Richard/Robin (*delete as*) was taken before his time.

And one thing is certain. We will never see his likeness again. For Sir Donald Sinden/Sir Richard Attenborough/Robin Williams (*delete as*) was literally a one-off. A star of the old school who could hold an audience in the palm of his hand.

And it was a hand that could turn itself to anything. Comedy, tragedy, tragi-comedy (and that counts as two words even though it's hyphenated), action and adventure. They were all grits to Sir Donald's/Sir Dickie's/Robin's (*delete as*) mill.

Comedy: Who can ever forget his side-splitting performance as a butler/murderer/alien (*delete as*) in Two's Company/10 Rillington Place/Mork and Mindy (*delete as*)?

Tragedy: Who can ever forget his heart-rendering performance as an antiques

Actor of hearts: Sir Donald Sinden/Sir Richard Attenborough/Robin Williams (delete as) will forever be remembered.

(Picture desk drop library pic of whoever in here)

dealer/dinosaur man/councillor (*delete as*) in Never the Twain/Jurassic Park/Good Will Hunting (*delete as*)?

Action: Who can ever forget his thrilling performance as a (*check imdb*)/dinosaur man/scientist (*delete as*) in (*check imdb*)/Jurassic Park II : The Lost World/Flubber (*delete as*)?

Adventure: He was also in some adventures which I will never forget for as long as we both shall live.

He gave us so much and yet asked for nothing in return. We will forever be in his debt for time in memoriam. And now it is time to repay that debt of joy with tears of grief.

But now is not the time to grieve over Sir Donald Sinden's/Sir Richard Attenborough's/Robin Williams's (*delete as*) death. For now is the time to celebrate Sir Donald Sinden's/Sir Richard Attenborough's/Robin Williams's (*delete as*) life. A life that was full. A life that was rich. A life that was full of riches.

A life that was rich in its fullness.

But that celebration of his life, a life that was rich, a life that was full, and yes, a life that was both full of riches and rich in its fullness, must wait. For now is the time to grieve. As grieve we indeed must.

For his tragic passing has left a Donald-sized/Dickie-sized/Robin-sized (*delete as*) hole in all our hearts. A Donald-sized/Dickie-sized/Robin-sized (*delete as*) hole in all our hearts that can never be filled.

It is a hole in all our hearts that can never be filled in a hundred years. It is a hole in all our hearts that can never be filled in a thousand years.

And yes, it is a hole in all our hearts that can never be filled in a million years.

It is literally a black hole at the centre of all our hearts. And like a black hole, it sucks in our tears of sadness until we there that's 750 words inc title inv follows by email.

MAJOR MISUNDERSTANDING

DW 43

THESE HONEYDEW MELONS WERE A REAL BARGAIN!

FRUIT PALACE

HERE'S THE BUS, DARLING!

GRAB A SEAT, LOVE!

IF YOU COULD HOLD JOSHUA AND THOSE MELONS, I CAN MANAGE THE REST.

DISGUSTING!

I BEG YOUR PARDON?

I'M SURE YOU'RE TERRIBLY PROUD OF BEING A MOTHER, AND EVERYTHING

BUT DO YOU REALLY HAVE TO INFLICT YOUR MATERNAL FUNCTIONS UPON EVERYONE ELSE IN THE BUS?

I DARESAY YOU'VE READ SOME NONSENSE ON THE GUARDIAN WOMEN'S PAGE ABOUT HOW BREASTFEEDING IN PUBLIC IS "PERFECTLY NATURAL AND HEALTHY"

OH YES, "LET IT ALL HANG OUT" VERY "ORGANIC", VERY "POLLY TOYNBEE".

WHEREAS IF I WERE TO EXPOSE PARTS OF MY BODY ON THE BUS, YOU'D BE CALLING FOR ME TO BE LOCKED UP AND CASTRATED.

YOU WOMEN DON'T WANT EQUALITY, YOU JUST WANT IT ALL YOUR WAY.

IT'S COMPLETELY UNNECESSARY.

IF YOU MUST FEED IT IN PUBLIC, USE A BLOODY BOTTLE.

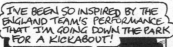

111

Butcher Saves Holidaymakers' Bacon

Winging it: Les took crash course in flying when pilot dropped dead.

IT'S EVERY nervous flyer's worst nightmare. An announcement over the cabin PA: "Are there any passengers on board who can fly a plane?" Last week that nightmare became a terrifying reality for 250 holidaymakers aboard an A33 Airbus bound for Tenerife. But, whilst everyone around him panicked, hero *Les Blackheads* calmly stepped forward and took the controls, safely getting the stricken aircraft and all its passengers to their destination.

Amazingly, until he sat down in the pilot's seat, the 55-year-old butcher had never even been in a cockpit before. And what made his feat even more remarkable was that he took over the controls even before the plane took off.

airport

The Cheapwings holiday jet was being refuelled at gate 6 of Leeds Bradford airport when the pilot and co-pilot both died of heart attacks and the emergency call went out to passengers. "I've flew a jumbo jet once on my grandson's computer flight simulator, so I thought I'd give it a go," said Les. "I went up to the cockpit, radioed the control tower to explain what had happened and they said they'd find someone to talk me through the take-off procedure."

safari

Eventually an off-duty pilot was found to give the Leeds pork butcher detailed instructions on how to control the plane. He told us: "While I was taxiing out to the runway he was explaining what all the different controls were for."

"I couldn't believe how complicated it was," said Les. "It was certainly a far cry from the joystick and button system I used on the Atari."

Sausage man Les steps up to plate on flight of terror

"Believe you me, an Airbus is much complicated than the bacon slicers I'm usually in control of."

preview

After five minutes waiting at the end of runway 2, the control tower finally gave Les the all-clear for take-off, and the 200-ton airliner began to gather speed. "It wasn't what you'd call a textbook take-off," laughed Les. "I brought the landing gear up far too soon and went into a steep climb. The man on the radio was shouting at me that I was about to stall and the passengers were all screaming."

garage band

"Then I pushed the stick down and we went into a

Taxi for Mr Blackheads: Les and his passengers wait for a take-off slot on the tarmac at Leeds Bradford airport.

dive. It was like a fairground rollercoaster, I can tell you," he continued. "But eventually I sort of got the hang of the controls and we reached cruising altitude."

At 35,000 feet, Les's instructor explained how to switch on the autopilot. "The next three hours were pretty uneventful," he told us.

photo booth

"The stewardesses went round with the duty free trolleys and I got a chance to enjoy the view from the cockpit windows and have a couple of whisky miniatures."

After flying over France, Spain and the Iberian Peninsula, it was soon time for Les to take over full manual control again and begin the tricky descent into Tenerife International airport. "There was a strong crosswind and the pilot on the walkie talkie was telling me to push this, pull that and twist the other to get the plane lined up with the landing lights," he said. "I didn't know what was going on."

The plane's landing gear clipped an electricity pylon,

the roof of a Hertz Car Rental office and the top of a coach before it finally came to rest fifty feet to the right of the runway, straddling the airport's perimeter fence.

iphoto

"It was an interesting landing, to say the least," Les told us. "Six passengers had to be taken to hospital with minor injuries and shock, and another thirty or so people on board shit themselves on final approach."

"And I was one of them," he added.

system preferences

Blackheads's heroism was last night honoured at the *Daily Mail Pride of Britain* awards, where he was presented with a commemorative plaque by 2008 King of the Jungle Joe Swash. "It's a great honour, but I don't think I'd do it again," he said. "In the future, if I'm sat on a plane and the call goes out for a volunteer to fly it, I'm going to keep my mouth shut."

"Some other bugger can do it next time," he added.

Hero

Hero: Pilot Wainscotting and the SliceMaster A330 (right) of which he took control.

STARS ☆ in their ☆ SKIES

FLYING THESE DAYS is safer than it has ever been. Advances in aircraft design mean that planes rarely break up in mid air and plummet to the ground any more. Similarly, pilot fitness is increasingly a priority for airline operators, meaning the chance of any captain dropping dead in the cockpit is extremely low.

But risk can never be completely eliminated. The more often you fly, the greater the chance that you will eventually get asked to take the controls in an emergency, and nobody flies more often than the STARS. With their jetset globe-trotting lifestyles, it's a matter of WHEN - not if - the celebs get called upon to land stricken jets. Here's a list of some of the more notable showbiz A-listers who have stepped up to the cockpit plate.

Boeing! Boeing! Gone!

WHEN both pilots of a 747 bound for Robin Hood Airport near Doncaster died of food poisoning mid-flight, the passengers were pleased that *Real Deal* star **DAVID DICKINSON** was on board. Without a second thought, the orange-skinned antiques expert calmly entered the cockpit and took the wheel of the 400-ton jumbo. "The control tower was talking me down," said the 68-year-old bric-a-brac guru. "As you can imagine, there was an awful lot of information to get over quickly, and they were speaking extremely fast, keeping me up to date with my bearing, airspeed and altitude."

"Most people would have been overwhelmed by such an onslaught of numbers. But I've worked in auction houses around the world and am used to thinking quickly while auctioneers reel off figures at great speed," he continued. "Though I say so myself, my landing was a real Bobby Dazzler. In fact, in the words of my copyrighted catchphrase, it was as smooth as chips."

Emu-gency landing

IN 1982 halfway between Sydney and London, both pilots of a Freddie Laker Skytrain choked to death on a Malteser. With no-one left at the controls, the plane went into a steep dive, plummeting nose down towards the ocean 35,000 feet below. Happily for all aboard, Aussie comedian **ROD HULL** was amongst the passengers, flying to the UK to appear in that year's Royal Variety Performance. Summoned by a stewardess, the ex-Air Force officer quickly made his way to the cockpit where he began wrestling with the controls with his one free arm.

However, the already difficult situation was made even more tricky by Hull's sidekick Emu, who grabbed the stewardess by the throat and wrestled her to the ground, ruffling her hair and stealing her shoe in the process. The uncontrollable puppet's slapstick antics continued throughout the rest of the flight, and by the time the plane touched down at Heathrow Airport 9 hours later, every single passenger on board was helpless with laughter.

Tom reached Cruise-ing altitude

PINT-sized Scientologist **TOM CRUISE** was relaxing with an in-flight magazine in the First Class section of a Boeing Dreamliner when the captain tripped and fell out of the window. With his experience playing a hot-shot Navy fighter pilot in *Top Gun*, Cruise was the obvious choice amongst the passengers to take the pilot's chair.

But like the Maverick character he played in the smash hit eighties film, the tiny actor ignored control tower pleas to take it easy and bring the plane in safely. Sitting on a pile of cushions to reach the controls, Cruise performed a series of hair-raising aerobatic stunts including loop-the-loops, barrel rolls and low level passes and buzzed the control tower at supersonic speed before finally landing safely.

Didn't he do well!

FIVE years ago, **BRUCE FORSYTH** was amongst 500 passengers relaxing on a jumbo jet flying to Gatwick Airport from Venezuela, where he had been to pick up a Miss World to marry. However, unbeknownst to the veteran *Generation Game* star and everyone else on board, up in the cockpit both pilots lay dead as the result of a homo-erotic auto-asphyxiation sex game gone wrong. When the alarm was raised by a concerned stewardess, the *Strictly* host calmly tap-danced up the aisle and took over the plane's joystick.

Carefully following instructions from air traffic controllers to watch his altitude, the *Play Your Cards Right* presenter pushed and pulled on the control column to take the aircraft "higher, higher" and "lower, lower", eventually landing safely two hours later. On a cabin announcement as the plane pulled up at the terminal, the chinny showbiz stalwart joked to passengers hat it had been "nice to fly you, to fly you nice."

Pilot Hailed

by our Butchery Aviation correspondent **Lester Pigshit**

AN OFF-DUTY airline pilot was last night being hailed a hero after he took the controls of a bacon slicer after the butcher operating it collapsed and died. Captain *Julius Wainscotting*, 52, was waiting to be served at Prendegast's Butchers in Colwyn Bay, Wales, when 63-year-old shop owner Clegwyn Prendegast suffered a fatal heart attack.

"He was halfway through cutting half a dozen rashers of streaky back for a customer when he suffered a fatal infarction," said onlooker Iorweth Llapp. "Things were looking bad but then this pilot stepped behind the counter and took over the controls of the slicer."

slicing

"He was on the phone to someone from the Guild of Master Butchers, who was explaining the controls of the machine and talking him through the slicing process," said Mr Llapp.

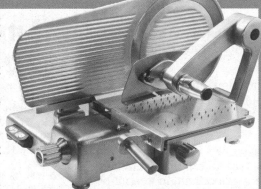

"Anyone else would have panicked, but he was cool as a cucumber."

"Some of the slices were a bit thick, others were a bit thin, but he got them all cut and that's the main thing," he added.

Captain Wainscottong was last night honoured at the *Daily Express Heroes of Courage* awards, where he was presented with a commemorative plaque by Paul Ross, presenter of Living TV's *Mystic Challenge* and *Tellystack* on UK Gold.

May-day! May-day!

Top Gear James's guide to Landing a Plane

WE'VE ALL wondered whether we've got what it takes to take over the controls of a plane if the pilots died. But would YOU know what to do in a mid-air emergency when a single false move could lead to disaster? We've teamed up with flowery-shirted TV presenter and keen amateur pilot JAMES MAY to bring you this step-by-step cut out and keep guide to safely landing any plane.

1 KEEP CALM. You're 5 miles up in the air and even if you go into a dive it's going to be several minutes before you hit the ground, so take your time to get comfy, have a cuppa and familiarise yourself with the controls.

2 LOOK OUT OF THE WINDOW. See if you can see airport where you can land. There's lots of them about and they're easy to spot; there's usually loads of planes parked around and a giant sock on a stick. If you're over the sea when the pilot dies, just keep flying round in circles till you spot some land.

3 LAND THE PLANE. Use the controls to point your plane towards the runway and land it. The steering wheel in front of you makes the plane go left and right just like a car, but it also goes backwards and forwards to make the plane go up and down. Once you're lined up with the runway, push the steering wheel forwards until the plane lands.

4 STOP THE PLANE. On the runway, you will still be travelling at 200mph. On the central console, you will see one, two or four sliders depending on how many engines your jet has. Pull them all the way back to stop the engines. On some types of planes you may have to push them forwards to stop the engines. Don't do the wrong thing or you'll take off again.

5 PUT THE WHEELS DOWN. I forgot to mention this before, but before you land the plane you have to put the wheels down. In most planes there's a button for it, marked "Wheels" or "Landing Gear" which lights up when you press it.

6 MAKE AN ANNOUNCEMENT. Once you've landed, press the cabin intercom button and give the passengers a brief summary of the local weather and time before reminding them to keep their seatbelts fastened until the plane has come to a halt. Then tell them that no smoking is allowed in the terminal building and thank them for flying with you today.

7 GO ON THE RADIO. I should probably have mentioned after No. 2 and before No. 3, but you should probably inform the airport of your intention to make an emergency landing so that they have plenty of time to get the fire engines out in case you crash.

Happy Landings *James*

Trolley DOLLY

IT WAS A flight that North Shields housewife *Dolly Piles* would never forget. For half way to Tenerife and five miles above the Mediterranean sea, one of the Boeing 727's senior cabin crew died of spontaneous human combustion.

And without sufficient staff to sell overpriced sandwiches and drinks, the Captain was forced to make an appeal.

"An announcement came over the tannoy asking if any passenger on board could operate a duty free trolley, hot drinks flask/tray combination and credit card machine," said Dolly, a former land girl and member of the North Shields Townswomen's Guild.

volunteer

Mrs Piles, 74, had some experience taking credit card payments in a shoe shop, and tentatively put up her hand to volunteer.

"During the next hour, I served in-flight meals and drinks, sold duty-free fags, booze, Toblerones and airline-branded teddy bears to countless passengers," she told us. "I even had to go round checking that all trays had been stowed and seats returned to upright position before landing."

Pensioner grabs controls of duty free cart at 35,000 feet

Mrs Piles's heroism was last night honoured at the *Lancaster Evening Post Prideness of Courage* awards, where she was presented with a commemorative plaque by disgraced former *It's a Knockout* presenter Stuart Hall.

Housewife pulls man off mid air

WHEN a woman passenger on board a DC10 died attempting mid-flight sex with her boyfriend in the toilets, a plucky Barnsley housewife came to the rescue.

23-year old Kurt Bumwad was attempting to join the Mile High Club with his fiance when she choked on a toffee and died. And when the call went out over the cabin interecom: *"Does anyone know how to pull off a cock?"* *Una Carbuncle* stepped forward.

cock

For the next 10 minutes the 48-year-old mother of five wrestled with the cock whilst Bumwad talked her through what to do.

"I used to do it for my husband,

so I wasn't a complete novice," she told reporters. "But I haven't been near one for such a long time and I was a bit rusty, so I was very glad of the instructions."

After fifteen minutes at his joystick, Bumwad went off and Una returned to her seat to applause from the rest of the passengers.

Mrs Carbuncle's heroism was last night recognised at the *Wednesbury Advertiser Deeds of Pluck* awards, where she was presented with a cut crystal vase by TV Physicist Professor Brian Cox.

There are Fairies *AT IT* at the Bottom of my Garden!

Woman calls cops over lewd sylvan folk

By our mythical sex correspondent **Aiken Drum**

A YORKSHIRE grandmother has called in police after being PLAGUED by sex-mad sprites. 68-year-old Pauline Foulage claims that the end of her garden in Cottingley near Bradford has become a regular haunt for fairies, elfs and pixies engaging in promiscuous sex, orgies and dogging. And Mrs Foulage says the randy Tinkerbells leave their rubbish, including marital aids, discarded underwear and used prophylactics, lying around where her grandchildren could pick them up.

Dell of vice: Mrs Foulage in the glade at the bottom of her Cottingley garden where pixies regularly indulge in sordid group sex.

"It's disgusting," she told her local newspaper *The Bingley Telegraph and Anus*. "Every night there's five or six little fairy cars parked up in the dell between the shed and the compost heap. There's always a couple doing their filthy business in one of the cars whilst the others mill around and watch them."

Sexual elf: Mrs Foulage's drawing of the goings-on she is subjected to night after night.

"I shan't tell you what they're doing with their little gossamer hands while they're stood there watching, but it turns my stomach, the dirty pigs," she continued.

shock

Mrs Foulage first noticed that her garden was being used for al fresco supernatural sex parties last year, when she saw lights in the undergrowth. "I was taking the bins out when I noticed twinkling coming from the undergrowth," she told the paper. "I went to investigate and got the shock of my life."

"I'm a broad-minded person, but I've never seen anything like it," she said. "There was a leprechaun having sex with a glittery fairy across the bonnet of a little car, with a queue of elves waiting their turn behind him. They were all drunk, shouting encouragement and manipulating themselves. I was disgusted."

Mrs Foulage told the fairies to get off her property, but says that in return she was subjected to a barrage of four-letter abuse. "You just don't expect that sort of language from fairy folk," she added. "They ought to be ashamed of themselves."

Mrs Foulage, a retired piano teacher, decided to call 999, and an officer from the station at nearby Keighley arrived half an hour later to investigate. "The fairies were having a gang-bang when the panda car arrived," said Mrs Foulage. "But unfortunately, the constable they had sent didn't believe in fairies so he couldn't see them."

board

"I asked him if there was another officer at the station who did believe in fairies, who could come down and arrest the dirty little beasts or give them a caution, but he said there wasn't," she added. "In the end I drew the police some pictures so they could see the disgusting stuff I have to put up with night after night."

Over the following weeks, the sprites' behaviour got worse and even more of them started turning up for the nightly open air orgies. On each occasion, Mrs Foulage summoned police, but they were never able to see the offenders. "They've got divers, forensics experts and dog-handlers in the force," she said. "Why oh why can't they have just one officer in West Yorkshire who believes in Elvenfolk to stop them using my garden like their own private sex playground?"

six

Mrs Foulage says it's now reaching the point where she can't let her three grandchildren play in the garden any more. "What if one of them picks up one of the tiny little used prophylactics they leave everywhere?" she fumed. "They could catch fairy AIDS and allsorts of off it."

boogaloo

A spokesman said West Yorkshire Police were taking Mrs Foulage's complaints seriously, but there was little action they could take at the present time. He told us: "We recognise the upset that the fairies' sexual activity is causing, and we are actively seeking the loan of an officer who believes in the magical thistledown realm on secondment from Greater Manchester CID."

RAFFLES THE GENTLEMAN THUG

AH, RAFFLES! ALLOW ME TO INTRODUCE YOU TO THE NOTED SUFFRAGIST MRS EMMELINE PANKHURST AND HER HUSBAND MR PANKHURST.

HOW DO YOU DO.

CHARMED, I'M SURE.

I CONFESS, MRS PANKHURST, THAT I AM SHAMEFULLY UNACQUAINTED AS TO THE WHYS AND WHEREFORES OF THE DEBATE OVER FEMININE EMANCIPATION.

IS THAT SO?

WELL IT HAS ALWAYS BEEN MY FERVENT BELIEF THAT PARLIAMENT SHOULD BE THE REFLECTION OF THE WISHES OF THE PEOPLE...AND PARLIAMENT CANNOT FULLY SERVE THAT FUNCTION WHEN THE VOICES OF WOMEN ARE WITHOUT ANY DIRECT REPRESENTATION.

WOULD YOU AGREE WITH THAT, LORD RAFFLES?

INDUBITABLY, YOU PUT FORWARD A COUPLE OF IMPRESSIVE POINTS, MRS PANKHURST. MOREOVER, IF THOSE TWO PUPPIES ARE FOR SALE, I'D LIKE TO EXPRESS AN INTEREST IN PURCHASING THE ONE WITH A ROSEATE PROBOSCIS.

WELL REALLY!

LORD RAFFLES- SUCH AN IGNORANT AND BOORISH MANNER ILL SERVES A GENTLEMAN OF SUPPOSED BREEDING.

ALRIGHT, PROFESSOR PISSFLAPS. KEEP YOUR FUCKING COIFFURE ENSCONCED. I WAS ONLY HAVING A CACHINNATE.

SIR! HOW DARE YOU ADDRESS MY WIFE THUSLY? I DEMAND THAT YOU APOLOGISE TO HER IMMEDIATELY!

OH YEAH? YOU GOING TO MAKE ME, ARE YOU, CUNTY-MANDIBLES?

RIGHT! THAT'S IT! I'VE HAD AN ELEGANT SUFFICIENCY OF THIS IMPUDENT MOUNTEBANK...! EMMELINE- KINDLY HOLD MY TAIL-COAT.

YOU AND ME! OUT IN THE AUTOMOBILISTS' LIVERY YARD...INSTANTANEOUSLY!

EFFECTUATE IT ON.

ALTERCATION! ALTERCATION! ALTERCATION!

SHORTLY... GOODNESS! YOU LOOK LIKE YOU'VE INCURRED A SOUND BELABOURING!

YOU SHOULD SEE THE OTHER FELLOW.

FARMER PALMER

♪ WE ROAMED THE FIELDS AND PASTURES, WHEN WE WERE YOUNG AND GAY... WE CHASED THE BEES AND PLUCKED THE FLOWERS...IN THE MERRY MERRY MONTH OF MAY..! ♪

♪ IN SUNNY GLADES WHERE WILLOWS WEEP OUR CHILDISH GAMES WE'D PLAY... ♪

BLAM!

♪ THAT DOG WUZZ WORRYING MOY SHEEP... ♪ IN THE MERRY MERRY MONTH OF MAY! ♪

CAPTAIN FIRESTONE of the DESERT RATS

DON'T WORRY, FRITZ, WE'LL SEND YOUR SECRET PLANS STRAIGHT BACK AFTER MR CHURCHILL'S HAD A BUTCHERS AT THEM!

HO-HO!

YOU TELL 'EM, CAP!

The story so far: Algeria 1942. Captain Monty Firestone and his maverick platoon of Desert Rats have just stolen the secret plans for a Nazi doomsday device from under the very noses of Rommel's 8th Army. With the Gestapo in hot pursuit, the plucky foursome must now race across 20 miles of hostile North African terrain to reach the safety of Casablanca.

Suddenly.

LUMME! THAT'S TORN IT!

A BLOOMIN' PUNCTURE! THAT'S ALL WE NEED!

BANG!

CRIPES! IT'S WRECKED AND WE AIN'T GOT A SPARE.

WANT TO BET?

Thinking quickly, Captain Firestone wrapped himself round the jeep's wheel hub.

CHALKIE, GET THE PUMP AND STICK IT WHERE THE SUN DON'T SHINE. 40 PSI SHOULD DO IT!

RIGHT YOU ARE, CAP!

38 PSI!

THAT'LL HAVE TO DO. JERRY'S GETTING CLOSER!

PUT YOUR FOOT DOWN, SPIKER!

HOLD ONTO YOUR HATS, LADS. THIS IS GOING TO BE A BUMPY RIDE.

The platoon was soon back on the road, but the blowout had cost them valuable time.

GEZUNDHEIT! THE ENGLANDER PIG-DOGS ARE USING THEIR CAPTAIN AS EIN TYRE.

VE VILL SOON CATCH THEM, MEIN KOMMANDANT. THEY VILL HAVE NICHT GRIP, ESPECIALLICHT VEN CORNERING!

MIND THAT ROCK, SPIKER!

GNNN!

CRASH!

LOOK OUT FOR THAT CACTUS!

OOYAH!

CRUNCH!

UPTURNED PLUGS AND LEGO!

The End

LETTERBOCKS

Viz Comic P.O. Box 841
Whitley Bay NE26 9EQ
letters@viz.co.uk

☐ **I'VE** heard that if you die without making a will and none of your relatives can be found, then all of your estate goes to the Crown. I'll bet the Queen sits watching *Heir Hunters* every morning, hoping that they can't trace anybody so that she'll pocket the loot. Greedy cow.

G Rumblemuffin, Tooting

☐ **THESE** so-called French people claim they're intelligent, yet yesterday on their Tour de France they were actually in Yorkshire. How are we supposed to take them seriously if they don't even know what country they're in?

Glen Hattersley, Stockport

☐ **I VISITED** Canterbury Cathedral recently and was saddened to note a large amount of scaffolding attached to the structure. 1,400 years of construction and still not finished. Another sad reflection of the 'rip-off Britain' building trade.

S Dentten, e-mail

☐ **I AM** currently sitting outside a vegan bar drinking coffee with soya milk and writing in a little notebook. Can any of your readers equal how much of a cunt I am?

Peaspod Manure, Glasgow

☐ **I DON'T** know why people use the phrase "slave wages" when they are poorly paid. I watched *Ben Hur* the other night and those galley slaves looked like they hadn't got a pot to piss in. They were very likely getting no wages at all.

Anthea Schneider, Barrow

☐ **WHILST** on holiday in Italy recently, I spotted the actor who played Jim Baines, the boss of the garage where Miss Diane-obsessed simpleton Benny worked in the 70s soap *Crossroads*. If it wasn't him it was someone who could easily make a VERY lucrative living as a Jim Baines-lookalike.

Keith Adams, e-mail

STAR LETTER

☐ **AN** Australian eastern brown snake can deliver enough poison in a single bite to kill 20 humans. Now what is the point of that? Does the snake think that once it has bitten someone, that person will then go and bite another 19 and save it the bother? This sounds like the height of laziness to me.

Alan Heath, e-mail

☐ **THEY** say the early bird catches the worm, but what if the worm is having a lie-in?

Dean Young, e-mail

☐ **IMAGINE** my shock and consternation on a Spanish holiday recently, when I heard the handsome barman at our hotel asking my wife if she wanted sex on the beach. It was only when I realised that it was actually the name of a popular cocktail that I could laugh to myself. Unfortunately though, I couldn't share the joke with my wife or the barman as they had mysteriously disappeared somewhere shortly after.

Trenton Hewitt, Barnsley

☐ **I AM** a little upset about Rolf Harris being included in the Operation Yewtree investigations. Surely Operation Eucalyptus Tree would be more apt for him? Yewtree should be reserved for genuine British kiddy fiddlers.

Vincent Blood, e-mail

☐ **I'LL** tell you what, in *Jurassic Park*, if Richard Attenborough had concentrated on setting up a gourmet sausage business instead of resurrecting dinosaurs, it would have resulted in a very different film.

Marvyn Russelcow, e-mail

☐ **IF** there's no smoke without fire, why are smoke alarms so-called, and not called fire alarms? I wonder if the boffins can answer that one, dare I ask?

Hollander Barrett, Truro

☐ **I JUST** spilled an entire bottle of Flash floor cleaner on the kitchen floor. Not sure if that counts as a mess or not.

Christina Martin, e-mail

☐ **THOSE** *'Taste the Difference'* sausages are a rip off. I bought a pack and they all tasted exactly the same.

Ed O'Meara, e-mail

☐ **OLD** grannies go on about the symbolism of reading your fortune in the leaves left at the bottom of a tea cup, so I wonder what they would make of my recent experience, where I was faced with an erect white Siberian tiger's cock at the bottom of my Cappuccino.

Nearly Normal Norman, Larne

☐ **HOW** is it that Tarzan, raised by apes, can speak "chimp," yet my dog who has lived with humans all his life can't speak a word of English? As always it's one rule for long lost aristocrats and another for dogs. Do I win £5?

Jan, e-mail

☐ **THERE** ISN'T a human being alive who doesn't constantly wonder what it would be like to be Bing for a Day. But given the chance, which

Michael Fish, Ineffectual Meteorologist

I've spent the vast majority of my life making wildly inaccurate predictions about the weather. So, if I was Bing for a Day, I reckon I'd be American crooner *Bing Crosby*, who famously dreamt of a "White Christmas" in his eponymous 1941 hit. Considering that Bing's hometown of Spokane, Washington, remains one of the USA's coldest cities, with a higher than 70% chance of snowfall throughout December, it's probable that Bing saw his "dream" of a white Christmas realised many times. For me, to enjoy this – or indeed any – level of meteorological accuracy, even for 24 hours, would be a fantastic experience.

David Dickinson, Daytime Telly Orangeman

I'm best known for presenting the programme *Bargain Hunt*, in which I used to help members of the public hunt for bargains. So, if I got the opportunity to be Bing for a Day, I'd probably choose the internet search engine, *Bing*. That way, I could just type the word 'Bargain'

☐ **IMAGINE** if money did grow on trees. We'd all be so rich and there'd be no poverty in the world. Except for people who lived in deserts and Eskimos.

Edna Rowbotham, e-mail

☐ **IT'S** been nineteen years since Princess Diana died. And, coincidentally, I lost my virginity on that very same day. Thank you your highness.

S Clapperton, e-mail

☐ **I DON'T** need David Attenborough to tell me that bats are blind. I saw a wildlife programme the other night, and a bunch of them were living in a scruffy old cave with bat-shit and cockroaches all over the floor. If they had eyesight they'd realise what a shithole they were living in, and look for somewhere better.

Tunbridge Weller, East Ham

TOP TIPS

CLAIM a restricted view ticket discount on your next theatre visit by taking a hatstand with you and putting it directly in your line of vision.

Neil Steadman, e-mail

AVOID being conned by companies offering hair growth tonics by first asking for a tester bottle and trying it on your bell end.

Garry Clarke, e-mail

MAKE visitors to your house think you buy organic free range eggs by purchasing a normal box of eggs and putting a feather in it.

Julian Hargreaves, e-mail

MATHS professors. Make beer from soft drinks by putting root beer in a square cup.

Rik Crompton, e-mail

RUGBY players. Make it easier to predict where the ball will bounce by replacing it with a football.

Stabilo Boss, e-mail

GIRLS. Impress men in your 'selfies' by putting your finger on your chin and pulling a face like a catfish.

Grant B Warner, New Zealand

TOM Cruise. Make people think you are taller by standing next to a wallaby and referring to it as a kangaroo.

Tam Dale, e-mail

OLD ladies. When the bus is five minutes late, get on board and berate the driver for his tardiness. Then spend the next fifteen minutes fumbling in your handbag for your bus pass.

Stan Butler, e-mail

JEANS manufacturers. Rapidly expand your market share in the US by producing XXXL to XXXXXL waist sizes, stitching in a holster-shaped pocket for a handgun, and increasing the size of the back pockets to comfortably fit a couple of magazine clips and a bible.

J Brownhagen, e-mail

toptips@viz.co.uk

Bing would YOU choose? We lined up some of country's top celebs and put the simple question to them: *Which Bing would you be if you could be...*

BING for a DAY

nto myself and then find a list of he closest bargains to me within seconds. Obviously, it would be more effective to use Google for his, as it's a far more efficient and popular search engine, but Google doesn't have the word Bing in t, and this column is only about being things called Bing for a day.

Michael McIntyre, Excitable Comic

Despite making a very respectable living as a professional comedian, I'm not in the slightest bit funny, so if I could be any Bing for a Day, I think I'd pick wise-cracking *Friends* character *Chandler Bing*. He's always quick with a quip, and constantly has his pals in stitches with his willy one-liners, so it would be fascinating for me to understand what it's like to be genuinely amusing, if only for 24 hours.

☐ **WHY** are so many injured people always described as being "serious" after a massive accident. Isn't there enough misery in broken Britain already? Come on accident victims, cheer up.

James Brown, Edinburgh

☐ **HOW** about a picture of a man being bitten on the arse by a lion?

Bradley Crumbhorn, Devon

* *Sorry, Mr Crumbhorn, but a picture of that nature would simply be too distressing for the pages of a family magazine like Viz. But here's a picture of the statue, 'Ow! Me Arse!' by Rodin, which depicts the scene.*

☐ **I WAS** watching the World Cup and noticed that a lot of the England players also turn out for clubs in the English Premier League, Italian Serie A, etc. People say that footballers are overpaid, yet it seems they have to play for 2 teams to make ends meet. Just goes to show that you shouldn't believe everything you read in the papers.

Martin Smith, e-mail

☐ **THERE'S** a lot to be said for watching historical programmes and learning from them. Until I saw *Carry On Henry* I hadn't a clue that Anne Boleyn had such enormous tits and a saucy giggle.

Guillermo Frey, Derby

☐ **HOW** disappointed my mother and I were to travel on the Eurostar. We were expecting that the tunnel would at least have some windows so that we could enjoy the marine life. Instead it just went dark for 20 minutes and then we were in France.

Kate Unwin, e-mail

☐ **IF** the Olympic swimming was held in a pool of Gatorade, the competitors could take sips to rehydrate during a race. Perhaps they could even choose the flavour they want in their lane, although I don't think the technology is up to that yet.

Gareth Price, e-mail

☐ **AS** a North Korean national, for many years I was crushed by my pointless life in the Hermit Kingdom. But I never gave up hope and as a result I planned and made my perilous escape into the outside world. Now I am safely here in the west, I intend to let others know of the dreadful and oppressive conditions the people of my country live under. But before I do, any chance of printing that picture of that bloke kissing that bird's arse?

Ho Chi Sung, e-mail

Fuck the Coppers

~ Get your own back on the police with *The Man in the Pub*

HERE'S A THING. Borrow a cow from a farmer and walk it down you local high street at 8.00 in the morning. More, if you like, a whole bloody *herd* of them. And when the coppers turn up and try to arrest you, tell them to fuck off, because it's only illegal to drive cattle down the street between *10.00 in the morning and 7.00 at night!* That's the Metropolitan Streets Act or something and it's never been took off the books. Watch them fuck off back to the station, red-faced with embarrassment.

AND GET THIS. Go out to your local park next Sunday with a fucking great big bow and arrows and start shooting the fuckers all over the shop. The coppers will probably tip up with fucking marksmen and make you put your weapon down and lay spread-eagled on the ground. Only when they come up and try to nick you, you make a citizen's arrest on *them*. Because under an old medieval law, everybody has to practice archery on the village green on a Sunday morning, and it was them what was breaking the law by not doing it. That'll shut the fuckers up.

HERE'S ONE FOR the ladies. Go up to a copper and tell him that you're pregnant and that you need a piss. And under an old law, he's got to put his cloak round a pregnant woman and let her piss in his hat. When you've done, tell him that you're not really pregnant and watch his face. He can't arrest you unless he's in uniform, and he's technically out of uniform if he's not wearing his hat. And he can't put that on because it's full of your piss. He'll be fuming but he'll know there's fuck all he can do. Priceless. Are you in the chair, eh? Mine's a pint.

Viz Comic and the Man in the Pub accept no responsibility for any arrests and subsequent prison sentences resulting from advice given in this column.

☐ **ACCORDING** to the Expansion Theory, if you fold a bit of paper 100 times it has the same width as the known universe. So logically, if I fold my knob 101 times it would be bigger than the known universe. I tried it and could only fold it once. I could have tried twice but feared rupturing my bellend. These physicists have too much time on their hands with their harebrained nonsense if you ask me.

Tam Dale, e-mail

☐ **"AN** apple a day keeps the doctor away," or so they say. But which one? My local surgery has two GPs, and one of them is quite fit.

Britt Roberts, e-mail

☐ **YOU** have to feel sorry for actor Sean Bean. After years of cultivating his tough-guy image, he still has to answer to the name of Mr Bean. On the other hand, I'm betting nerdy comic actor Rowan Atkinson isn't complaining, and is getting lots of pussy action because of the inevitable confusion.

Hong Dillard, Mablethorp

☐ **IMAGINE** how wide an owl's eyes would go if you stuck your finger up its arse.

James Brown, Edinburgh

☐ **I ALWAYS** used to resent having to pay the extra sewerage charge on my water bill, but after last night's vindaloo I almost feel obliged to cough up double. I pity any poor sod who has to miraculously extract fresh drinking water from what just dropped out of my arse.

Brendan Perkins, e-mail

GENOME TRUTHS

GENOME TRUTHS

THE NEW science of DNA sequencing allows boffins to examine every aspect of what makes us who we are. By analysing these miracle molecules in a laboratory, geneticists can not only tell us our eye colour, body shape and shoe size, they can also identify chromosomes that may make us prone to heart disease or cancer.

Not only that, they can even predict if we'll develop a sweet tooth, be a mathematical genius or excel at roller disco.

They can even determine even whether we are likely to commit MURDER.

WE OBTAINED DNA samples from a number of leading celebrities, and sequenced them to see what secrets they revealed about the real people behind the famous faces we invite into our living rooms each night ...and our findings will shock every man, woman and child in Britain.

Little Jimmy Krankie

Source of sample: *Chewing gum stuck under school desk*

Scientific analysis: There are lots of genes you'd expect to find in a schoolboy; such as ones that suggest a predisposition for getting up to mischief and a liking for sweets. Unfortunately, these are combined with another chromosome that gives him a 70% chance of developing tooth decay. The combination of these genes makes it odds-on that Jimmy's dad/husband Iain will soon be taking his son/wife to the dentist for fillings. But there is an upside. A mutation on gene 14 gives him a tendency to scrump apples, which should be very good for his teeth. However, the most surprising thing revealed when we sequenced Little Jimmy's DNA was that he was a woman; genes on Chromosome 3 are known to code for tits and a fanny.

Brian Cox

Source of sample: *Sock under bed in dormitory at CERN*

Scientific analysis: Whilst the TV boffin spends his days looking into outer space, we focussed on the inner space of his DNA. We found that he shares genes with both Liberace and Albert Einstein, which explains his twin careers as both a D:Reem keyboardist and a theoretical physicist. However, he also possesses genes which make him talented at many other occupations which he has probably never even tried. Although he may not realise it, Cox could also make an excellent living as a chicken sexer, water diviner or elephant mahout.

Uri Geller

Source of sample: *Spoon we asked him to rub in the street*

Scientific analysis: At first glance, there seems to be nothing unusual about the paranormal cutlery-bender's DNA. Geller's genes code for the typical features you'd expect in a human being; two eyes, hair, knees, buttocks... all the usual things. But on the end of one of his chromosomes was a gene that left the experts baffled. It coded for nothing they'd ever seen before. When this mystery gene was injected into a laboratory mouse, the animal suddenly became able to bend spoons, re-start broken watches, and reproduce a drawing that had been sealed in an envelope earlier that afternoon by somebody it had never met before.

Mo Farah

Source of sample: *Saliva flobbed out during Great North Run*

Scientific analysis: Olympic 5,000 and 10,000 metre gold medal winner Mo's DNA is exactly what you'd expect for a successful middle distance runner, as his dominant genes code for muscles that have endurance rather than sprinting ability. Indeed, when we ran Mo's human genome through the computer, it identified chromosomes that would allow him to complete a half marathon in 60 minutes 10 seconds - amazingly the exact time he ran in the 2013 Great North Run. Sadly for him, DNA never lies, and no matter how hard he tries or how much Quorn Mince he eats, he will never be able to better this time; the sub-one hour half marathon will forever remain outside Farah's grasp.

Sting

Source of sample: *Swab taken from gusset of boxer shorts at launderette*

Scientific analysis: When we sequenced the former Police frontman's sample we found several genes that are often found in Geordies, so it is quite likely that he originally came from somewhere in the north east of England. This fits the facts, as it is known that his father was a milkman in the Newcastle area. Although the gene on his Y-chromosome for having sex is perfectly unremarkable, the one for going off after a normal amount of time is mutated, explaining why it always takes him five-and-a-half hours to shoot his stack. Chromosome 24 also has a allele for a fine singing voice. However, it is recessive and not expressed, which is why he sounds like a bullfrog eating sandpaper on his records.

Russell Brand

Source of sample: *Manuel's granddaughter's knickers*

Scientific analysis: 70% of human genetic make-up is so-called "nonsense DNA"; endless chains of letters strung together seemingly at random and with no discernible meaning. However, when our scientists sequenced the pipecleaner-legged funnyman and political philosopher's DNA, they found that an amazing *99%* of it consisted of nonsense DNA! This may go some way towards explaining how Brand talks and writes; endless chains of letters strung together seemingly at random and with no discernible meaning.

Spelling it Out
What your DNA says about YOU

YOUR DNA is made up of millions of nucleotide molecules, each one a different combination of just four molecules - *Adenine, Cytosine, Guanine* and *Thymine*. For convenience, scientists label these four nucleobases **A, C, G** and **T**, and the unique way they are arranged in your genes says a lot about the sort of person you are. Look at some of your DNA under a microscope and tot up the number of different bases to unlock the hidden secrets of your true personality...

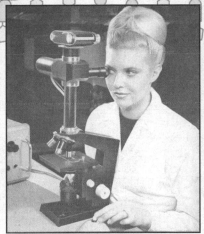

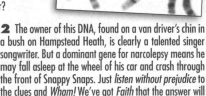

```
A T T C G C T G A A T C G A C
T A A G C G A C T T A G C T G
```

Mainly As

You're fun-loving and outgoing and live life to the full. Always up for a laugh, you're the life and soul of the party and always the first one onto the disco dancefloor or karaoke stage.

Celebrity examples: *Chatty Man Alan Carr, Benefits Queen White Dee, US Foreign Secretary Henry Kissinger*

Mainly Cs

You're a quiet, home-loving person who would always prefer a night in by the telly to a rowdy party or social event. But your love life can be complicated, as you are promiscuous and prone to embark on casual flings.

Celebrity examples: *Master Baker Paul Hollywood, Singer Badly Drawn Boy, Angel of Mercy Mother Teresa of Calcutta*

Mainly Gs

You're a hopeless romantic, forever falling in love and having your heart broken. You're reliable, loyal to a fault and prone to sudden rages and murder, and your favourite pop star is Neil Sedaka.

Celebrity examples: *Novelist Barbara Cartland, Wrestler Giant Haystacks, Convicted Perjurer Lord Archer*

Mainly Ts

You're a serious-minded, studious person who's never happier than when you've got your nose buried in a book. You also love gardening and soup, and enjoy the Fred Basset cartoons in the *Daily Mail.*

Celebrity examples: *Telly Lord Melvyn Bragg, Astronaut Buzz Aldrin, Trololol Man Eduard Khil*

Who Do YOU Think They Are?

Have a go at our fun quiz and see if you can identify the stars from the information held on their DNA fingerprints...

1 An allele on chromosome 6 of this DNA found in some pants in a caravan on Scarborough cliffs shows that the owner had a liking for big cigars and shiny tracksuits. *Goodness gracious! How's about that, then?* Have you fixed it for yourself to get the answer?

2 The owner of this DNA, found on a van driver's chin in a bush on Hampstead Heath, is clearly a talented singer songwriter. But a dominant gene for narcolepsy means he may fall asleep at the wheel of his car and crash through the front of Snappy Snaps. Just *listen without prejudice* to the clues and *Wham!* We've got *Faith* that the answer will *wake you up before you go go.*

3 This DNA, recovered from a fag-end in the *Top Gear* studio car park, comes from someone with curly hair, knock-knees and a pot belly who loves driving fast cars with all smoke coming off the wheels. *And on that bombshell,* it's time for you to name the *star in this reasonably-priced DNA.*

Answers: 1. Jimmy Savile, 2. George Michael, 3. Jeremy Clarkson

---

126

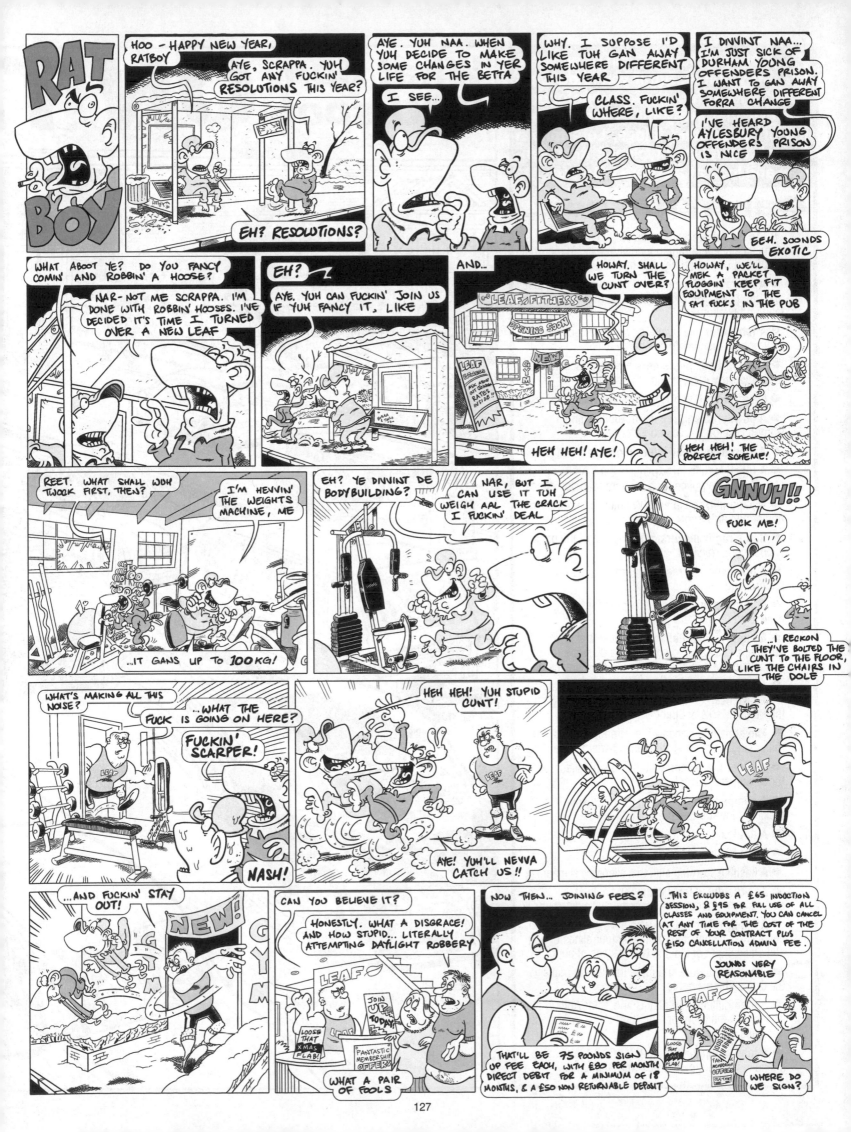

LONG car journeys can often seem very boring. But if you know what to look for, those monotonous, endless motorway miles are actually full of fascinating things. Lets take a 70mph trip down a typical British highway and look at all there is to see.

Can *YOU* spot...

- [ ] **An HGV driver** whose favourite film is *Duel* altruistically encouraging a newly-qualified motorist by driving 6" behind her and flashing his lights.

- [ ] **A 90-year-old woman** who's never taken a test and can't see over the dashboard driving the wrong way up the sliproad.

- [ ] **A footballer** in a black Range Rover doing 130mph on his way to "a charity event".

- [ ] **The *Top Gear* presenters** having a race in three unroadworthy cars.

- [ ] **A lorry driver** dumping a rolled-up carpet into a bush.

- [ ] **A powdered egg rep** in an Audi holding a 90mph Bluetooth sales conference.

- [ ] **A pissed-up rugby international** in a golf cart.

- [ ] **A black man** in an expensive car who has been stopped by the police for a random roadside check.

- [ ] **A paperclip rep** in a BMW enjoying a refreshing power nap at 90mph.

- [ ] **Some rugby players** mooning out of the back window of a minibus.

- [ ] **A man** who you recognise from *CrimeWatch* hitch-hiking.

- [ ] **A caravanning couple** stopping for their elevenses on the hard shoulder.

- [ ] **A highway maintenance vehicle** that looks sufficiently like a police car from a distance to cause everyone to start slamming their brakes on.

- [ ] **An elderly couple** who live 800 miles away, who have been on the road for a week looking for their local Marks & Spencer.

- [ ] **The start** of a coned-off section to protect one man using a strimmer 20 miles further up the road.

- [ ] **Another black man** who has been pulled over for driving at 70.1mph.

- [ ] **A camper van** containing a film crew who are making a low-budget porn film.

- [ ] **A flat fox**.

- [ ] **A flat hedgehog**.

- [ ] **A flashing warning sign** that everyone is ignoring.

- [ ] **An articulated lorry** in the 60th mile of an overtaking manoeuvre past another articulated lorry.

- [ ] **A family** off on holiday who have just spent their entire week's spending money on four plates of egg and chips, a pot of tea and two glasses of pop.

- [ ] **Petrol** being sold at a price that would make Bill Gates shit his pants.

- [ ] **A man** pulling in to play Grand Theft Auto in the services game room and print off some humorous business cards.

- [ ] **A load of shaven-headed football fans** having a piss in the hedge 15 yards from the toilets.

What can YOU spot ON T[...]

AUCTIONS Speak Louder than WORDS!

THESE DAYS you can't switch on the television in the afternoon when everybody else is at work without seeing an auction. However, whether it's the final, tense face-off between the Reds and the Blues on *Bargain Hunt*, the nail-biting moment when a seller finds out if a much-loved heirloom is going to make its reserve on *Flog It*, or the dramatic instant when the bidders discover what they've just spent thousands of dollars on in *Storage Wars*, all these shows have one thing in common: They make the business of attending auctions look downright squalid.

What a lot he got: Antiques expert and bric-a-brac dealer Dixon Davidson makes and loses millions every day bidding at high-stakes auctions.

If the scenes we see on our screens are to be believed, auction rooms are populated by hoards of seedy, overweight, unattractive people who spend their days grubbing about in mouldy cardboard boxes full of other people's junk. Invariably, the sums to be made as the various chipped, cracked and unloved lots are knocked down to the highest bidder are tiny. As a lifestyle, it looks like only a small step up from being a rag and bone man or one of those people who roots through the skips at your local recycling centre when the attendants are on their tea break.

But one man who turns this reputation on its head is professional bargain hunter, antiques dealer and international bric-a-brac entrepreneur **DIXON DAVIDSON**. In a glamorous forty-year career at the front-line of the bidding game, Dixon has made - and lost - literally millions more times than he cares to remember.

EXCLUSIVE!

By our Auction and Boot Sale Correspondent
Tolpuddle Marter

"I'm one of the auction world's highest rollers," he told us. "And just like a gambler in a Monte Carlo Casino, I'm addicted to the thrill of winning. But instead of the roll of the craps or the turn of the next card, I get my rush when the auctioneeer's hammer hits that round little bit of wood on his desk and he points at me and says: 'Sold! To the man in the brown anorak!'"

"That's the real deal in my book!"

Wigan-based Davidson, 58, got his first taste of the gavel game when he attended a sale at a local auction house back in the mid-1970s.

❝A young woman who lived on the council estate in Platt Bridge had got behind on her rent and been evicted. The bailiffs had been in and put all her stuff up for auction. I went to the viewing and had my eye on a chest of drawers that was still full of her knickers. Obviously, I wasn't at all interested in the contents, it was just that it was a nice piece of melamine and I was willing to splash out up to a tenner on it.

However, there were a couple of seedy-looking characters in the saleroom and I was pretty sure it wasn't the furniture they were looking to buy.

They started driving the price up, bid after bid. I got caught up in the excitement of the bidding battle and suddenly, without knowing how it happened, the lot was with me at twelve quid. Before I knew it, my rivals dropped out and the hammer came down. The drawers were mine. And by that I mean the chest of drawers, not the knickers inside it. Although, obviously, they were mine too. Not that I wanted them. As I said before, I had no interest in them whatsoever.

naive

As this was the first auction I had attended, I had been very naive. I hadn't realised that there was also a buyer's commission of 15% and VAT to pay on top of my winning bid. I knew I'd have to sell the chest of drawers for sixteen quid before I broke even. But I needn't have worried, because without knowing it I'd just bought one of the best bargains of my life.

strange

Anyone who's ever watched *Storage Hunters* knows that even the most unlikely lots may contain treasure. As long as you search through your purchases thoroughly you're practically guaranteed to find something valuable. And my melamine bedroom cabinet was no exception. Once I got home I started rifling through the contents and there, hidden away in the bottom of a drawer, I saw something sparkle. My hands were shaking as I pulled a load of knickers out of the way to reveal a diamond necklace.

My hands were shaking as I pulled a load of knickers out of the way to reveal a diamond necklace...

Bargain hunter Dixon makes bid for fame

I thought it might be just costume jewellery, but when I went into Ratners in Wigan the next day to get it valued, the man behind the counter's magnifying thing fell out of his eye with surprise as he examined it.

mcqueen

He told me the necklace was made out of Koh-i-Noor diamonds, and he gave me a million pounds cash for it there and then.

A million notes for a sixteen quid outlay? That's a jewel of a deal in my book!

But in the wheeler-dealer auction business, fortunes can be lost as easily as they can be made, as Dixon was shortly to find out.

I'd travelled over to Runcorn for an auction of the effects of a local bloke who'd died. There were some nice soft furnishings, curtains, sofas, rugs and what-have-you, but most of them had been spoilt because he'd lain undiscovered in his flat for eight months. Anyway, I wasn't interested in any of that stuff. I had my eye on another lot entirely - a large cardboard box full of well-thumbed pornographic magazines.

The good, the bid and the ugly: Dixon bags bargains at auction, then sells them on for huge profits at high class car boot sales like this one.

I know what you're thinking, but let me make it clear that I had no interest in those mags. No interest whatsoever, and that's true. No, at the viewing my eye had been caught by something I glimpsed underneath them, hidden away at the bottom of the box - an unmistakeable glint of gold.

newman

This could have been anything - an antique candelabra, a valuable solid gold Ming vase or the death mask of King Tutunkhamen. I had a hunch that it was something valuable, but I didn't investigate any further for fear of drawing attention to what I'd discovered. I simply sauntered off nonchalantly to have a look at the next item in the room, a mixed lot consisting of an infra-red heat lamp, a pillar drill, some old ice skates and six bunches of keys.

Once the bidding started, I realised that one other person was interested in the box of mags. A box of 1970s scud like that would normally get knocked down for about a fiver, so when the bidding reached a hundred quid I realised my rival must have clocked the gold too. I doubt the auctioneer at Runcorn Cattle Mart had ever seen anything like it as the two of us relentlessly drove the price up and up. But I held my nerve until my adversary finally lost his bottle. He'd clearly set himself a limit of a million pounds and the lot was mine for a million and one.

jerry

I may have won the bidding battle but I was actually the loser on the day. When I got home and began rooting through the bongo mags to discover the treasure that lay beneath, I was disappointed by what I found. The golden treasure I had glimpsed the day before turned out to be nothing more exotic than a few Quality Streets.

Blowing a cool million and one pounds on some gummed-up Escorts

> **Blowing a cool million and one pounds on some gummed-up Escorts and a handful of mouldy toffees was certainly not the best deal I ever made...**

and a handful of mouldy toffees was certainly not the best deal I ever made. But we've got an old saying in this game... *Easy come, easy going going gone.*

After getting their fingers burned so badly, most people would decide to give up, but not Davidson. And it wasn't long before he was back in the saleroom, bidding just as enthusiastically as before.

I'd been to a viewing for a police auction of seized goods, all the proceeds of crime. The saleroom was like an Aladdin's Cave - there was everything from a flatscreen telly or an onyx table to a MIG welder or a pallet of car radios. But there was one lot that caught my eye in particular - a beautiful work of art that was propped up in a dusty corner.

Now I may not know much about art, but I like to think I can spot a masterpiece by a famous artist like Leonardo da Vinci, Van Gogh or Pablo Picasso. And this painting of a nude woman in thigh-length boots with a sword and a big snake was definitely by Leonardo da Vinci, Van Gogh or Pablo Picasso and the estimate in the catalogue was for just £5-£10 with no reserve. I couldn't believe my luck - the clip frame must've been worth that much on its own.

In the event, nobody else bothered to bid and I got the lot for the starting price of two pounds.

A Van Gogh of some flowers had sold at Sothebys the previous week for ten million pounds, so I was expecting a ten million profit from my painting, minus the two pounds I'd paid for it. I was mentally spending the money as I carried my prize up the front steps of Leigh Art Gallery. But my hopes of selling my painting for a fortune were to be cruelly dashed. It turned out that my "original work of art" was a worthless, mass-produced print. Not only that, the frame was a fake too.

tom

Not only had I failed to make ten million on this deal, I'd actually made a two pounds loss. Four pounds fifty if you include my bus fare from Wigan to Leigh. I even had to buy two singles rather than a return ticket, as I had been fully expecting to drive back to my lodgings in a brand new Rolls-Royce.

As any Container Wars viewer can testify, it's often the least promising objects that turn out to be the most valuable. And the hidden history behind one seemingly mundane purchase led to Dixon pocketing a seven figure profit.

I was at a storage auction on a fenced-off patch of ground next to the retail park in Standish. The proprietors

Value added tat: An ordinary-looking storage unit could well be hiding valuable treasures.

were flogging off the contents of units where the owners had stopped paying the rent. One of the lock-ups in particular caught my eye; it had been used as a stockroom by the owner of a local sex shop, and contained several pallets of shrink-wrapped Scan DVDs with lurid covers. The auction got off to a lively start.

pot

There were a few of us bidding for it, but I was the only one who wasn't interested in the hardcore vids. No, that sort of thing doesn't interest me at all. I had spotted something much more exciting hidden away in the gloom at the back of the unit.

The dirty mac brigade dropped out of the bidding war one by one and pretty soon the auctioneer brought his gavel down and the lot was mine. I moved all the mucky films back to my flat to dispose of at a later date, before turning my attention to my real prize hidden away at the back of the unit. There it was - a box of old tools, including a well-worn claw-hammer with a rusty head and a worm-eaten handle. Something that was only fit for the bin, you might think.

kettle

But you would be wrong. For I have read quite a few Dan Brown novels and I had a powerful hunch that this was no ordinary hammer. It was the very tool that had been used to nail Jesus to his Cross in the Bible. I took it round to my local church, where the vicar confirmed it was indeed the fabled "Hammer of Destiny" and immediately gave me two million pounds for it.

silicon

God must have been smiling on me when I made that deal, I can tell you. But the Lord giveth and he taketh away, because my miraculous profit got wiped out the very next day. I blew the lot on a bin bag full of assorted used bras and tights that I wrongly suspected of containing Henry VIII's coronation robes.

Next Week: The time Davidson lost £25 buying a load of Betamax Electric Blue videos when he thought the vinyl suitcase they were in was a Louis Vuitton one that once belonging to Jackie Onassis, Elizabeth Taylor or Wallis Simpson.

TINRIBS

YOUNG TOMMY TAYLOR'S BEST FRIEND WAS A REMARKABLE ROBOT NAMED TINRIBS

I'M LOOKING FORWARD TO THIS SCHOOL HILL-WALKING TRIP IN THE SCOTTISH HIGHLANDS, TINRIBS!

SCHOOL MINI BUS
HIGH ROAD

HI. I'M BARBIE I LOVE YOU VERY MUCH.

GOOD GRACIOUS! THIS PLACE IS SWARMING WITH MIDGES!

WE'LL BE BITTEN TO DEATH BEFORE WE REACH THE HILLTOP!

CLIMB ABOARD MY ROBOT CHUM HEADMASTER!

YOU SEE, MIDGES ARE ATTRACTED TO HUMAN PERSPIRATION...

...SO IF MR SNODWORTHY TOWS US ALL UP THE HILL, HIS FAT SWEATY BODY WILL BECOME AN IRRESISTIBLE "MIDGE MAGNET"

SWARM STING

GASP WHEEZE PANT

AN EXCELLENT IDEA, YOUNG TAYLOR!

AHH, JUST LOOK AT THAT MAGNIFICENT VIEW!

SUMMIT

gasp! gasp! gasp!

COME ON SNODWORTHY, SHOW A BIT OF AESTHETIC APPRECIATION!

THE ONLY TROUBLE IS — NOW WE'VE GOT TO CLIMB ALL THE WAY DOWN THE HILL AGAIN!

WHAT A BORE!

A ZIP WIRE WOULD BE A MUCH MORE FUN WAY OF DESCENDING THE HILL, HEADMASTER..

RIP!

MY SHIRT!

AND TINRIBS CAN HELP US TO CONSTRUCT ONE!

FIRST WE PULL OUT MR SNODWORTHY'S NIPPLES UNTIL THEY'RE SEVERAL METRES LONG..

STRE-T-CH!

BEEEP!

THEN WE TIE THEM TO THIS GIANT PRICKLY THISTLE AT THE FOOT OF THE HILL.

AROO-GA!

NOW I PUSH TINRIBS'S ARMPIECE THROUGH THE SIDE OF ONE OF HIS TIN CANS: LIKE SO!

THAT'S SUPER, TAYLOR! ME NEXT ON YOUR ZIP WIRE...

DIGNITAS APPLICATION

SCRAPE!

WHEE!

..OR SHOULD THAT BE "NIP" WIRE?! HO HO!

SOON

DINNERTIME! WE'LL LIGHT A CAMP FIRE BY THE BONNY-BONNY BANKS OF THIS LOCH!

LOCH PUTRID

AND A BIT OF TRADITIONAL SCOTCH MUSIC WILL WHET OUR APPETITES FOR OUR PORRIDGE DINNER.

OH NO! MY BAGPIPES HAVE BEEN EATEN BY MOTHS!

MY ELECTRONIC BUDDY WILL COME TO THE RESCUE AGAIN!

I'VE RIPPED OPEN MR SNODWORTHY'S TORSO AND REMOVED ONE OF HIS LUNGS ALONG WITH A SECTION OF HIS TRACHAEA.

GACK BUBBLE

NEXT I JUST PUSH TINRIBS'S HOLLOW ARMPIECE INTO THE LUNG'S UPPER NODE TO SERVE AS A BAGPIPE "DRONE."

GOOD WORK, TAYLOR!

PARP!

gasp bleed

I'LL PLAY A FEW VERSES OF 'AMAZING GRACE' WHILE WE'RE WAITING FOR THE PORRIDGE TO COOK.

THAT DOES IT!

DRONE WHINE

THIS SCHOOL TRIP IS MAKING ME AS MAD AS HELL, AND I'M NOT GOING TO TAKE IT ANY MORE!

I'LL USE THAT STUPID ROBOT'S TIN CANS TO SABOTAGE THE HEADMASTER'S PORRIDGE WITH THIS REEKING LOCH WATER!

RANCID STENCH

WITH DINNER RUINED, WE'LL JUST HAVE TO PACK UP AND GO HOME!

MR SNODWORTHY, IF YOU WANT TO HELP COOK DINNER OUR CAMP FIRE IS OVER HERE!

EH?

McGURR!

RUIN MA HAGGIS DINNER, WOULD YE?

WELL YE'RE GAUIN' TAE PROVIDE ME WITH ANITHER ONE...

SHORTLY

WELL CHILDREN, WASN'T THAT AN INSTRUCTIVE LESSON IN HOW TO MAKE A HAGGIS?

YES, IT WAS REMARKABLE HOW NEARLY ALL OF MR SNODWORTHY'S PULPED BODY COULD BE STUFFED INTO HIS SCROTUM!

BIG VERN

WELL DONE, VERNON. YOU'VE HAD A VERY GOOD FIRST WEEK HERE AT MACBURGERS.

IN FACT, YOU'VE DONE SO WELL I'M MAKING YOU EMPLOYEE OF THE MONTH.

CHEERS, BOSS!

I'LL JUST PUT YOU IN THE FRAME.

DO FACKIN' WOT?! NO WAY ARE YOU PUTTIN' ME IN THE FRAME FOR THIS JOB, YOU CAN'T!

BLAM!

I DIDN'T MEAN TO DO IT! I'M NOT GOIN' BACK INSIDE!

BLAM!

DO YOU WANT FRIES WITH THAT?

ROGER MELLIE THE MAN ON THE TELLY

LET'S SEE... JACKET AND TROUSERS, DRY CLEAN AND RE-TEXTURE... THAT WILL BE £26, PLEASE, MR. MELLIE.

LISTEN, NEVER MIND MONEY, PAL. I'VE GOT A BUSINESS PROPOSITION FOR YOU...

OH?.. WHAT'S THAT?

A BIT OF THE OLD CELEBRITY ENDORSEMENT. YOU DO MY DRY CLEANING FOR FREE AND YOU CAN STICK **THIS** IN YOUR WINDOW

HOW'S THAT, EH?.. AN EXCLUSIVE DEAL WITH FTV'S ROGER MELLIE

TV STAR ROGER MELLIE GETS HIS CLOTHES DRY CLEANED AT DAISY FRESH

YOU WATCH THE PUNTERS FLOOD THROUGH THE DOOR...THEY'LL ALL WANT THEIR DUDS WASHED AT THE SAME PLACE AS YOURS TRULY

HMM! WELL, I THINK WE'VE GOT A DEAL, MR. MELLIE

GREAT... REMEMBER, IT'S TWO JACKETS, TWO TROUSERS AND FIVE SHIRTS A WEEK, OKAY?

RIGHT YOU ARE

AND I WANT THEM IRONED AS WELL...I'M FUCKIN' **BIG LEAGUE**

GOSH! AN EXCLUSIVE DEAL WITH ROGER MELLIE... WHAT A COUP!

SEE YOU NEXT WEEK

LetteRbocks

Viz Comic, P.O. Box 841, Whitley Bay, NE26 9EQ - letters@viz.co.uk

THE Government could reduce the cost of expensive badger culls by building more roads instead. I have just seen 3 laying dead by the side of the road on a 5 mile car journey and this isn't the first time.

Bill Tardy, e-mail

ALTHOUGH the death of Richard "Jaws" Kiel must have been a deep personal tragedy for his friends and family, I for one will sleep more soundly in the knowledge that a 7-foot giant with metal teeth won't be biting through the roof of any cable car I may be travelling in.

James Brown, Edinburgh

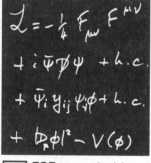

FOR years, physicists have been unable to incorporate gravity into the standard model equation to produced a unified theory of fundamental reactions. But they still keep their jobs. I'm a binman, and every time I miss a few bins on my round I get a bollocking off my gaffer at the depot. I missed half the round last week because I wanted to knock off early and I was given the push. Once again, it's one rule for theoretical physicists and another for the rest of us.

Terry Crockwitt, London

I DON'T think Her Majesty would be looking quite so smug on those bank notes if she knew she was sharing my wallet with a Stringfellows drinks card, a small personal stash and two ribbed condoms.

Peter Busby, e-mail

WHY doesn't Michael Portillo do the Middlesbrough to Thornaby line on his *Great Railway Journeys* TV show? The rubber-lipped prick.

Dibz, e-mail

✳ *What a shame. A programme about the Middlesbrough to Thornaby line with Michael Portillo is an excellent suggestion, Mr Dibz, but then you spoil your letter by hurling abuse at the presenter. He may not represent your political views and you do not have to vote for him in any election, but the prick cannot help having rubber lips, and to point it out is rather a cheap shot.*

I WISH these Premiership footballers wouldn't go sliding along the ground on their knees every time they score a goal. They might be millionaires who only work on Saturday afternoons, but their mums aren't, and it's them who have to try and wash the grass stains out of their socks.

Edna Scrotum, Cheadle

EVERY week I recycle dozens of wine bottles and countless beer cans, whereas my neighbours only manage a couple of jam jars. Come on people! I can't fix global warming on my own.

Rik Crompton, e-mail

HOW long is a piece of string? Well I found one in the kitchen drawer that measures 11 3/4 inches. Now that we know, can everybody please stop using this moronic rhetorical question?

Tommy O'Neill, e-mail

THERE'S no doubting the mathematical capability of *Countdown*'s Rachel Riley. I have checked her quick mental calculations carefully on a calculator and can confirm their accuracy. But why does this seemingly bright young woman have to flaunt herself so cheaply, parading her shapely body in scanty, revealing outfits and flouncing about before the cameras like some lusty tart in an Amsterdam shop window? If I wanted to watch pole dancers flaunt themselves I'd go to my local pole dancing club, which, incidentally, is ludicrously over-priced.

Maurice Gladiola, e-mail

IS it me or were Fruit Polos really shit? Well, the ones I found in my Gran's pocket were. She's been dead twelve years.

Mick H, e-mail

THESE women are always going on about the pain of childbirth, but what about us poor blokes during conception, eh? All that bouncing up and down on our elbows, pulling stupid faces.

Peter Busby, e-mail

I THINK the town of Kidderminster is the ideal place name to be spoken in the voice of late controversial Irish MP Ian Paisley Snr. I wonder if any of your readers can match other towns and cities to the voices of our parliamentary representatives.

Brummy Savage, e-mail

I'M sick of sports commentators saying "you couldn't write a script like this." If people can write scripts about dystopian futures in which life is in fact a simulation made by sentient machines to harness humans' heat and electricity as an energy source, they can probably write ones about Gary Taylor-Fletcher scoring a last-minute equaliser against Stoke.

Joey, e-mail

I LIVE in a block of flats on the 13th floor, so I don't bother pulling the curtains when I have a wank. Do any other readers get accused of living an easy life?

Gareth Price, e-mail

LIKE Mr Price *(above letter)*, I live in a block of flats on the 25th floor and I too am able to masturbate with the curtains open. Lets face it, if anyone passes my window and sees me pulling the Pope's cap off, they're not going to be around long to tell anyone about it.

Kirby Cardenas, Manchester

I BET that Hitler fella wouldn't have been such a dick if the kids in his class has called him 'Adolf Titler'. A nickname like that sticks and I reckon he'd have kept his head down.

Brian Rest, e-mail

THEY say any publicity is good publicity. Well, my mate Andy was in the newspaper for punching an old lady in between the tits last week, yet I fail to see how he could come out of this smelling of roses.

T Clements, e-mail

AS part of my new healthy diet, I have chosen to take two teaspoons of cod liver oil every morning. However, as a health regime it's not really working as it tastes so fucking disgusting, I have to down a bottle of whiskey afterwards to get rid of the taste.

Bongo Andy, Ipswich

FOR years I really fancied my best mate's mum. So imagine my disappointment when I discovered that during all that time she had been working as a prostitute. For the cost of a tank of petrol, I could have had her from any direction I wanted.

Stephen Rice, e-mail

ON a recent school trip to Paris, our young son brought me back an Eiffel Tower key ring which digs in to my knackers through my pocket. It may be a global cultural icon of France and one of the most recognisable structures in the world, but I can't help thinking the architects didn't think the design through properly.

Terence Trent, Derby

Are They Still YOUNG?

with Augustus Fieldhouse
Professor of Ageing at the Max Plank Institute

I WONDERED if you knew of anywhere I might get a cupboard featuring a mural of Barnes-Wallis's Bouncing Bomb attacking the Möhne Dam, as this one has just been sold.

Ian Andrews, e-mail

* *Well readers, do you have a cupboard depicting RAF's heroic 1943 airborne assault on the Ruhr Valley for sale? If so, get in touch and we'll pass your details on to Mr Andrews.*

IF horseshoes are lucky, how come horses have four of them but usually end up either carrying some fat bastard around on a fox-hunt or fighting off Millwall supporters on a weekly basis?

Martin Maximus, Derby

MY mate's name is Rolf Savile. Poor bastard!

Jimmy Harris, e-mail

SOUL SINGER WASTE DISPOSAL

"Hello... is it a skip you're looking for?"

Then look no further. Your home, garden or garage could be Once, Twice, Three Times as Tidy with a skip from...

RICHIE SKIP HIRE

• Mini, Midi and Maxi skips
• Daily and Weekly rates available
• Tipper and Grab Hire

Fast, Friendly and Efficient - Lionel Richie Skip Hire is the Number 1 Skip Hire in Spalding and South Lincs.

Don't Delay - Call Today on Spalding 45612

"The prices at Lionel Richie Skip Hire had me dancing on the ceiling!" Mr S, Peterborough

"Hiring a skip from Lionel Richie was easy like Sunday morning." Mrs B, Lincoln

---

I WAS walking along Westgate Road in Newcastle last week and I saw a woman who looked like Kim Wilde in the 80s, and it got me thinking. I know she was 21 when she recorded her debut single *Kids in America*, but is she still 21 today?

Harold Bobbins, Trimden

* *That's a very good question, Mr Bobbins, and the simple answer is no. Since that song was recorded, Ms Wilde has piled on the years - thirty three of them to be exact. And far from being 21, she is now in fact 54.*

LIKE most fifteen year-old boys, I fancied Jane Fonda like mad when I saw her in *Barbarella*. But as I reckoned she was about 30 in the film, twice my age, I thought she wouldn't be interested in me as the age gap was too much. Well it was 20 years ago when I first saw the film and now I'm 35. I was just wondering if Miss Fonda is still about 30, as the age gap now doesn't seem quite such a problem and I might be in with a chance.

Steve Wankshaft, Trowbridge

* *I'm afraid I have to disappoint you, Mr Wankshaft. Although Jane Fonda was indeed 31 when she made Barbarella in 1968, she was in fact 57 by the time you saw it in 1994. So rather than a 15 year age difference you imagined, it was actually 42. And the bad news is that in the intervening years, Jane has matched your own ageing year for year, and at nearly 77, the actress still remains 42 years your senior.*

I WAS at stage school with Bonnie Langford in 1970, both of us six years old, when she was picked to go on *Opportunity Knocks*. She was a runaway sucess and went on to great stardom, whilst I went on to work in a pork pie factory in Nottingham. I am now 52 and have spent the last 46 years being very bitter and resentful that it wasn't me chosen to go on the show. It would make my day if the intervening years have been cruel to Ms Langford and that she is now in her late seventies or even eighties.

Edna Vitriol, Penge

* *What a sad life you appear to have led, Mrs Vitriol, and one bound to end in disapointment. I'm happy to say that in the last 44 years, Bonnie has aged just 4.4 decades, and today is a sprightly 52 year-old.*

Do YOU want to know if somebody is still young? Write to: Augustus Fieldhouse, Viz Comic, PO Box 841, Whitley Bay, NE26 9EQ

WHAT a con these so-called food banks are. I deposited a pack of Hobnobs there last week, and when I went to withdraw them today I was told they were gone.

Colin Devitt, e-mail

EVERY Sunday morning I get woken by the same racket of bells from a nearby church. That is not what I want to hear after a night out with the lads and a hangover. Why can't Christians do what Muslims do and have prayers on a Friday dinner time? That way everybody can go out on Saturday night and get completely sloshed and not have to worry about a racket the following morning.

Alan Heath, e-mail

I DON'T know why French waiters always think it's posh to stick one arm behind their backs when they're pouring wine. For all we know they could have their hand down the back of their trousers and having a good old root around down there. Disgusting I call it.

Matilda Byrne, Luton

HOW come we never see any doggers on things like *Autumnwatch*? The woods round the back of my house are full of the dirty bastards most nights of the week. Come on BBC2, let's have some realism. It's supposed to be a factual programme after all.

Bramley Peartree, Surrey

I JUST met a man in my local who told me that Prince Philip is a lizard and is part of an overlord species of super lizards that rule the planet. Upon reflection, that sounds like something nobody could make up and this man had absolutely no reason to lie to me. That being the case I'm absolutely flabbergasted at what I've learned.

Leo Stitch, e-mail

I THINK it's outrageous that female BBC television presenters are considered past their prime when they reach a certain age. Many of them still have nice tits and legs and I for one wouldn't kick them out of bed. Come on, BBC, enough of this ageist, sexist behaviour.

Chester Conker, Droitwich

The Sausage Dog who would be KING

The amazing story of a four-legged friend who rose to become monarch of all England

IN ALL THE annals of history, no tale is more extraordinary than that of Fritz, a miniature dachshund who was crowned King of England in 1132. Although his reign was as short as his legs, he nevertheless remains the only dog to have ever occupied the English throne.

The ailing King Henry I was on his deathbed, and had summoned his sons - the Duke of Gloucester, the Earl of March and the Bishop of Durham - to

his quarters at Richmond Palace in order to name his favoured successor. The country was awash with pretenders, and the three princes jostled at his bedside, each one claiming that he was more loyal than the others. In truth, all of them were traitors who would go to almost any lengths to secure the crown for themselves.

With his dying breath, Henry lifted his hand and pointed, proclaiming: "I name you my heir and next King of all England." But the King was so weak that he could barely lift his finger, and instead of one of his sons, he only succeeded in pointing at a small sausage dog that happened to be in the room. Then, before he could make his wishes any clearer, he fell back on his pillow and expired from a combination of a pox, an ague and a surfeit of lampreys.

Nobody knew where the little dog had come from or how he came to be in the King's chamber. The only clue to his identity was a disc hanging from his collar on which was engraved his name - "Fritz".

This was a time when the King's word was law, so as the anointed heir, Fritz was immediately gathered up by Archbishop of Canterbury Thomas a Beckett and taken to Westminster Abbey to be crowned. The coronation took place the next day, and was carried out with all the pomp and splendour that such an ancient and important ceremony demanded. The majestic sense of occasion was only marred when the newly-enthroned King Fritz - his bottom irritated by a bad case of worms -decided to yacht across the altar carpet.

The early days of his rein were eventful ones; a peace treaty with Portugal was in the offing, England was courting Burgundy and the Black Death had reached Aquitaine. The monarch's role as head of state had

never been more important, but the new King elected to spend his time chasing cats, eating socks and getting his lipstick out to frotter himself to orgasm against the legs of everyone at court.

As he was just two years old (fourteen in dog years), King Fritz was still in his minority and found himself surrounded by advisers, chief among whom were the old King's three sons. Still bitter about being usurped to the throne by a sausage dog, they plotted together and decided ... The King must die.

Under the cover of night and after drugging the palace guards with wine, the Duke of Gloucester stole into King Fritz's bedchamber, bent on malfeasance. Like any dog would, the unsuspecting dachshund leapt out of his bed and rushed to greet his midnight visitor with his tail wagging. "What have I got for you here, then? What have I

got? What's this? What's this, your majesty? Do you want this? You do, you want this," Gloucester exclaimed. The King ran around in small circles, wagging his tail excitedly.

Gloucester reached into a leather pouch hanging from his belt and produced a Terry's Chocolate Orange and three Yorkies. The delighted King snaffled the lot, wrappers and all. Little did the unsuspecting dog realise that he had signed his own death warrant.

Fritz's body was found the next morning by the servant who let him out each morning to do a shit on the lawn. He had died in his sleep - poisoned as he slept by the chocolate that the regicidal Duke had fed to him. In his turn, Gloucester seized the reins of power and immediately had himself crowned King, disingenuously swearing himself loyal to the memory of his canine predecessor.

Fritz had been on the throne for a mere three weeks, yet as the only dog ever to have ascended the throne, he left an indelible mark both on his country and on the carpet at Richmond Palace.

HIS MAJESTY

Next Week: *The Hamster who would be Pope*

137

OH, LORDY! IT'S THE FAT SLAGS

D'Y WANT THE LAST SLICE, SAN?...WELL, THE LAST SLICE OUT OF *THIS* BOX, ANYWAY

I DON'T KNOW WHY YOU ORDERED 'EM

NO...YOU 'AVE IT... I'M FED UP O' PIZZA WE *BOTH* ARE...

COS WE'VE GOT T' GET US *FIVE* A DAY, SAN.

'AVE YER? *WHEN?*

I'VE ALREADY 'AD ME FIVE TODAY...

I 'AD THE METER READER THIS MORNIN'... THEN THE WINDOW CLEANER... THAT YOUNG OFFENDER SELLIN DUSTERS AFTER ME DINNER, DAVE AT TEA TIME AN BAZ ABOUT AN HOUR AGO

...PIZZA DELIVERY BLOKE MAKES IT SIX, TRAY.

NO... BAZ AN' DAVE ARE PENCIL- DICKS, SAN... THEY ONLY COUNT AS HALF A PORTION EACH... AN' THAT YOUNG OFFENDER WI' THE DUSTERS WERE *YESTERDAY*, COS HE COME BACK AN HOUR LATER WI' HIS MATE...

REMEMBER?

AYE!

...SO Y'VE ONLY ACTUALLY 'AD *FOUR* OF Y' FIVE TODAY

KNOCK! KNOCK!

OOH, THERE'S THE DOOR... I'LL GERRIT

GOOD MORNING, MISS...I'M FROM THE CHURCH OF THE LATTER-DAY SAINTS...

...HAVE YOU HEARD THE GOOD NEWS?

'OO IS IT, TRAY?

BRING 'IM IN.

IT'S YER FIFTH PORTION

HEY, SAN... GIRLZMAG SAYS Y' NEED *SEVEN* A DAY T' KEEP YER LIBIDO HEALTHY.

EEH! THERE'S THEM TWO BLOKES WHO TAKE THEIR DOGS FORRA SHIT ABOUT THIS TIME EVERY NIGHT...

UGH! UGH! PRAISE THE LORD!

...GIVE 'EM A SHOUT WHEN THEY GO PAST, WILL YER?

---

mr. LOGIC

HE'S AN ACUTE LOCALISED BODILY SMART IN THE RECTAL AREA.

hmmm...

hmmm...

YOU'VE GOT THAT WRONG.

EH!? THERE'S TWO T'S IN LITTER, ISN'T THERE..?

YES, BUT "LITTER", BY DEFI-NITION, IS RUBBISH THAT IS DISCARDED AND LEFT LYING IN AN OPEN OR PUBLIC PLACE...

AS SOON AS IT IS PICKED UP AND DEPOSITED IN A DESIGNATED BIN, IT IS NO LONGER LITTER... IT IS "REFUSE".

A "LITTER BIN" IS, THEREFORE, AN OXYMORONIC IMPOSSIBILITY. YOU HAVE MADE A SIMPLE, YET FUNDAMENTAL ERROR OF LEXICOLOGICAL MIS-NOMENCULATURISATION.

WELL THANKS FOR POINTING THAT OUT. HOLD ON... I'LL JUST CHANGE THE WORDING.

CRUMP!

hmm...INASMUCH AS MY ANAL SPHINCTER IS INDEED WITHIN THE BOUNDARIES OF THIS RECEPTACLE...

LITTER ARSEHOLES

...THAT IS AN ACCURATE DESCRIPTION OF THE PRESENT SITUATION.

Blackpool gears up for RAT-MAGEDDON!

Blackpool Tower of terror: Lord Mayor Councillor Eddie Collet (left) says it will be holiday business as usual despite epidemic of giant rats the size of dinosaurs running wild along the Lancastrian resort's world famous Golden Mile (artist's impression, below).

RECENT newspaper stories about a plague of giant poison-proof rats sweeping across the country have provoked widespread alarm. Luridly-worded stories in the *Daily Mail* about an epidemic of vicious rodents the size of cows laying waste to our towns and cities have rightly led to panic throughout the population.

"Bring it on!" says Lord Mayor

But now it seems that, if anything, these scare-mongering headlines may have **UNDERESTIMATED** the scale of the problem. For scientists from a Lancashire University now believe that a tidal wave of rats the size of **ELEPHANTS** could be about to engulf the UK.

And it gets worse, because according to Professor Adrian Street of the University of Fleetwood, there is a very real danger that these elephant-sized rats could then **MUTATE** and grow to the size of **DINOSAURS!** Professor Street told us: "It's a doomsday scenario, but there is a very real prospect that 60-foot-high, 100-ton rats could be scurrying round your bins and nesting under your shed within the next few months."

But one local authority is refusing to let the threat of the oncoming rat-pocalypse from upset its summer season. "It'll take more than an infestation of Brontasaurus-sized furry vermin to spoil the fun," Lord Mayor of Blackpool Eddie Collett told reporters, at a press conference to announce the emergency measures being put in place by the council to deal with the expected nationwide invasion of giant rats.

holiday

"We don't intend to let these overgrown mice stop Blackpool being the perfect

By our vermin correspondent **Myson Ratz**

family holiday destination it has always been," he said. And Councillor Collett outlined a ten point plan to reassure this summer's visitors that it's going to be business as usual along the Golden Mile, including ...

● *The bottom 50-ft of the Blackpool tower to be coated with special anti-climb grease to prevent giant rats from scrambling up the structure King Kong-style.*

● *Tourists will be restricted to travelling downstairs only on the trams along the Golden Mile between Starr Gate and Fleetwood, to prevent passengers being plucked from the open top decks and eaten alive by ravenous rodents. To keep overall passenger numbers up, the frequency of trams between 8.00 am and 5.00 pm will be doubled, with services running on the quarter hours as well as the halves as at present.*

● *The floral clock to be fenced in with heavy duty chicken wire to discourage the T-Rex-sized behemoths from digging up expensive bedding plants.*

● *All food outlets will be allowed to continue serving customers at existing pavement tables, but all cheese-based foodstuffs (eg. Toasted cheese sandwiches, tuna melts, cheesy chips and Quavers) must be eaten indoors so as not to attract the hungry rats.*

● *Any residents with cats will be asked to remove the bells from their collars.*

● *Bins to be put out on the morning of scheduled collection only. Anyone putting their bin out the night before will receive an official warning letters. Subsequent breaches will be dealt with via a red warning, followed by a final*

warning and then a £50 fine (reduced to £40 if paid within 14 days of being served).

● *Several hundred-foot-high stools to be erected at various places around the town for ladies to jump on top of and scream should they encounter one of the outsize rodents.*

Meanwhile the Fylde Coast Civic Works Department have already started constructing a rat trap about the length of a tennis court. The Mayor said: "We're going to bait it with 4 hundredweight of bacon rind that has kindly been collected from breakfast plates by the Blackpool Landladies' Association."

"Unfortunately, we've been having trouble setting it," Councillor Collett continued.

"So far, the Blackpool & Fylde Panthers rugby players, the police tug-of-ward team and a squadron of local army cadets have all tried and failed to pull the bar round far enough to get the hook on the hasp. Sadly sixteen volunteers have so far perished during attempts to set the thing."

"It's got quite a powerful spring on it," the Mayor added.

The Pie Pipers

THE answer to Britain's giant rat woes could lie in the hands of just three celebrities, according to a leaked government dossier. The stars charged with solving the country's pressing vermin problem are the unlikely trio of Blur bassist *Alex James*, *Great British Bake*-off Judge *Paul Hollywood* and seventies folk rock legend *Ian Anderson* out of Jethro Tull.

Three Mice Men: James, Anderson and Hollywood carry hopes of Britain

According to the secret report, in the event of the expected rodent invasion, the three men will be brought together and appointed 'Rat Riddance Tsars'. Former rock star James - now one of the country's leading artisan cheese producers - will bring his expertise to bear in producing strong-smelling cheeses that will be very effective at attracting rats.

mutiny

These cheeses will then be baked into an enormous pie with a flaky yet delicious crust by tidy-bearded *GBBO* star Hollywood.

The giant cheese pie will then be rolled to Beachy Head, with Ian Anderson leading the way dressed in gaily-coloured attire including felt shoes with bells on the end, stripy tights and a jester's hat,

Radical plan to tackle rat problem

whilst playing a selection of his band's hits - including *Locomotive Breath, Minstrel in the Gallery* and *Aqualung* - on his flute.

Government pest control experts believe that, enticed by the smell of the cheese pie and enchanted by the lilting tones of Anderson's trademark flute-playing, the rats will follow the procession all the way to Beachy Head. Here, hypnotised, it is hoped that the rats will fall off the edge of the cliffs to their death on the jagged rocks hundreds of feet below.

Prime Minister David Cameron gave the scheme his backing. He told Radio 4's Eddie Mair: "I don't know whether this project is going to work. But what I do know is this: *not doing anything is not an option.*"

"This government will not sit back and allow the country to be overrun by a tsunami of giant, warfarin-resistant rats. And we will do everything within our power to protect the British public, even if that means getting the bassist out of Blur, Paul Hollywood off Bake-Off and Ian Anderson out of Jethro Tull to roll a big cheese pie to Beachy Head," he added.

Chews at Ten

Newsman Huw bitten on bellend by rodent

BBC NEWSREADER *HUW EDWARDS* was recovering at home last night after his penis was savaged by a giant rat live on air. The rodent - estimated to be eighteen inches long including its tale - is understood to have run up the Welsh broadcaster's trouser leg during the *10 o'Clock News* and sank its teeth into his bobby's helmet.

Millions of viewers watched unawares as Edwards, 53, continued to calmly read out headlines and reports throughout the five-minute attack. A BBC News insider told us: "Huw is a consummate professional and doesn't let anything ruffle his feathers when he's on air."

"His lip went slightly higher than usual, and there was a bead of sweat on his brow when the rat launched its attack on his farmer's hat, but the average news watcher at home would never have guessed there was anything amiss," he added.

trousers

After introducing the local news and weather summaries from around the country, Edwards leapt from behind his desk, pulled his trousers down and started beating the rat with a rolled-up script in an attempt to get it to loosen its grip.

The source told us: "He was screaming in pain, but the rat wasn't going to let go. It was hanging off the

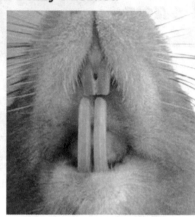

end of his unit for grim death, and the more Edwards flailed at it the deeper it sank its gnashers into his herman jelmet."

shave

Fortunately, animal expert Chris Packham was in an adjoining studio filming an edition of *SpringWatch* at the time. He heard the commotion in the newsroom and rushed through

to help. "Packham knows all about animals, and he explained that the only way to stop the rat biting someone would be to stick your finger up his arse," said the source. "The rat, that is, not Huw Edwards."

scratch

The ex-*Really Wild Show* presenter duly inserted his finger into the angry rodent's backside, but it refused to let go of the newsreader's glans. "Its grip slackened off a little bit, but it wasn't going to give up its prize without a fight," said the source. "Then the floor manager started the five second countdown to the 10.29 headlines round-up."

"As the green light went on Huw leapt back into his chair and calmly delivered the closing bullet-points. The millions of viewers watching at home would have had no idea that under his desk he had his pants round his ankles and a giant rat with

Breaking News: There's a rat on my lid. BBC anchorman Huw Edwards (above) bravely continued reading the headlines despite eighteen-inch rodent sinking its razor-sharp teeth (left) into his cocknuckle live on air.

Chris Packham's finger up its arse chewing his lid."

sniff

The rat eventually released its grip after weather forecaster Helen Willetts hit it several times on the head with her shoe. Father of five Edwards was later taken to hospital where he was given a precautionary series of rabies shots, and received ten stitches in his purple pearler.

Following the attack, the BBC has introduced new Health & Safety guidelines, prohibiting newsreaders from bringing cheese or bacon into the newsroom and requiring them to tie up the bottoms of their trousers with string.

Rat's Life!

FORMER *That's Life* presenter *Esther Rantzen* last night choked back the tears as she told reporters she "knew nothing" about the giant rats that have infested the BBC since the 1970s.

"Of course one heard rumours about rats at the time," she said. "But I can honestly state 100% that I never saw any rat activity myself or was aware of it taking place whilst I was one of the BBC's biggest stars."

action

"If I had, rest assured I would have taken action and immediately reported it to the relevant authorities," she continued.

isle of

"The problem is, the place was crawling with sex offenders and

"I knew nothing about rodents at Beeb" ~ Rantzen

paedophiles at the time, and we were so busy trying to stamp them out that we didn't notice that there were loads of rats everywhere too," she added.

How to get over your FEAR of RATS

by Now Un-disgraced Telly Psychiatrist **Dr Raj Persaud**

Aratnophobia - the irrational fear of a rat - is thought to affect more than 90% of the population. The idea of one of these disease-ridden, pink-eyed, scaly-tailed vermins swimming up the U-bend, sinking its yellow teeth into your barse and frantically scrabbling at your clockweights with its sharp claws whilst emitting a high-pitched shriek is everyone's secret nightmare.

To get over your fear of rats, simply print out the picture of the small mouse *(left)* and keep looking at it until you are no longer afraid of it. Then blow that picture up by 25% a week for 10 weeks until it is the size of a big rat. Hey presto! You are no longer afraid of rats.

© Dr Raj Persaud Enterprises Ltd.

RAT THREAT TO DR WHO

HE MAY HAVE beaten the Daleks, vanquished the Master and conquered the Cybermen, but now DR WHO may have finally met his match. For the galaxy-hopping Time Lord, who first hit TV screens way back in 1963, is sensationally set to be AXED when the expected invasion of giant rats hits our shores.

Not exterminated: Out-of-control rat infestation at Beeb now threatens flagship sci-fi series.

Fans fear that when the unstoppable tide of huge rodents begins its relentless sweep across Britain, the long-running BBC series could be amongst their first casualties, meaning that the science fiction hero's latest incarnation, played by foul-mouthed actor Peter Capaldi, could well be his last.

giant

A source in the pub told us: "The producers are worried in case Capaldi gets killed and eaten by a giant rat halfway through filming a series."

"All the epsodes they'd completed up to that point would have to be binned. It would cost literally millions to re-shoot them all with a new actor in the title role, so they've simply taken the decision to pull the plug on the whole show,"

EXCLUSIVE!

he said, adding that he had this on very good authority from a friend of his brother's who knew somebody who sometimes did the traffic reports on BBC Radio Derby.

Devastated viewers have already taken to social media in their droves to protest at the controversial decision to can the top-rated show, with the hashtags *#DontlettheratskillDrWho* and *#BringBacktheDoctor* trending worldwide within seconds of the news beginning to spread.

kendo

Meanwhile former Doctors queued up to criticise the plan to axe the series, which has

been a fixture in the Saturday night schedules for more than fifty years. Except for a break of about 16 years in the middle. "I am gutted to hear that the series is to be cancelled over the fear that the Doctor could be eaten by giant rats," said Peter Davison, Colin Baker or Sylvester McCoy. "After defeating every alien in the universe, it seems ironic that he should finally come a cropper courtesy of a load of jumped-up cheese-nibblers."

mick

In 2011 the BBC announced its decision to axe the popular 6 Music radio network after fears that a plague of giant locusts might descend on the station's studios and strip the flesh from presenters including Shaun Keaveny, Liz Kershaw and Stuart Maconie.

YOU DIRTY RAT!

BBC Director General Tony Hall was last night clinging to his post by a thread after a fresh scandal threatened to engulf the corporation. The row blew up after it was revealed that the famous rat in a biscuit tin that appears in the 'Health Inspector' episode of *Fawlty Towers* may have been FAKE.

"I was there in the studio and I know for a fact that it wasn't a real rat in that tin," says former BBC assistant floor manager Angus Gaybody. "It was made of cloth and Connie Booth was operating it with a stick."

biscuit

The episode, first broadcast in 1979, features a scene where waiter Manuel's pet rat Basil emerges vertically from a biscuit tin and slowly turns 90° to the left and right before the lid is replaced on top of it. Previously the rat was thought to have been real, but now whistleblower Gaybody's allegations suggest that TV watchers were cynically **DUPED** by the BBC.

"Fawlty Towers' viewers have been systematically lied to," he said. "It's time to tell the truth."

Cleese comes clean as fake footage row envelops Beeb

The show's star John Cleese last night apologised unreservedly for the deceit. "I have harboured the secret of how that footage was faked since 1979," he told the media scrum that had formed an encampment outside his Hampstead home. "I cannot

Was it a rat I saw?: Cleese (left) is fully at Fawlty for the deception and subsequent cover up.

describe the relief after finally coming clean and clearing my conscience of this burden I have been carrying around for thirty-five years."

mickey

But Cleese's weasel words cut no ice with millions of viewers, who said they felt cheated and deceived by the BBC. "I used to love Fawlty Towers but if I watched it now I would just feel sick," said licence payer Geoff Foreskin of Hull. "Cleese lied to us and I will never forgive him for that." Whilst ex-viewer Maureen Clitoral-Hood said: "I've watched that episode a thousand times

with my son. Now I have to look him in the eye and tell him that the rat in the biscuit tin wasn't real. How do I do that?"

piss

Whilst many fans called for *Fawlty Towers* to be axed and Cleese to be sacked, one viewer went even further. "Cleese should be fired without his pension for what he's done," said Frank Gleet of London.

"Then he should be stripped to the waist, handed a big Samurai sword and forced to commit hari-kari live on television on a Saturday night, just after *Strictly* so it gets lots of viewers."

10 THINGS YOU NEVER KNEW ABOUT RATS

THEY eat babies in their cradles, they spread the bubonic plague and you're never further than six feet away from one. They're RATS, and according to experts by 2020 there'll be 1000 of them for every man, woman and child in the country. But how much do you really know about these whiskery little critters? How big are they? What do they eat? And which was the first one to climb Mount Everest? Here's 10 flea-ridden facts about these fascinating rodents.

1 RATS are a very adaptable species and have colonised every continent on earth - including Antarctica. Indeed, when rescuers finally located the remains of Captain Scott's ill-fated expedition to the South Pole in 1913, the rat that they had never been more than six feet away from during their trek was found frozen in the snow... exactly five feet eleven inches from the tent.

2 AS EVERY scientist knows, rats are very good at solving mazes.

In fact, a rat is kept at Hampton Court for this express purpose. If any visitors become lost whilst exploring the Tudor Palace's famously complex box-hedge labyrinth, the rat is sent in and they are told to follow it to safety.

3 BELIEVE it or not, Ratty - one of the most popular rats in literature - who lives by the riverbank in Kenneth Grahame's classic children's book *The Wind in the Willows*, is not actually a rat at all. He's a water vole, a sort of swimming rat.

4 "THERE'S a rat in mi kitchen, what am I going to do?" sang the members of UB40 in their 1986 hit of the same name. Instead of writing a song about it, the Birmingham-based band would have been well advised to call in an experienced professional pest control operative to set glue traps, put down warfarin-laced bait or hit it with a cricket bat when it ran out from behind the cooker.

5 THEY say that rats are the first thing to leave a sinking ship, but in the case of the Costa Concordia it was the liner's Captain Francesco Schettino - whose name translates as Frank Rollerskates - who according to prosecutors was the first person to make it into the lifeboats.

6 THE WORLD'S smallest man Calvin Phillips was never more than six inches away from a rat that was the size of a small mouse.

7 THE FIRST woman in space, Valentina Tereshkova, was shocked to see a rat floating round her Vostok 6 space capsule. The 6" rodent had somehow crept into the cockpit during preparations for launch in June 1963, and the lady cosmonaut spent her three days in space standing on a chair, screaming and holding her space suit up round her knees.

8 SINCE elephants are famously scared of mice in case they run up their trunks, you might suppose that they'd be even more frightened of rats. But this isn't the case, and in fact they get on with them quite well.

9 THE FIRST man to be bitten on the tintis by a rat that had swam up the U-bend of his toilet was Thomas Crapper, who was sitting on a toilet that he had just invented at the time.

10 ALTHOUGH many US presidents have had cats and dogs, none of the 44 men to hold the office has owned rats. 1996 Republican Bob Dole candidate bred pedigree Variegated, Cinnamon Rex and Russian Blue rats for show, but he was narrowly defeated by Bill Clinton in the New Hampshire Primary.

"Give Poison-Resistant Rats my Wife's Cooking!"

A LONDON taxi driver yesterday came up with a revolutionary plan to deal with poison-resistant rats. "Get my missus to cook dinner for the buggers," laughed *Gary Tiptree* of Lambeth. "That would soon sort them out."

Tiptree, 48, told passengers: *"Poison-resistant rats? Don't make me laugh. A portion of the wife's steak and kidney pie would finish them off, I tell you."*

lambeth

Scientists believe that the rats have become immune to the anti-coagulant poison warfarin due to years of indiscriminate use, but the 48-year-old taxi driver from Lambeth claims he has an ideal solution. *"Get her indoors to cook them a meat and potato pudding,"* he told fellow cabbies in a Kings Cross Cafe.

moon

Researchers are working on new, more powerful toxins to counter the rodent threat. It's a difficult task as the chemicals used must only be harmful to rats whilst leaving other wildlife unharmed. But according to Tiptree, the answer is staring them in the face.

"They should bring them over to my house and give them some of the wife's steak and kidney pie," he told a woman in the back of his taxi who was in the middle of a phonecall. *"Kill anything, that would, my wife's steak and kidney pie."*

Cambridge University's Dr Alison Barnyard said: "Many poisons kill

Cabbie suggests simple solution to rodent problem

rats, but we have to be very careful to control the toxins we introduce into the ecosystem. For this reason it is very difficult to produce a safe vermicide that will be effective against the rodent population."

But 32-stone Gary said he knew of one. *"My missus's meat and potato pie would do the job. Hahahaha,"* he told XFM phone-in host Jon Holmes. *"I tell you. It'd kill them stone dead, that would."*

flint

Warfarin resistance was first identified in the rodent population in the early 1980s, when it was a localised problem. But it has spread rapidly in the intervening years, and now almost every area of the country has a significant rat population that is immune to the widely-used Vitamin K epoxide reductase inhibitor.

"They want to give them a slice of my wife's steak and kidney pudding," Tiptree told a cycle courier who he had knocked off his bike on Westminster Bridge. *"I say,*

they want to give them a slice of my wife's steak and kidney pudding."

richards

According to Dr Barnyard, more powerful rodenticides, such as Courmatetralyl - also known as "super-warfarin" - are longer lasting and effective against rat populations that are warfarin-resistant. But she warns that these should only be used as a last resort. "If we over-use these extra-potent pesticides, it won't be long before the rat population develops resistance to them as well," she told us.

But Gary knows something that no rodent on earth could eat and survive. *"My wife's meat and potato pie would kill any rat stone dead,"* he told a Japanese tourist who he was taking from Kings Cross to St Pancras via Kew Gardens and Hendon Police College.

"Mind you, we wouldn't have so many rats if they didn't keep letting all these bloody immigrants in," he added.

Drunken bakers

BAXTER BASICS MP

LADIES AND GENTLEMEN, AS YOU MAY KNOW, I WAS RECENTLY THE VICTIM OF A "STING" OPERATION PERPETRATED BY A DOWNMARKET TABLOID NEWSPAPER.

IN MY CAPACITY AS MINISTER FOR FAMILY VALUES, I FEEL IT IS INCUMBENT UPON ME TO TAKE THIS OPPORTUNITY TO PUT MY SIDE OF THE STORY.

I WAS APPROACHED VIA SOCIAL MEDIA SOME WEEKS AGO BY AN OSTENSIBLY PLAUSIBLE YOUNG FEMALE POLITICAL RESEARCHER, CALLING HERSELF "SOPHIE TITWANK".

THIS PERSON, I NOW REALISE, WAS IN FACT AN UNDERCOVER REPORTER.

WE ENGAGED IN AN EXCHANGE OF INCREASINGLY EXPLICIT PRIVATE MESSAGES WHICH CULMINATED IN ME SENDING TO HER A SERIES OF INTIMATE PHOTOGRAPHS - PIXELLATED VERSIONS OF WHICH WERE LATER SPLASHED ACROSS THE FRONT PAGE OF A SUNDAY NEWSPAPER.

...PHOTOGRAPHS, I AM ASHAMED TO SAY, THAT SHOWED MY PENIS STICKING OUT OF MY PAISLEY PYJAMAS... PYJAMAS, I MAY ADD, THAT WERE A PRESENT FROM MY WIFE TO MARK OUR WEDDING ANNIVERSARY.

THESE PICTURES OF ME IN PAISLEY PYJAMAS DO NOT SHOW ME IN A GOOD LIGHT.

THEY WERE A STUPID MISTAKE.

MY COCK WOULD'VE LOOKED MUCH BETTER STUCK OUT OF SOME BLACK CALVIN KLEINS.

...AND IT IS AS A RESULT OF THIS GRAVE ERROR OF JUDGEMENT THAT, WITH REGRET, I WAS FORCED EARLIER THIS AFTERNOON TO ACCEPT MY WIFE'S RESIGNATION AS MY SPOUSE.

BIG SMILE OVER HERE FOR THE TELEGRAPH, MR BASICS!

ROGER MELLIE THE MAN ON THE TELLY

MORNING, TOM. YOU SAID YOU HAD A JOB FOR ME

YES... **TOP GEAR** WANT YOU TO APPEAR ON THEIR 'STAR IN A REASONABLY PRICED CAR'.

WHAT!?.. FUCK ME RAGGED, TOM...THAT'S FANTASTIC!

NEXT DAY...

OKAY... THREE... TWO...ONE...

GO!

YES... THEY'RE FILMING IT AT THEIR DUNSFOLD AERODROME STUDIO TOMORROW, ROGER.

SCREEECH! SCREEE! SCREEF!

WOOOOAH!

CHRIST! THAT WAS TIGHT!..

OH FUCK! I'VE OVER COMPENSATED...I CAN FEEL THE BACK END SLIDING OUT...

KEEP HOLD OF IT, MAN

VROOM! BANG! VROOOM!

OH, SHIT!... I'M DOING NINETY!...IT'S TOO FAST FOR THIS CORNER...

OH! FUCK! SHIT! FUCK! SHIT! FUCK! SHIT!

NEARLY THERE!... PEDAL TO THE METAL ON THIS STRAIGHT. ...LAST CURVE COMING UP... EASE OFF A BIT... I CAN SEE THE FINISH...OUT THE FINAL BEND AND **GO FOR IT!**

SCREEEE!

...YES!

ALRIGHT, SWEET TITS?...CAN YOU GO AND TELL JEREMY THAT ROGER HAS ARRIVED...

DUNSFOLD AERODROME
ALL VISITORS PLEASE REPORT TO RECEPTION

...AND THAT I'VE GOT MY OWN HELMET

Martin Lewis's Money-Saving Ice Cream Top Tips

> *We all love ice cream, but before you spend your hard earned money on the stuff, here are a few tips that will make the ice cream fat cats work a little harder for your ice cream pound.*

BUDGET supermarket Cornettos are nowhere near as nice and are also about two-thirds the size of the genuine article, but they are a lot cheaper, so buy those instead.

EVER NOTICED how monkey blood slides straight off ice cream? When you buy a cornet with monkey blood from an ice cream van, get the man to put crushed nuts on it first. Then, when he puts the monkey blood on, it will fill the gaps between the nuts and you'll get more for your money. He may charge you extra for the crushed nuts, but that will be more than offset by the extra monkey blood you'll be getting for free.

ICE CREAM is 90% water, which is at its most dense at 4˚C. So when you go to the supermarket, take a thermometer with you and walk around the aisles with your ice cream until it warms up to 4˚C before taking it to the till. When you get home, pop it in the freezer and it will expand by 0.02% volume. Hey presto! More ice cream for your hard-earned money.

ON WINTER nights when the temperature drops below freezing, switch the fridge off and store your ice cream outside.

More money saving ice cream tips next time... *Martin*

Computer_News
A roundup from the World of Information Technology...

Man Sits Through Whole Youtube Advert

A Hull man is believed to be the first person ever to sit through the entire thirty seconds of a YouTube commercial. "I sat down at my computer to watch a clip of an old Spanish lady being mounted by a priapic labrador, and was poised to click and skip the ad at the five second stage as usual," said unemployed forklift driver Terry Meatus, 48. "But the batteries must have run out in my mouse, and I had no option but to keep on watching until the half-minute commercial had run its full course." Surprisingly, Mr Meatus said he was none the worse for his ordeal. "In fact, I was really impressed by the ad, which was beautifully shot with much higher production values than the average YouTube clip," he told us. "I think it was for a bank or a car or possibly a mobile phone company," he added.

Printer Prints What Man Wanted it to Print

A Goole man was celebrating last night after his printer actually printed out a document that he wanted. "I clicked to print a nice picture of the cat," said unemployed foundry worker Terry Sulcus, 48. "But to my amazement, instead of it coming out cropped off the side, really tiny or indeed getting six copies of something I tried to print out yesterday, it just printed out the picture I wanted at the correct size." A Hewlett Packard spokesman told us: "If Mr Sulcus would like to return his printer to us, we will happily replace it with one that makes a lot of whirring and chugging noises, then suffers a non-existent paper jam and a flashing message saying that the Cyan ink is low."

Woman Forgets Password for Millionth Time

A Luton woman yesterday clicked the 'forgot password?' button on a web account log-in for the one millionth time. Attempting to buy some fire logs from the Home Bargains website, Barbara Glans tried the name of her cat, her budgie and her date of birth to no avail before requesting a new password. "Thinking about it, it might have been my mum's maiden name followed by my first house number," she told *MacUser* magazine. "But then that might be the one for my banking or pehaps Amazon," she added. "But I'll not forget it again. I've writtien it down and put it somewhere safe," she said.

BAG Bloopers
Bag-related gaffs, geffs, giffs, goffs and goofs from the movies

• **IN** the 1964 Disney classic *Mary Poppins*, the magical nanny played by **Julie Andrews** removes a stepladder from her bag. However, the ladder is about seven feet tall, whilst the bag can be clearly seen to be no more than eighteen inches deep at most. It would be a physical impossibility for the ladder to fit inside.

• **IN** a scene from 1994's Oscar-winning *Shawshank Redemption*, Red, played by **Morgan Freeman**, is released from prison and gets a job packing groceries in a supermarket. In one shot, he takes a brand new paper bag from a pile and begins placing a woman's shopping inside. However, when Freeman hands the shopping back to her, the previously perfectly flat bag can clearly be seen to be creased and bulging in several places.

• **IN** *Breakfast at Tiffany's* (1961), Holly Golightly, the character played by **Audrey** Hepburn, checks her appearance in the mirror before leaving her Manhattan apartment. Her handbag can clearly be seen to be over her left shoulder, yet in the mirror's reflection it is over her right.

• **AFTER** the climactic scene of 1995's *Braveheart*, starring **Mel Gibson**, a lone piper can be seen walking across the battlefield at Falkirk. The film is set in 1280, yet the bagpipes can clearly be seen to be wearing a digital watch.

Mark Commode

STAR LETTER

I'VE just watched a video on the internet where a decorator visited a lady's house to give her a price to paint her kitchen. When the lady said she didn't have £900, he suggested they had sex instead, to which she agreed. Now I'm a painter myself and I can tell you that £900 to paint a small kitchen is way too much. Perhaps if he gave more realistic estimates, he wouldn't have to go through the rigmarole of having sex every time he went to price a job.

Nick Steal, e-mail

I'M sick of people saying "good boy" to their dogs. Your dog has no idea what good or bad is, it has no moral compass. It is at best an obedient, subservient little shit machine.

Paul Jones, Cambridge

A BLOKE at work saw me looking for my keys and very helpfully said, "they're always the last place you look." So I searched in two extra places after finding them, just to make him a liar.

Ed O'Meara, London

I WONDER if Tony Robinson and his *Time Team* chums could come by and have a dig around my back garden? I think that's where the dog has buried my television remote. If it helps, I could tell them it used to belong to Shakespeare or some other old famous dead twat.

L. Worsley, Tring

IMAGINE my disappointment after following a right tasty arse down the street for ten minutes last week, when she turned around and was my wife.

Harry Harrison, Norwich

A LOT of people were mightily impressed by Hannibal Lecter when he told agent Clarisse Starling that he could tell she wore L'Air du Temps perfume – "but not today." Personally, I was more impressed with Miggs, the bloke in the next cell who reckoned he could smell her minge. Hats off to him, I say.

Hampton Twelvetrees, Hull

"GIRL, I'm just a Jeepster for your love," sang Marc Bolan in 1971. Seriously, what the fuck was he on?

Blooby Shint, Sheffield

"I WISH I had a hundred quid for every time I heard the name Harry Potter," I said the other week. Then I remembered I was the Actor Daniel Radcliffe, and that this was probably the case.

Daniel Radcliffe, Hogwarts

DAVID Cameron has just announced "jobs for all." Imagine the look on the face of my uncle who enjoyed a wonderful retirement party only last week.

Ian Shapton, Frant

HOW come I am expected to lift and bin my dog's turds, yet the Queen does not have to lift the turds from her swans when they shit all over the place? As usual it's one law for the monarch and another for the rest of us.

Alan Gibson, Lurgan

AS A keen Man United supporter, I have been in a bad mood lately because they have lost a few games. I much prefer to see the lads get a victory.

Nick the Red Devil, Ireland

IN response to Nick the Red Devil (above), I am actually the opposite. In a game between Man United and Aston Villa, I would much rather see Manchester United lose as I am a keen Villa supporter. I suppose it's just horses for courses.

Ian the Villain, Waterford

I DON'T understand Mark Kermode. All he does is talk on the radio about films he doesn't like. If he hates films so much, why does he keep going to see them?

Jake Cuthbertson, M'bro

PARKING in my local village can be a complete nightmare. I hope those people with disabled badges realise just how fortunate they are.

Eddie Beergarden, Berkshire

What's in the Bag, Ma'am?...

HER MAJESTY the Queen never goes anywhere without her handbag. It's as much a part of her image as waving from a Rolls-Royce, setting fire to her castles and scowling. *But what does she keep in it?* We know she doesn't carry money, so chances are it simply contains a lipstick, some tissues and a pair of reading glasses. But that's not very interesting, so we went on the street to see if the great British public had any more exciting ideas about what Her Majesty keeps in the right royal handbag...

...**I'D** imagine that it probably *is* simply lipstick, tissues and glasses, but they will be magnificently expensive ones. The lipstick will be top-of-the-range La Prairie and the tissues will be silk and monogrammed in gold thread. And the reading glasses probably have Swarovski crystals in the frame, or more likely Koh-i-Noor diamonds. Magnificent.

Nicholas Witchell, BBC fartsucker

...**I THINK** she keeps a live rat or two in there in case she gets peckish between official engagements. That's because I know for a fact that the Queen is a shape-shifting lizard from outer space, and that's what they eat, like on that science fiction programme *V* from the 1980s.

David Icke, Ex-Hereford Utd goalkeeper and Messiah

...**IF SHE'S** anything like my missus, she'll have a can a Red Bull, a bottle of Jagermeister, 20 Regal, a disposable lighter and a Dutch cap in there. But I doubt she's anything like my missus who isn't majestic in any way. So I'm not sure what she'll have in her bag.

Frank Bolus, unemployed

...**I THINK** she carries a box of rubber johnnies in her bag in case she gets lucky with a Lord Mayor or civic dignitary whilst opening a hospital ward or something. The dirty bitch.

Alderman Ray Brocolli, council leader

...**MR BROCOLLI** ought to be ashamed of himself saying that the Queen carries jimmy hats in her handbag on the off chance of having casual sexual intercourse with men she meets on official visits. I hope he gets tried for treason, sent to prison and gang-raped by the other prisoners.

Edna Meek, church warden

...**MRS MEEK** needs to wind her fucking neck in. Mr Brocolli never suggested that the Queen was going to have full penetrative sex with these Lord Mayors. For all she knows her majesty might just be giving them all a posh wank. I think she stashes little cartons of ketchup and barbecue sauce from McDonalds in case they haven't got any at a state banquet. Also them little jams.

Lance Persilautomatic, juggler

TOP TIPS

REPLICATE the festival experience for free by getting 50 of your mates to come round and pile into your living room, then ask the people across the road to put on some music videos.

Peter Cassidy, Newcastle

A LARGE spoonful of poppy seeds with every meal means that the next day's dump will scratch away any embarrassing itching around the ringpiece. For more persistent itching, replace poppy seeds with builders' sand.

James Brown, Edinburgh

NEXT Christmas, celebrate Jesus's birthday by giving a vicar the bumps.

Chunky, e-mail

CHURCHGOERS. Save money by choosing a place of worship with a new roof.

Mark Spoors, e-mail

PRETEND you're dining out in a fancy "gastro-pub" by serving your oven chips in a plant pot, and everything else on a chopping board.

M Bowers, York

IS MEMBERS. When making a video about the evils of the West, be sure to waggle your finger at the camera as you speak or we could doubt your sincerity.

Mick Bollocks, e-mail

WHOLE black peppercorns make ideal black balls for a very snooty Action Man golf club selection committee.

Robert Cordon, Sheffield

HYSTERICAL American Christians. Safely enjoy devilled eggs by boiling them in holy water and eating them on crucifix shaped toast.

Tam Dale, Blantyre

SAVE £s on thrill seeker holidays or F1 track days by travelling on the 255 bus to Halifax when the driver's busting for a piss.

Phil, Cleckheaton

toptips@viz.co.uk

THE other day I found a bench in the park, so I took it into my nearest police station to hand it in. I couldn't believe it when they cautioned me for wasting their time. So much for my honesty. The next bench I find lying about I'll take home.

Nicholas Tarte, e-mail

WHY didn't they use courier parrots instead of courier pigeons during the war? Instead of tying a written note to the bird's leg, they need only have spoken the message to the bird and released it. It would the n have flown to the recipient and delivered the message in a high-pitched voice on presentation of a cracker or similar baked item.

Matt, Bolton

THESE so called experts think they know everything. Well I bet they can't guess what number I'm thinking of right now. And if they do I'll just pretend I was thinking of a different one.

Wilbur Alan, Ipswich

I THINK Alcoholics Anonymous would probably get a lot more members if they didn't keep advocating the "Twelve Steps". Most turps-nudgers I know can't even manage a very short mobility ramp, never mind having a shitload of stairs to negotiate.

Hector Golightly, Bodmin

HOW come Dracula has always got bloodshot eyes? I could well understand if he was out on the piss the night before and wasn't getting enough to kip, but the lazy bastard hits the sack at dawn and doesn't get up until it's dark.

Tommy Helsing, Whitby

MY sat-nav told me to go left, and I went left, so I think it most unfair that I got fined for driving through a red light. I shall certainly be expecting TomTom to reimburse me for this.

Alan Heath, Newcastle

IT'S that time of year when all you hear on the radio and see on TV is people banging on about dancing, singing and baking. What about the football? Come on execs, give us fans of minority sports a look-in for once.

Rob Hudson, e-mail

ON page 120, a letter from Nearly Normal Norman told how he found an image of a white Siberian tiger's cock at the bottom of his cappuccino. I was horrified to find this image of a cock on the foil lid of some sour cream and chive dip I got in McDonald's.

James Burrell, e-mail

I'M sick and tired of hearing about sustainable fishing and all that bollocks. What ever happened to "There's plenty more fish in the sea"? I wonder how the "so-called" boffins will explain that one away?

Stan Handlebars, Leeds

Merry Coxmas

The Festive Season Around the Universe with *Brian Cox* Professor of Particle Physics out of synth band D:Ream

● **WIZZARD** famously sang: *"I wish it could be Christmas every day."* But believe it or not, it really is Christmas every day in some places. That's because the Multiple Universe Theory states that there are an infinite number of parallel realities in which everything that can possibly happen actually happens... including one where Christmas happens 365 times a year!

● **IF YOU BUY** a 12lb turkey this Christmas, make sure you're on the Earth, because if you buy it in the gravity-free vacuum of the Moon, it will only weigh 2lbs - not enough to feed the family on Christmas Day, let alone any leftovers for Boxing Day. That's one small turkey for you... *one giant profit for butcherkind!*

● **THERE ARE** so many scientists working at CERN - the European Science Agency's Large Hadron Collider - searching for the elusive Higgs Boson, that they couldn't possibly buy each other Christmas presents. As a result, the institute's Director General Professor Rolf-Dieter Heuer organises a yearly "Secret Santa" amongst the 3,500 researchers, with a maximum spend of £5.

● **CHRISTMAS** Day on Jupiter would last less than 10 hours... hardly enough time to defrost the turkey and watch the Bond film. On the plus side, because of its massive orbital period around the Sun, you'd only have to sit through the Queen's speech once every 11.9 years!

● **ANYONE** who tried to put up their Christmas tree in a black hole would be doomed to failure. For even if their fairy lights worked first time, they wouldn't be able to tell as the intense gravity at the heart of the super-dense collapsed star would prevent the twinkle from ever reaching their eyes. In fact they could easily end up spending infinity fiddling with the bulbs, looking for the duff one.

● **ACCORDING** to Sir Isaac Newton, two Christmas puddings exert an attractive gravitational force towards each other which is proportional to the product of their masses and inversely proportional to the square of the distance between them. The force between a pair of 2lb puddings is thus a quarter that between a pair of 4lb puddings, but diminishes as they are moved further apart on the table.

...And that's why I love Physics and Christmas!

Bri x

I MET an interesting old man at the bus stop a few years ago. I remarked on the irregularity and unreliability of the bus service, and he replied "Tell me about it, mate. I could write a fucking book about it." I have often wondered if he ever managed to write that novel, and although I have trawled Amazon and several branches of Waterstones, unfortunately it has so far been to no avail.

Nickolas Curtis, Dulchester

I ONCE had a wank up a stepladder over a picture of my mate's sister. Can any of your readers beat that?

Grenville Harpic, Bolton

HOW are energy-saving light bulbs supposed to save energy if people keep turning them off?

Paul Jones, Cambridge

151

Take a Shit

Rude Spirit

"Benny Hill's back and he's up to his old tricks again" says Essex man

Once one of the most popular comedians on the telly, **BENNY HILL** disappeared from our screens in the 1980s, when his brand of near-the-knuckle humour became too un-PC for modern viewers and his long-running show was axed by ITV bosses. But now, more than two decades after his death, it seems that the bawdy entertainer is back and up to his old tricks ...*and he isn't about to let a small matter like being six foot under slow him down.*

And one man who knows this only too well is Essex-based former septic tank cleaner Fishburn Trimdons. "Amazingly, it turns out that I am the only man on earth who can see Benny Hill's ghost," says Fishburn, 47. "And now I'm on a one-man mission to protect Britain's scantily-clad young women from his perverted spectral attentions."

Trimdon's first encounter with the saucy spook happened a couple of years ago, when a simple evening outing to go bird-watching near his home in Dagenham turned into something much more sinister.

❝I'd heard that a rare meadow pippit had been seen in the grounds of the local nurses' home, so I grabbed my binoculars and went out to see if I could spot it. I knew that it was a particularly nervous species, so I was being as quiet as possible as I crept through the bushes round the back of the building.

Pippits are also nocturnal in their habits, so I had waited until after midnight before venturing out on my ornithological expedition.

I climbed up a tree where I'd heard the bird had made its nest, but as I edged along the branch I suddenly felt the temperature drop. I soon saw why - there, crouching at the end of the branch amongst the foliage was a terrifying apparition... the ghost of

As told to *Take a Shit* reporter Fanny B'Terr

Benny Hill! It was unmistakably him, I recognised him from his trademark Fred Scuttle beret, cheeky leer and wire-rimmed National Health glasses. He was a familiar figure from his popular comedy shows back in the 1970s.

The only difference was, he was now see-through and glowing a bit. Not only that, the phantom funnyman was peering through a pair of binoculars just like mine. But unlike me, he wasn't looking for birds - at least not the feathered kind. The filthy-minded phantom was using his field glasses to spy through the window at a student nurse who was getting changed out of her uniform after a long shift.

Suddenly, the nurse must have seen the ghost, because she screamed in terror. Simultaneously, I made a lunge to grab the binoculars out of Hill's spectral hands and the branch snapped with a loud crack. The ghost vanished into thin air as I fell awkwardly to the ground, severely winding myself in the process. In fact I had only just got my breath back when a panda car arrived; apparently, there had been reports of a peeping Tom lurking in the area.

The filthy-minded phantom was using his field glasses to spy through the window at a student nurse who was getting changed out of her uniform

Is there Benny's body there? Clairvoyant septic tank worker Fishburn Trimdons claims he is the only person on earth who can see the supernatural shade of late funnyman Hill.

I explained to the policemen about the ghost of Benny Hill that I had just seen up the tree, but they just looked at my binoculars and the broken branch, put two and two together to make five and arrested me on the spot. The nurse could easily have confirmed my story and got me off the hook, but I didn't want to cause her any more distress after her haunting experience, so I accepted a caution. ❞

Trimdons thought that his late night brush with Hill's spook would be a one-off, but it seemed that the late comedian's restless spirit had other ideas. And their next encounter took place in broad daylight.

❝I'm a keen amateur photographer, and I set out bright and early one summer's morning to photograph a sunrise to send into my local BBC weather

Hill spectre: The cheeky comic died in 1992, but he's back as a ghost.

picture competition. As I walked up the street, I heard the hum of an approaching milk float, and I froze in horror when I saw who was at the wheel. It was Benny Hill's ghost again ... and this time he was dressed as a milkman. Back when he was alive, he'd made a hit record about the fastest milkman in the West, who died at the end of the song following a fight with Two Ton Ted from Teddington. Chillingly, in a macabre case of life imitating art,

When a fit young housewife opened the door in her skimpy nightie and bent down to pick up the bottle, he'd cop a ghostly feel

BENNY HILL

Ernie
(The Fastest Milkman In The West)

Benny Hill himself had also died at the end of his life, only to come back now as his famous alter-ego Ernie!

I watched the randy wraith doing the same thing again and again: he'd put a milk bottle on a doorstep, then ring the doorbell. When a fit young housewife opened the door in her skimpy nightie and bent down to pick up the bottle, he'd cop a ghostly feel. Because he was a ghost, the vile pervert's victims felt nothing.

I was horrified at Hill's depraved behaviour, and I knew that only I could stop him. To collect evidence, I fitted a powerful telephoto lens to my camera, then hid behind some bins and secretly photographed him molesting eleven different scantily-clad women as they bent over to pick up their morning pintas.

Unfortunately, when my photos were developed there was no sign of the ghost on them. They just showed young housewives in their nightdresses bending over on their doorsteps. I had completely forgotten that supernatural entities don't show up on film. Worse still, the assistant at my local branch of Snappy Snaps put two and two together to make five and thought I'd been spying on the women myself. She called the police and I got 200 hours' community service for milk theft and voyeurism, while Hill's ghost - the real criminal - got away Scot-free. **"**

As the only man who could see Benny Hill's ghost, Trimdons now made it his mission to protect the women of Essex from the late comedian's unwanted attentions. And he had a hunch that the next horny haunting might take place on a beach.

" It was a glorious, sunny day so I got the bus to Southend, where I had a strong feeling that Hill would launch his next attack. In hot weather the beach is always crowded with bikini-clad beauties and I knew that the sex-mad spook wouldn't be able to resist the temptation to turn up and slake his insatiable appetite for crumpet.

I wandered up and down the beach, keeping a sharp lookout for any supernatural goings-on. And as usual, I didn't have to wait long for the risqué wraith to show up. I heard ethereal saxophone music from the other side and suddenly there he was

again, zig-zagging quickly along the beach. He was see-through again, but this time he was dressed in a stripy, one-piece Edwardian swimming costume, with a rubber swimming cap pulled tightly down

I knew that if I didn't act fast, Kara would be left knickerless at the next costume change and the audience would see everything

onto his head and a beach ball tucked under one arm. It was a truly terrifying apparition.

Nobody on the beach reacted to Hill's presence and it dawned on me that, once again, I was the only one capable of seeing the ghost. My blood ran cold as I realised that he was about to attack again. And sure enough he did.

Hill went up to a woman in a skimpy bikini who was blithely drying herself off after a swim. If she'd known that the sinister shade of the 1970s telly favourite was hovering just inches behind her with a wicked glint in his ghostly eye, she would have run a mile. But as it was, she continued towelling her long, lithe limbs, completely unaware that Hill was lining her up as his next innocent victim.

I watched in horror as Hill's transparent hand reached out and pinched her bottom. I was disgusted at his outdated, sexist behaviour and decided to act to protect the young woman from this sordid attack. I ran across the sand and lunged forward to push the ghostly groper's arm away. Unfortunately, as Hill was a ghost, my hands went straight through him and I ended up grabbing hold of his victim's bikini bottoms.

As I did so, I tripped on something - probably a crab - and fell to the ground, pulling the bottoms down with me as I fell. The woman screamed, and I didn't get the chance to explain about the ghost before her boyfriend came over, saw what was happening, and put two and two together and made five.

He'd just got through beating me senseless when the police arrived. Again they wouldn't listen to my story, and thanks to my record I got six months suspended and a place on the sex offenders register. **"**

Despite acting from the best of intentions, misunderstandings arising from Trimdon's encounters with the ghost had now cost him his career at a local septic tank emptying company. And it was whilst he was looking for a new job in his local paper that he was spotted the likely scene of Benny Hill's next sinister manifestation.

" It was an advert for the touring production of *Strictly Come Dancing* that was coming to a local theatre. I've always loved the show for the music and the imaginative choreography, but I had a feeling that Benny Hill would have a far more sinister interest in going to see the show. There would be a bevy of vulnerable, leggy young women taking part, and I knew that only I could protect them from the late comedian's perverted attentions.

Lewd of the dance: Strictly star's lingerie was next target of dirty-minded phantom's attentions.

End of the leer show: Hill's ghost was pinching bottoms on Southend beach, says Fishburns.

I'd been out of work for six months at this point and couldn't afford a ticket, so I smuggled myself in through the stage door in a laundry basket. There were a lot of dressing rooms backstage, but I guessed that Hill's ghost would target Kara Tointon as she was the prettiest and had the best figure and everything.

I wasn't wrong. I knocked on her dressing room door and when no-one answered I quietly snook in. Once inside, I was shocked to see the spectral figure of Benny Hill. The dirty devil had been in Kara's underwear drawer and her lacy panties, bras, stockings and suspenders were now strewn all around the room.

Once again, I was outraged at his depraved, outdated and politically incorrect behaviour. I knew that if I didn't act fast, Kara would be left knickerless at the next costume change and the audience would see everything, so I started grabbing back the sexy lingerie off of the ghost and hastily shoving it back in her knicker drawer.

Hill retaliated by pulling down my trousers and pants to my ankles, leaving me naked from the waist down just as the dressing room door opened and Kara Toynton walked in, fresh from the dress rehearsal. She screamed the place down - maybe she too had caught a glimpse of Hill's ghost as it vanished into thin air. The theatre manager then appeared to see what all the fuss was about, put two and two together and made five, and called the police. **"**

This time, following psychiatric reports, Trimdons was placed under observation in a secure unit for eight months. Since his release, he says he's only seen Benny Hill's ghost a few times.

"Once I saw him getting up to his old tricks at Dagenham swimming baths and I've also seen him a couple of times haunting the women's changing rooms at Debenhams in Barking. But on both occasions I managed to escape before the police came, misunderstood my intentions and put two and two together to make five."

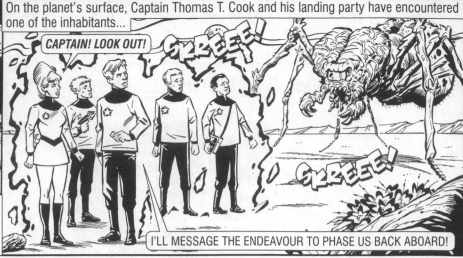

Next Week: The Endeavour crew decide to uninstall Outlook Express and download the free version of Mozilla Thunderbird, only to discover that their Java Applets need updating before they can configure the incoming mail server.

Sid the Sexist

TITS OOT!

TYNESIDE'S SILVER-TONGUED CAVALIER

CAB FOR MR. SMUTT?

FUCKIN' 'ELL. IT'S A LASS TAXI DRIVER!

NEVER 'AD A TAXI DRIVER WI' TITS BEFORE.

WELL THAT'S A LIE, ACTUALLY. THE ONE WOT BROUGHT W'HURM LAST NEET 'AD A PAIR BIGGER THAN YOURS, PET.

AYE. FAWATY STURN 'E MUST'VE BEEN.

REET PET, Y'CAN PULL OOT NOW...THE RURD'S CLEAR... DIVVEN'T FORGET T'SIGNAL.

MIND THIS PARKED CAR. Y'Z'RE A BIT CLURSE...

OOH! FUCKIN' MILLIMETRES, THAT. THICKNESS O' THE FUCKIN' PAINT!

THAT'S THE TROUBLE WI' LASSES AN' CARS... NEE SPATIAL AWARENESS...

AN' THAT'S NOT SEXIST PET, BEFORE Y' START BLEATIN' ON... DOON THE GEARS, LUV... DOON THE GEARS...

IT'S JUST THE WAY Y'FLUFFY LITTLE HEEDS IS WIRED. Y'Z'RE NOT CUT OOT T'BE DRIVAZ. DIVVEN'T GET W'WRANG... THEZ PLENTY O' STUFF YUZ **ARE** GOOD AT...

THORD GEAR...YUZ COMIN' UP TIV A ROONDABOOT, LUV...

NORSIN'... LASSES ARE GOOD AT THAT...COOKIN'...BETTA THAN BLURKS. APART FROM PROPA CHEFS.

MIDDLE LANE...YUZ'RE GANNIN' STRAIGHT AWA.

Y'Z'VE GOT NEE 'AND-EYE COORDINATION, Y'SEE. DIVVEN'T TEK IT THE WRANG WAY, I'M NOT GETTIN' AT YEE PORSONALLY...IT'S AALL WOMEN DRIVAZ...YUZ'RE DRIFTIN' OOT T'WARDS THE WHITE LINE PET... LURDS O' ROOM ON THE KORBSIDE.

Y'NEVER SEE BORDS DRIVIN' FORMULA 1 CARS, DEE YA? WELL, MEBEEZ ONE OR TWO... BUT THEY DIVVEN'T WIN NOWT.

TRAFFIC LIGHTS AHEAD. COVER Y'BRAKE, PET.

Y'COULD'VE GONE THERE. THEY WAS ON AMBA. Y'DIVVEN'T NEED Y'HANDBRAKE. Y'CAN RIDE THE CLUTCH.

Y'SEE, IT WUZ BLURKS WHAT INVENTED THE CAR... IT WUZ DESIGNED AROOND W'. AALL THE CONTRURLS IS JUST WHERE A MAN CAN REACH 'EM.

LEFT 'AND DOON A BIT, HINNY.

IN FACT, IT'D BE NEE EXAGGERATION T'SAY THAT THE WORST MAN DRIVA IS BETTA...AN' SAFER...THAN THE BEST BORD DRIVA IN THE WORLD.

UP 'ERE ON THE LEFT, PET...

DIVVEN'T FORGET T'INDICATE.

FUCKIN' 'ELL TYPICAL LASS'S PARKIN'.

DIVVEN'T WORRY, PET. I CAN WAALK T'THE KORB FROM 'ERE.

WAIT 'ERE FORRUZ, WILL YUZ? I'LL AANLY BE ABOOT TWENTY MINUTES.

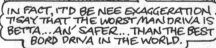

TWENTY MINUTES LATER...

DRIVING THEORY TEST CENTRE

FAIL

Y'SEE... BLURKS CAN THINK IN THREE DIMENSIONS, WHEREAS LASSES CAN AANLY THINK IN TWO DIMENSIONS...

...ABOOT SHOES AN' BABBIES.

157

Welcome to the fla

It's An

I'M A CE

Get Me

IKE

BOAR

ASK ANYONE to name their favourite D-lister-baiting ITV gameshow and they'll tell you it's *I'm a Celebrity!* Meanwhile, trailing round IKEA is everybody's favourite way to spend Sunday morning at their local out-of-town retail park. Well, now we've teamed up with cheeky Geordie funnymen *Ant & Dec* to bring

LIVING ROOMS

A pre-autotune recording of you singing your latest single is the laugh of the internet. Cheer yourself up by buying a desklight that takes a bulb with a fitting you have never seen before and will never see again.

Whilst you are in the furniture jungle, a bitter ex-partner sells their story to the press, accusing you of being a cheating love-rat. Miss a turn whilst you tweet a picture of a 'TESTIKUL' wall-mounted TV bracket to your 109 followers.

Buy a bag of 100 tealights.

Buy a BILLY Bookcase

Buy a small plywood box for £1 with no idea what you are going to use it for.

CHAIRS

Restaurant Tucker Trial
You drink a can of Swedish pear cider that smells like nail varnish remover. Go back two squares while you sit down on a 'Lundkvist' sofa and wait for your head to stop spinning

You flirt outrageously with one of your fellow competitors and climb onto an 'ULVAEUS' futon with them in the sofabeds section. However, you have to get off it immediately because it's like lying down on a wooden pallet covered in thin sliced bread. Miss a turn.

BEDROOMS

RESTAURANT

Restaurant Tucker Trial
You fancy a bit of chocolate but they've only got some peculiar foreign type for sale. Miss a turn whilst you wonder whether "Daim" is the Swedish spelling of "Dime"

Following a racist outburst, you lose your job as the face of a budget supermarket chain. Miss a turn whilst you chuckle at a bedside cabinet called a 'KOKK'.

You have grabbed a handful of impractically shor pencils that you don't want. Miss a turn whil you conceal them in your coat pocket.

FOYER

Your latest single fails to make it into the Top 100. Miss a turn whilst you take a picture of a coffee table called a 'KLITTORIS' and put it on Facebook.

CHECKOUTS

You get to the tills and the queues are so long that you abandon all your shopping. Go back to the start.

INSTRUCTIONS: Cut out the D-List celebrity counters, enter the shop and start the game

ENTER

You've made it back to the car park! You're the King or Queen of the Flat-pack Jungle! You'll be rewarded with a slight resurgence in your career for about three weeks before returning to abject obscurity.